Scholastic Literacy Skills

Comprehension

Teacher's Book

Author	Helena Rigby
Editor	Clare Gallaher
Series designer	Joy White
Designer	Rachel Warner
Cover illustration	Joy White
Illustrations	Beverly Curl

Designed using Adobe Pagemaker
Processed by Scholastic Ltd, Leamington Spa

Published by Scholastic Ltd, Villiers House, Clarendon
Avenue, Leamington Spa, Warwickshire CV32 5PR

© 1998 Scholastic Ltd

2 3 4 5 6 7 8 9 0   9 0 1 2 3 4 5 6 7

British Library Cataloguing-in-Publication Data
A catalogue record for this book is available from the British Library.

ISBN 0-590-53892-6

Contents

Acknowledgements

The publishers would like to thank the following for permission to reproduce copyright material.

(pages 70, 164) Addison Wesley Longman for 'Your name, sir?' based on an extract from *I See What You Mean* by Alison Kilpatrick, Patricia McCall and Sue Palmer © Kilpatrick, McCall and Palmer 1982 (1982, Oliver and Boyd) and 'A Devon disaster', based on an extract from *Reading Routes Blue Box: Rain and Floods* © Addison Wesley Longman.

(page 66) Enid Blyton Ltd for 'Mr Lion's Soup', a play adapted from *Brer Rabbit* by Enid Blyton © Enid Blyton 1948 (1948, Latimer House Ltd).

(page 81) Eric Finney for 'Coming Home' from *Another Very First Poetry Book* selected by John Foster © Eric Finney 1992 (1992, Oxford University Press).

(page 182) HarperCollins Publishers for the use of an extract from *The Stone Book* by Alan Garner © Alan Garner 1976 (1976, Collins).

(page 114) HarperCollins Publishers USA for the use of an extract from *No Roses for Harry* by Gene Zion © Eugene Zion 1958 (1958, HarperCollins USA).

(pages 150, 159, 144, 146, 120, 88, 107, 128, 98) Dave Higham Associates for the use of 'The cave' from *Stig of the Dump* by Clive King © Clive King 1970 (1970, Puffin); 'The Chief Rabbit' from *Watership Down* by Richard Adams © Richard Adams 1973 (1973, Puffin); and extracts from the following books: 'Dreams' from *The BFG* by Roald Dahl © Roald Dahl 1984 (1984, Penguin); 'Cinderella' from *Revolting Rhymes* by Roald Dahl © Roald Dahl 1984 (1984, Puffin); *Charlie and the Chocolate Factory* by Roald Dahl © Roald Dahl 1973 (1973, Puffin); two extracts from *The Twits* by Roald Dahl © Roald Dahl 1982 (1982, Puffin); 'The Story of Giant Kippernose' from *John Cunliffe's Giant Stories* © John Cunliffe 1994 (1994, André Deutsch); and an extract from *A Birthday For Frances* by Russell Hoban © Russell Hoban 1983 (1983, Hippo Books).

(page 94) Julie Holder for 'A centipede' by Julie Holder from *The Flumps* Annual © Julie Holder 1978 (1978, World Distributors Ltd).

(page 106) Barbara Ireson for 'John and Jim' from *Over and Over Again* © Barbara Ireson 1978 (1978, Beaver Books; 1984 Hutchinson Books Ltd).

(page 112) Karla Kuskin for 'The witches' ride' from *Dogs and Dragons, Trees and Dreams* © Karla Kuskin 1980 (1980, HarperCollins).

(page 103) Sheila Lavelle for 'Ursula Bear' from *Ursula Dancing* by Sheila Lavelle © Sheila Lavelle 1977 (1977, Hamish Hamilton).

(page 122) Brian Lee for the use of his poem 'Bones' from *A First Poetry Book* © Brian Lee 1979 (1979, Oxford University Press).

(page 174) Little, Brown & Co (UK) for the use of 'El Niño' based on an extract from *Weird Weather* by Paul Simon © Paul Simon (Little, Brown & Co (UK)).

(page 176) Macmillan Children's Books for 'The cure' from *William Again* by Richmal Crompton © Richmal C. Ashbee 1983, adapted by arrangement with Macmillan Children's Books, London.

(page 100) Sarah Matthews for the use of 'Crayoning' by Stanley Cook from *A Very First Poetry Book* edited by John Foster © The Estate of Stanley Cook 1984 (1984, Oxford University Press).

(page 160) Brian Moses for 'Shoot the messenger!' by Brian Moses from *Rice, Pie and Moses* by John Rice, Pie Corbett and Brian Moses © Brian Moses 1995 (1995, Macmillan Children's Books).

(page 138) Thomas Nelson & Sons Ltd for the second and third paragraphs in 'Canal locks' from *Targets 4* by Dorothy Brogden © Dorothy Brogden 1983 (1983, Thomas Nelson & Sons Ltd).

(pages 86, 168, 79) Penguin Books Ltd for the use of an extract from *Jim and the Beanstalk* by Raymond Briggs © Raymond Briggs 1970 (1970, Hamish Hamilton); an extract from *The Watchers* by Helen Cresswell © Helen Cresswell (1993, Puffin); and 'Growing' by Max Fatchen from *Songs for my Dog and Other People* by Max Fatchen © Max Fatchen 1980 (1980, Kestrel Books).

(page 126) Penguin Putnam Inc. (USA) for the use of an extract from *Cam Jansen and the Mystery of the UFO* by David A Adler © David A Adler 1980 (1980, Viking Penguin, a division of Penguin Putnam Inc.).

(pages 130, 170, 162, 137) Peters Fraser and Dunlop for 'Thirty-two lengths' and 'Tricks' by Michael Rosen from *Quick, Let's Get Out Of Here* © Michael Rosen 1985 (1985, Puffin); 'The Bakerloo flea' by Michael Rosen from *Nasty!* © Michael Rosen 1984 (1984, Puffin); and 'Grammar' by Michael Rosen from *Excuses, Excuses* compiled by John Foster © Michael Rosen 1997 (1997, Oxford University Press).

(pages 74, 97, 101, 80) Reed Consumer Books Ltd for 'The first house' by Syd Hoff from *Stanley* in the *I Can Read* series (1978, World's Work Ltd, William Heinemann); 'Otto, the penguin chick' from *Penguin's Progress* by Jill Tomlinson © Jill Tomlinson 1991 (1991, Mammoth); an extract from *'The Owl Who Was Afraid of the Dark'* by Jill Tomlinson © Jill Tomlinson 1991 (1991, Mammoth) and extracts from 'The Little Girl Who Got Out of Bed the Wrong Side' by Ruth Ainsworth from *Three Bags Full* © Ruth Ainsworth (William Heinemann, a division of Reed International Books Ltd).

(page 92) Clive Riche for 'These Are The Clothes That My Big Brother Wore' by Clive Riche from *A Very First Poetry Book* compiled by John Foster © Clive Riche (Oxford University Press).

(page 73) The Society of Authors as the Literary Representatives of the Estate of Rose Fyleman for the use of 'Mice' by Rose Fyleman, which appeared in *Tiny Tim* poems selected by Jill Bennett (1981, Heinemann).

(page 148) Stanley Thornes Ltd for the use of 'The Beatles' from *People in British History* by Tony T Triggs (1985, Basil Blackwell).

(page 84) Transworld Publishers Ltd for an extract from *Chalk and Cheese* by Adèle Geras © Adèle Geras 1996 (1996, Corgi, a division of Transworld Publishers Ltd).

(page 180) A P Watt Ltd on behalf of Crystal Hale and Jocelyn Herbert for the use of 'To the lady behind me' by A P Herbert which appeared in *Faces In A Crowd* edited by Anne Harvey © A P Herbert (1991, Puffin).

(pages 134 and 69) A P Watt Ltd on behalf of Dick King-Smith for the use of an extract from *Harry's Mad* by Dick King-Smith © Dick King-Smith 1986 (1986, Puffin) and permission on behalf of Fox Busters Ltd for 'Pete's mouse' from *Happy Mouseday* by Dick King-Smith © Dick King-Smith 1996 (1996, Corgi Pups).

Every effort has been made to trace copyright holders for the works reproduced in this book and the publishers apologise for any inadvertent omissions.

What is Scholastic Comprehension?

Comprehension means 'understanding' and, in its narrowest sense, comprehension material tests children's understanding of what they read. However, true 'comprehension' goes much deeper than this, and therefore the main objective of the *Scholastic Comprehension* series is to foster reading and comprehension skills in the widest possible sense, so that children not only learn how to read, and extract information from a variety of types of text, but also begin to appreciate the enjoyment and learning they can gain from a range of books. While the children are working on the units in this series, they will become more aware of the different features of various types of text genres, and will begin to understand how organisation of language, choice of vocabulary, grammar, layout and presentation all influence meaning.

The complete series is made up of four Pupil's books, with one book aimed at each year of Key Stage 2. These are supported by this Teacher's book which, as well as answers, offers further photocopiable activities at each level.

Working at text level

This series of comprehension books gives children opportunities to work at text level. It is well known that text-level work gives an essential context for work at sentence and word levels. It is also an essential part of the meaning-making process which is at the heart of effective reading.

Typical activities in text-level work are identifying main points, awareness of organisation and linguistic features of different text genres, differentiating fact, opinion and persuasion, and awareness of tense, mood and person in writing and how they affect meaning. You will find all these aspects of comprehension, and more, represented in the *Scholastic Comprehension* series.

Reading strategies

In order to learn to read well, a reader must be motivated. The variety of reading material offered by this series will ensure that children's interest will be captured so that their reading confidence will be developed.

Testing comprehension can never be a precise art. Any reader brings to new text a considerable 'baggage' of opinions, knowledge (or lack of it) and personal experience. All of these factors are bound to affect how that person responds to what they are reading and how much, or what type, of information they will retrieve from it.

To be able to fully understand a text, the reader will need to have acquired the skills of detailed (close) reading, and search reading (including skimming and scanning). To answer questions on the content of the text, the reader will require retrieval skills to locate and select the appropriate information, as well as communication skills to express responses verbally or in writing.

Close reading

Reading the text in detail gives a reader a clear understanding of what it contains. The passage should usually be read more than once, particularly if its content or subject matter is difficult or unfamiliar. This initial read through should allow the reader to fully grasp the meaning and intent of the author.

Skimming and scanning

Once the reader is familiar with and understands the text, search skills are required if the information needed to respond to a particular question is to be located swiftly. The reader needs to be able to skim through the passage quickly and scan the parts of the text where the answer might lie.

Answering the questions

Answering comprehension questions can be challenging for a young reader, particularly in the early stages. It would be of value to the children if the texts, and possible answers to the questions, could be discussed in small groups before they are asked to work individually. This will help pupils to structure their answers and will also support any children who have limited reading and writing skills. Children should always be encouraged to answer the questions in complete sentences as this will also enhance their writing skills.

Types of question

The four aspects of comprehension covered by questions in the Pupil's books and the photocopiable material in this book are literal, inferential, deductive and evaluative comprehension. Each of these tests a different facet of the reader's understanding of the texts. Explanations of these four types are given below, but it should be recognised that there is a considerable amount of overlap and that questions may sometimes fall between two, or more, categories.

✿ **Literal comprehension** centres on ideas and information that are quite explicit in a particular text. The reader is required to locate the response to a question, the clues to which lie on the surface of the text. In its simplest form, literal comprehension can be the recognition or recall of a single fact or incident, but it can also take more complex forms, such as the recognition or recall of a series of facts or the sequencing of incidents.

✿ **Inferential comprehension** requires the reader to 'read between the lines'. The information needed to respond to an inferential question is implicit in the text, and the reader needs to make inferences based on what has been read to formulate an answer. This type of question is more challenging, as it explores the extent to which the reader is aware of the nuances of meaning in the text. Pupils may, initially, need help to look for hidden clues and to link cause and effect.

✿ **Deductive comprehension** demands that the reader delves even deeper into the passage to make inferences based, not only on the text, but also on the reader's own experience and background knowledge. The reader is required to draw on personal knowledge and demonstrate a broader understanding of the text using links of cause and effect drawn from experience. Again, pupils may need support and guidance in formulating their answers.

✿ **Evaluative comprehension** asks the reader to make an evaluation of arguments or ideas suggested by the text. In order to do this, readers need to compare the information provided with their own experiences, knowledge or values. Answers given to this type of question depend on readers' assessment of a situation and how they would react to it, given their own inclinations and experiences. Generally, it is not possible to provide set answers to these questions, although pointers to the areas that should be covered are sometimes offered.

Introducing the Pupil's books

Each of the four Pupil's books has a standard format – 30 double-page units, with each unit made up of a reading comprehension passage followed by questions which address the four types of comprehension outlined above. The passages cover a variety and balance of eight different fiction and non-fiction genres. The genre of each passage is given in a strip on the left or right of each page. The eight text genres (which are used in random order throughout all four books) are:

Non-fiction
✿ recount;
✿ instruction;
✿ report;
✿ explanation;
✿ argument.

Fiction
✿ poetry;
✿ drama;
✿ narrative.

Each of the 30 units in the Pupil's books follows the same pattern. It begins with an introductory section, which gives some brief information on the purpose or structure of the relevant genre. This is followed by a 'Before you read' section, which offers one or two questions to engage the reader's attention and raise awareness of the content of the unit. These questions could form the basis of a small group discussion before the reading task is attempted.

The introductory sections are followed by a reading passage. These passages gradually increase in length and difficulty throughout the four books to extend children's reading experience and foster reading development. The reading passage is followed by about ten comprehension questions based on the text. The questions are designed to test the four main types of reading comprehension already discussed.

In the early stages, the emphasis is on literal comprehension, and appropriate answers to the questions could be discussed in small groups. The children should then be encouraged to answer the questions in their own words, using full sentences. This approach would be particularly helpful to children who need guidance in locating the specific relevant information and making the appropriate inferences from the text. Children will respond in different ways to the evaluative questions, as answers depend on their own experiences and preferences. For these too, discussion would help them to formulate responses. As children gain experience and confidence, they will become more able to work through the units on their own, with the minimum of adult help.

The final section of each unit offers suggestions for further activities, loosely related to the content of the unit, which more able pupils might wish to try.

Suggested answers to the comprehension questions in Pupil's books 1–4 will be found on pages 24–63 of this Teacher's book.

Using the Teacher's book

The photocopiable material

The photocopiable section in this book complements and reinforces the work of the Pupil's books. Individual units of work, with gently graded tasks, match the target age group of each Pupil's book. The questions posed are balanced to give equal weight to the four types of comprehension already discussed.

Book 1 contains examples of the genres represented in the Pupil's book – instruction, report, explanation, argument, recount, drama, narrative and poetry, thus offering the reader a variety of fiction and non-fiction texts. The first 18 units use relatively short passages, with six comprehension questions for the children to answer. These are followed by longer passages, which usually have ten comprehension questions for the children to answer.

Book 2 again reflects the different genres covered in the Pupil's book. The passages in Units 1–16 are slightly shorter in length than the later passages in Book 1 and have eight comprehension questions, thus offering reinforcement and consolidation of the earlier work. Units 17–24 have longer passages, with ten comprehension questions based on the texts.

Books 3 and 4 follow the same format and structure as the previous two books. The first set of units have shorter passages for reinforcement and consolidation, while the final units offer longer passages for a more sustained read (with 12 comprehension questions being given in Book 3 and 15 questions in Book 4).

Children working on one of the photocopiable units should first read the passage, preferably in a small group. They should then be given the opportunity to discuss the passage and possible answers to the comprehension questions. Next, the children should answer the questions, trying always to use their own words rather than repeating sections of the text. It is important that pupils develop the habit of reorganising and rephrasing the information they take from a text. The ability to do this demonstrates children's understanding of what they have read. As always, questions should be answered in complete sentences, rather than with one word or a phrase. This will have the added benefit of developing children's writing skills.

The suggested answers to the comprehension questions in the photocopiable material will be found on pages 184–208 of this Teacher's book.

How to use the answers

All answers are laid out clearly, unit by unit. At the start of each section, a listing of question types for the passage is given, which (in the Pupil's books) identifies whether a particular question addresses the skills of literal, inferential, evaluative or deductive comprehension. The answers for the passages in this Teacher's book simply list how many questions there are in each category.

For the Pupil's books, this is followed by a language focus – a few lines which suggest the main features of the genre and any other points worthy of note or discussion.

Answers are given as directly as possible. Where children are likely to give a range of replies, this is introduced by the phrase 'Answers may vary', followed by suggestions of the types of points answers should cover. Where questions depend almost entirely on the individual's experience and opinions, the phrase 'Your own answer' is given. Obviously situations may arise where children's answers may differ greatly from those suggested. It is usually worth checking the child's understanding and method of expression while also rejecting (though kindly) inventive or purely hopeful answers.

Models of eight text genres

Report genre

✿ focuses on a specific subject or idea

✿ is usually in present tense

PLANET EARTH

There are many planets in space. Earth is one of the nine planets in our Solar System. It is the only planet that we know of where there are living things. This is because living things, such as plants and animals, need water to live.

Water covers a lot of the planet called Earth. There are oceans, seas, rivers and lakes. If you could look at Earth from space you would see why astronauts call it 'The blue planet'.

The Earth moves around the Sun. It takes 365 days (one year) to move around the Sun. As the Earth moves, it spins round. Because it spins, we have day and night. When our part of the Earth is turned away from the Sun it is night-time. When our part of the Earth is turned towards the Sun it is daytime.

✿ provides facts, diagrams and examples to support the subject

Narrative genre

✿ there are different types of narrative – realistic, folk, historical, myth and so on.

THE NAUGHTY KITTENS

Beginning

✿ involves characters,

setting,

Once there were two little kittens called Tilly and Tommy. Tilly was ginger with little white paws and Tommy was black and white with a black tail. They lived with their owner in a large house.

dialogue and plot that work together to open the action

✿ presents a problem to solve

Middle

One day, their owner had to go out to do the shopping. 'Now, have a nice sleep, you two,' she said. 'Great,' thought Tilly and Tommy. Now they could really have some fun.

In the morning they played hide-and-seek behind the plant pots in the kitchen. 'CRASH!' went the green plant pot all over the floor. Next they played with a ball of wool from the sewing tin. 'CRASH!' went the tin, and everything fell out over the floor.

In the afternoon they played 'Chase the fly around the bedroom'. 'CRASH!' went the china doll, all over the floor. Then they played 'Hunt the spider'. But the spider didn't want to play and ran up and hid in a vase of flowers. 'CRASH!' went the vase, and the water and flowers spilled out across the room.

End

Tommy and Tilly were now very tired. They curled up next to each other and soon fell asleep. A little while later the front door opened. It was their owner returning from shopping.

✿ ends the narrative with a solution to the problem

'Oh dear! What a mess!' she cried. 'I can't have locked the door when I went out. That big, clumsy dog from next door must have got in again.' She smiled fondly at the two little kittens who were still asleep. She had brought them a special treat to eat for tea. Well, kittens who are always as good as gold deserve a special treat, don't they?

Instruction genre

✿ describes how to carry out a process or procedure

✿ lists materials needed to carry out a procedure

MAKING SCRAMBLED EGGS (SERVES 2)

Ingredients
4 fresh eggs
butter or margarine
milk
salt
parsley
bread

You will need
whisk or fork
mixing bowl
medium-sized saucepan
wooden spoon
chopping board
sharp kitchen knife
toaster

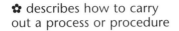

Making the dish
1 Break eggs into bowl and beat well.
2 Add small amount of milk and pinch of salt.
3 Beat again until well mixed.
4 Melt small amount of butter or margarine in pan.
5 Pour mixture into pan.
6 Cook until egg is not runny, stirring constantly with wooden spoon.
7 Chop parsley finely.
8 Toast and butter one or two slices of bread per person.
9 Spoon egg on to toast.
10 Sprinkle with parsley.

✿ features action verbs

✿ is usually a series of steps in a specific order (which may be numerical, chronological and so on)

✿ frequently omits definite articles

✿ is in present tense using imperatives

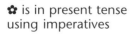

Recount genre

✿ usually in past tense

✿ deals in facts

✿ uses action verbs

✿ may be personal (involves 'I' or 'we')

✿ may involve personal feelings and opinions

✿ contains details

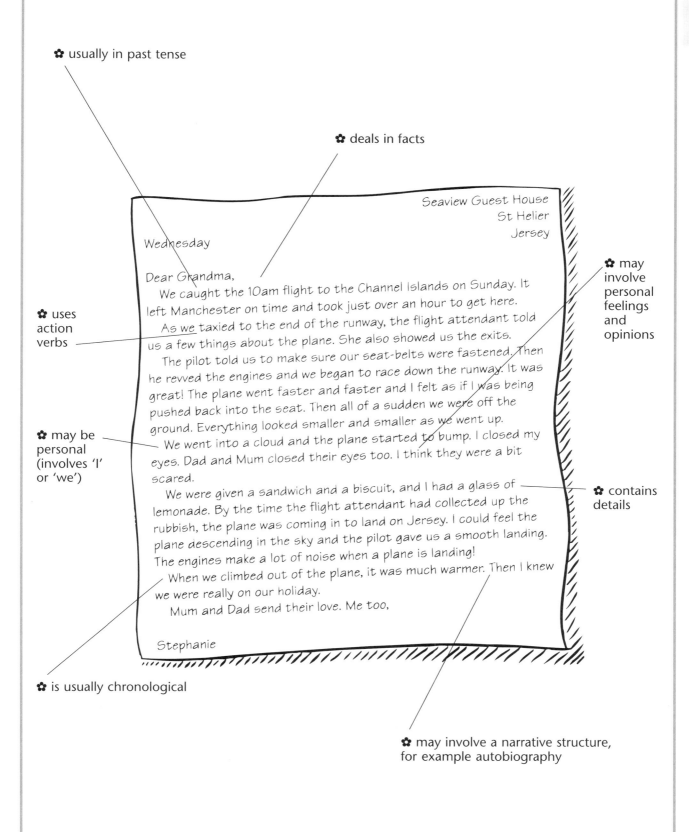

Seaview Guest House
St Helier
Jersey

Wednesday

Dear Grandma,
  We caught the 10am flight to the Channel Islands on Sunday. It left Manchester on time and took just over an hour to get here.
  As we taxied to the end of the runway, the flight attendant told us a few things about the plane. She also showed us the exits.
  The pilot told us to make sure our seat-belts were fastened. Then he revved the engines and we began to race down the runway. It was great! The plane went faster and faster and I felt as if I was being pushed back into the seat. Then all of a sudden we were off the ground. Everything looked smaller and smaller as we went up.
  We went into a cloud and the plane started to bump. I closed my eyes. Dad and Mum closed their eyes too. I think they were a bit scared.
  We were given a sandwich and a biscuit, and I had a glass of lemonade. By the time the flight attendant had collected up the rubbish, the plane was coming in to land on Jersey. I could feel the plane descending in the sky and the pilot gave us a smooth landing. The engines make a lot of noise when a plane is landing!
  When we climbed out of the plane, it was much warmer. Then I knew we were really on our holiday.
  Mum and Dad send their love. Me too,

Stephanie

✿ is usually chronological

✿ may involve a narrative structure, for example autobiography

Argument genre

✿ puts forward a point of view

✿ has an opening statement

A VARIED DIET IS BEST

Humans need to eat different kinds of foods if they are to have a balanced diet. If they do this, they will grow fit and strong, have plenty of energy and enjoy good health.

Some foods provide us with proteins which make the body grow. Some foods are rich in carbohydrates or fats; these give us energy. Other foods are rich in vitamins and minerals; they help to keep us fit and well.

No one food can supply all the things we need. That is why it is important to eat a wide range of foods.

We need to eat foods like meat, fish, nuts, eggs and cheese for proteins; we should include grains, sugar and fats to give us energy; it is also important to eat fruit and vegetables for minerals and vitamins.

If we include these foods, and others, in our meals then we can be sure that we are eating a varied and balanced diet.

✿ a series of reasons or evidence for the argument which may include details and facts

✿ a closing statement which sums up the argument; usually in present tense

Drama genre

✿ tells a story via the setting, sound
effects and dialogue between characters

The storm

✿ layout and
punctuation
conventions

*Matthew and his sister Kirsty are hurrying to get home before a big storm
breaks. The sky has become very dark. Loud thunder is heard as the play
begins. Matthew and Kirsty have been to the cinema, but have no coats. The
weather has changed suddenly and they are feeling cold and frightened.*

MATTHEW: Come on, Kirsty. Can't you go any faster? We'll be caught in
this storm. I knew I shouldn't have taken you with me today.

✿ speaker's
name; colon

KIRSTY: Matthew, wait for me. I just *can't* go any faster. How long have
we got before the rain starts?

MATTHEW: How am I supposed to know that?! *(Lightning flashes very close
to them followed by loud thunder. A strong wind begins to blow and drops of
rain begin to fall.)* Run Kirsty, run! See if we can make it to that tall tree.

KIRSTY: But Matthew... you're not supposed to... OK.

*(They begin to run, but the rain is pelting down. They are soon soaked
through and the tree still seems a long way off. As they approach a corner, an
old lady appears. Her umbrella is blown inside out.)*

OLD LADY: Children, children, you must get inside and out of this terrible
storm. Come into my house till it blows over. You'll be safe there.

(Matthew keeps on running but Kirsty stops.)

✿ usually in
present tense

KIRSTY: Matthew, come back. This lady says we can go into her house
until the storm has passed. Matthew! Matthew! *(Matthew doesn't stop
running. The storm is so noisy that he can't hear Kirsty. Suddenly the old
lady takes out a whistle and blows it loudly. Matthew stops, looks around
and sees his little sister going into a house with a stranger. He races back
towards them. Just as he reaches them, there is a huge flash of lightning and
a deafening crack of thunder.)*

✿ involves
what characters
actually say

Explanation genre

✿ describes how something
works or why something happens

Hᴏᴡ ᴛᴏ ꜰʟʏ ᴀ ᴘʟᴀɴᴇ

Most modern aeroplanes are so complicated that they need a crew to fly them. Even so, there are certain basic things that work in much the same way for all planes and some of the controls are very similar to those used in cars.

✿ involves facts

Look at the diagrams below which show how a small plane is controlled. On the outside of the plane you can see the elevators, the ailerons and the rudder. Inside the cockpit you will find the wheel (often a 'stick' in older planes), foot pedals, and a number of dials in front of the pilot. There is also a throttle which controls the speed of the engine.

✿ is usually in present tense,

using a series of steps in a specific order

When the pilot wants the plane to lift off the ground and climb, the wheel is pulled gently backwards. This raises the elevators, so the air presses down on the tail and the nose goes up. When the pilot wants the plane to move downwards, the wheel is pressed gently forward.

The pilot uses the rudder bar to turn the plane left or right. The plane is also tilted to make the turn smoother. The ailerons on the wings make the plane tilt – these are moved by the wheel or stick.

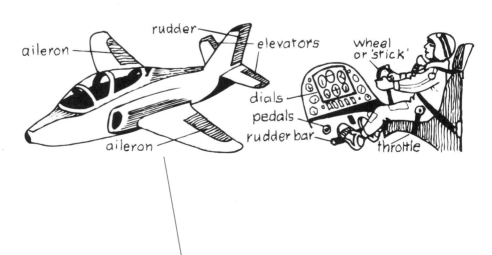

✿ may involve diagrams

Poetry genre

✿ there are different types of poetry, for example lyric (involving poet's emotions or feelings) and narrative (tells a story).

SNAKE

Suddenly the grass before my feet
shakes and becomes alive.
The snake
twists, and almost leaps,
graceful even in terror,
smoothness looping back over smoothness,
slithers away, disappears.
—And the grass is again still.

And surely, by whatever means of communication
is available to snakes,
the word is passed:
Hey, I just met a man, a monster, too;
Must have been, oh, seven feet tall.
So keep away from the long grass,
it's dangerous there.

Ian Mudie

✿ uses word pictures to build sensory impressions and create images

✿ plays with sounds of words and rhythms of phrases

✿ compresses ideas – uses less 'space' than prose

Assessment

Scholastic Comprehension can be valuable in helping you to assess a child's developing progress in English. Comprehension exercises test above all children's ability to read and make sense of text. Because the reading passages are appropriately labelled with a particular genre name, it is relatively easy to spot whether a child is less or more able to tackle and make sense of specific types of text. Moreover, by looking at whether particular questions are inferential, deductive, evaluative or literal, it is also easy to recognise areas where the child is having difficulty. In either case, there is a wide range of differentiated material to choose from in the four Pupil's books and this Teacher's book, which will challenge or build confidence in most children in the primary school.

Photocopiables for assessment and record-keeping

Pupil's record and evaluation sheet
This has been designed to be completed mainly by the children. It provides a record of the units covered by each child and allows each child to indicate his or her interest, level of difficulty and level of achievement. It is useful in highlighting individual patterns of needs, interests and strengths. It also builds a strong sense of achievement in each child.

Class record of progress
This follows the class as it moves through the school, providing a record of what has been covered in each year. It can help teachers find a starting point with a new class. It also helps with progression between year groups.

Pupil's record and evaluation sheet

[Name] _____'s record

✿ Fill in the chart for each unit you complete.
Use these symbols, or make up your own.

☺ ☻ ☹

Date	Book/Unit	Did I enjoy it?	Was my work good?	Was it easy?

Teacher's comments

Class record of achievement
Pupil's book 1

Unit	Title	Genre	Date
1	Abed's special day	Recount	
2	How to wash your hands	Instruction	
3	Trouble in the park	Drama	
4	The new girl	Narrative	
5	Whales	Report	
6	Our school trip to the farm	Recount	
7	Why do we need fire?	Explanation	
8	More care should be taken with rubbish	Argument	
9	How to cross the road safely	Instruction	
10	Sounds	Poetry	
11	The boy who cried 'Wolf'	Drama	
12	The little dog and the big, juicy bone	Narrative	
13	Planet Earth	Report	
14	The naughty kittens	Narrative	
15	Why is the Sun important?	Explanation	
16	You should look after your teeth	Argument	
17	In our playground	Poetry	
18	Sally Ann – Princess of the Chip Kingdom	Narrative	
19	How to make cheese on toast	Instruction	
20	Why do some animals sleep in winter?	Explanation	
21	Being able to swim can save your life	Argument	
22	Exercise is good for you!	Argument	
23	Time flies	Poetry	
24	The strange plant	Narrative	
25	The magic pencil	Narrative	
26	On the beach	Poetry	
27	In the rainforest	Drama	
28	A trip to the future	Narrative	
29	How a guitar makes a sound	Explanation	
30	Dinosaurs	Report	

Class record of achievement
Pupil's book 2

Unit	Title	Genre	Date
1	First day in year 3	Recount	
2	Making scrambled eggs	Instruction	
3	Trouble at home	Drama	
4	The Hare and the Tortoise	Drama	
5	Football	Report	
6	The Fox and the crow	Narrative	
7	We should look after our trees	Argument	
8	Tug of war	Instruction	
9	King Midas and the golden touch	Narrative	
10	A lesson for young James	Poetry	
11	Katy's dog	Narrative	
12	A letter to Grandma	Recount	
13	The fairy penguin	Report	
14	A close shave	Narrative	
15	Why the sea is salty	Explanation	
16	Going to school	Argument	
17	Grasshoppers	Poetry	
18	Catherine and the Carrot King	Narrative	
19	Learning to swim	Report	
20	How to find information in a book	Explanation	
21	Things were better then	Argument	
22	How to plant a tree	Instruction	
23	See the robbers passing by	Poetry	
24	A letter to a school friend	Recount	
25	The genie	Narrative	
26	Why there is lightning then thunder	Explanation	
27	Travel teaches you many things	Argument	
28	A narrow escape	Narrative	
29	Hare in summer	Poetry	
30	The haunted house	Drama	

Class record of achievement
Pupil's book 3

Unit	Title	Genre	Date
1	How to catch a train	Instruction	
2	How a rainbow is made	Explanation	
3	Theseus slays the Minotaur	Narrative	
4	Our trip to Shingle Cove	Recount	
5	Lauren and the Flying Dog (part 1)	Narrative	
6	How to grow tomatoes	Instruction	
7	Door	Poetry	
8	How we digest our food	Explanation	
9	The Hare with many friends	Drama	
10	Sports day	Report	
11	Lauren and the Flying Dog (part 2)	Narrative	
12	A varied diet is best	Argument	
13	Team games are more fun	Argument	
14	Too early	Poetry	
15	Why an iceberg floats	Explanation	
16	The storm	Drama	
17	The elephant	Report	
18	Androcles and the Lion	Narrative	
19	Flat Stanley	Recount	
20	The amazing Tamara Mudpuddle	Narrative	
21	Catching a fish	Instruction	
22	Big Black Bird	Poetry	
23	Why some spiders have webs	Explanation	
24	The Lion and the Mouse	Narrative/mime	
25	The earthworm	Report	
26	Julie of the Wolves	Narrative	
27	Cats make good pets	Argument	
28	Me-moving	Poetry	
29	Tom	Narrative	
30	Brer Rabbit and the Tar Baby	Drama	

Class record of achievement
Pupil's book 4

Unit	Title	Genre	Date
1	How bees 'talk'	Explanation	
2	The greatest tightrope walker in the world	Narrative	
3	A letter from Mozart	Recount	
4	How to make a kite	Instruction	
5	Your skeleton	Report	
6	A Remarkably Woolly Dog	Poetry	
7	How to fly a plane	Explanation	
8	Reading books is a good hobby	Argument	
9	The greatest tightrope walker in the world	Narrative	
10	When my cat died	Recount	
11	Wrecked in the Antarctic (part 1)	Narrative	
12	Making a creepy crawly caterpillar	Instruction	
13	Snake	Poetry	
14	Sharks	Report	
15	Computers or books?	Argument	
16	Return of the Deadeye (part 1)	Drama	
17	The greatest tightrope walker in the world	Narrative	
18	How to help	Instruction	
19	Beware Melanie Prosser	Narrative	
20	*Traffic Lights* and *The Wild Bulls*	Poetry	
21	Super Spuds	Instruction	
22	Horses through time	Report	
23	How a violin works	Explanation	
24	Wrecked in the Antarctic (final part)	Narrative	
25	Return of the Deadeye (final part)	Drama	
26	The Brumby Drive	Recount	
27	The Olympic Games has lost its way	Argument	
28	Magpies	Poetry	
29	A name for a kitten	Narrative	
30	How our writing system works	Explanation	

Answers

Unit 1 – Recount

Abed's special day

Question types: literal 1–3, 7; inferential 4, 8; evaluative 9; deductive 5, 6, 10

Language focus: discuss personal recount features; action verbs in past tense ('went', 'ran', 'made'); words which express emotion/feelings ('sad', 'happy', 'pleased').

1. Abed went to the seaside on Friday.
2. He felt very happy when he saw the blue sea.
3. He took off his sandals before he ran along the sand.
4. People stopped to look at Abed's sandcastle because they thought it was good; they stopped to admire it.
5. Answers may vary – shorts; swimming costumes or any other cool clothes because it was very hot.
6. Answers may vary – swimming; sunbathing; playing beach games.
7. This day was so special for Abed because it was the first time he had ever been to the seaside.
8. Answers may vary – he had to go home; he wondered if the sea would ruin his sandcastle.
9. Answers may vary – the waves would have washed away Abed's sandcastle as the tide came in.
10. took; made; felt.

Unit 2 – Instruction

How to wash your hands

Question types: literal: 1–3; inferential 7; evaluative 4, 10; deductive 5, 6, 8, 9

Language focus: verbs which command; order of instructions.

1. These instructions tell you how to wash your hands.
2. You need soap and water to wash your hands (you also need a sink).
3. Wet your hands. Put some soap on your hands. Rinse your hands in the water.
4. Answers may vary – warm water is usually better for getting dirt off.
5. Your own answer.
6. You can wash your whole body in the bath or shower.
7. Answers may vary – select two from: put; rub; rinse; empty; dry.
8. Answers may vary – towel; paper towel; hand dryer.
9. Answers may vary – clothes; crockery; cutlery; pets; car.
10. The numbers make the instructions easier to follow.

Unit 3 – Drama

Trouble in the park

Question types: literal 1–3, 5; inferential 4, 7, 8; evaluative 9; deductive 6, 10

Language focus: use of dialogue/characters in a play.

1. The play takes place in the park.
2. Tim has lost his watch.
3. He remembers putting his watch in his pocket.
4. Answers may vary – most likely it dropped out of his pocket when he was playing football.
5. Tim was worried about going home because he had lost his watch – it was a present from his aunty and he thought he would get into trouble.
6. Answers may vary – the children are expected to be home by a given time; perhaps it is time to have tea.
7. Tim and Chloe's mum did not look very happy because the children were late coming home.
8. We know that Tim is unhappy because Chloe tells him not to cry.
9. Tim and Chloe felt worried when they saw their mum because they would have to explain why they were late, and Tim would have to tell her that he had lost his watch.
10. Your own answer.

Unit 4 – Narrative

The new girl

Question types: literal 2, 4–6, 9; inferential 1, 3, 8; evaluative 10; deductive 7
Language focus: a story has main characters.
1. The main characters in this story are Rebecca, Kerry and Sarah (Mr Blake could also be considered to be a main character).
2. They were both tall with long dark hair.
3. Answers may vary – probably because they looked the same, perhaps because of their closeness.
4. The teacher's name was Mr Blake.
5. The new girl's name was Sarah.
6. Rebecca couldn't go to school because she had a bad cold.
7. Answers may vary – she may have felt nervous; scared; worried.
8. Rebecca was upset because Kerry was making up a dance for the school show with Sarah and she felt left out.
9. Sarah's great idea was for the three of them to make up a dance together.
10. Answers may vary – yes, because they were all friends in the end and were making up a dance together.

Unit 5 – Report

Whales

Question types: literal 1–5, 9; inferential 7; evaluative 8; deductive 6
Language focus: a report contains facts.
1. Whales live in seas and oceans.
2. Whales can hold their breath for an hour or more.
3. The blue whale is the largest animal in the world.
4. Most whales eat sea plants called plankton.
5. Whales have flippers to help them to swim.
6. Answers may vary – we use our legs to walk and run, for example.
7. It can weigh as much as 20 elephants.
8. Answers may vary – we do not want whales to become extinct.
9. Answers may vary – examples of facts are: whales can hold their breath for an hour or more; they have flippers to help them swim; the blue whale is the largest animal in the world; and they can talk to each other by making noises under water.

Unit 6 – Recount

Our school trip to the farm

Question types: literal 1, 4, 5, 10; inferential 2, 3; evaluative 7, 8; deductive 6, 9
Language focus: nouns.
1. The farmer was called Farmer Jones.
2. The children had to wear wellington boots because it was muddy.
3. Steven was always naughty.
4. The children saw cows, horses, pigs and hens at the farm.
5. Horses and cows were in the field.
6. Answers may vary – bread; pasta; breakfast cereal.
7. Answers may vary – the children may have felt annoyed, angry or unhappy.
8. Answers may vary – because he was always naughty and it served him right; it was funny.
9. Your own answer.
10. farm; mud; cows; clothes; coach. Other nouns include wellington boots, trip, crops, wheat, barley, corn, horses, field, pigs, chocolate and head.

Unit 7 – Explanation

Why do we need fire?

Question types: literal 1, 2, 9; inferential 5; evaluative 8; deductive 3, 4, 6, 7
Language focus: structure of an explanation.

Answers

1. Fire is a hot flame.
2. Fire needs air and fuel to make a flame.
3. Fire gives off smoke, which can make you cough.
4. People use light bulbs today to light rooms (light bulbs use electricity).
5. We need firefighters to extinguish fires which are out of control.
6. Answers may vary – useful: to heat food; to heat houses to keep them warm; to heat metal to make things; to see in the dark. Harmful: destroys things; sends out smoke.
7. You would dial 999 if you spotted a fire.
8. true; true; false.
9. Fire is a hot flame. Many years ago, people used fire to see in the dark. If a fire is spreading and becoming dangerous we need trained firefighters to put it out.

Unit 8 – Argument

More care should be taken with rubbish

Question types: literal 1, 3, 4, 9; inferential 8; evaluative 6, 7; deductive 2, 5, 8
Language focus: bringing out the main points of an argument; new vocabulary ('recycling').
1. Answers may vary – crisp packets; empty tins; cans; bottles and so on.
2. Answers may vary – they throw rubbish on the ground because they do not care about their environment; they are lazy.
3. It is taken to a rubbish tip.
4. Rubbish can be dangerous to animals and birds because they might eat the rubbish, thinking it is food, or they might get stuck inside empty bottles or tins.
5. Answers may vary – insects; mice; hedgehogs; foxes; cats; dogs.
6. Answers may vary – there may be broken glass, rusty, sharp tins and germs.
7. Your own answer.
8. The writer wants us to take care with our rubbish by putting it in a bin or recycling it.
9. throw; hurt; recycling.

Unit 9 – Instruction

How to cross the road safely

Question types: literal 1–3; inferential 4; evaluative 8; deductive 5–7
Language focus: order of instructions.
1. The instructions tell you how to cross the road safely.
2. There are seven instructions.
3. Find a safe place to cross (a pedestrian crossing). Press the crossing button and wait. Wait for the 'walking person' to turn from red to green.
4. Answers may vary – to be aware of any traffic that may be coming.
5. Answers may vary – a parent; an older brother or sister; a guardian; the school crossing patrol.
6. Answers may vary – knowing the Green Cross Code; taking time and care when crossing the road; being sensible when you are crossing the road (not running).
7. Answers may vary – lorries; buses; motorbikes; minibuses.
8. Answers may vary – hopefully yes, they tell you how to cross the road safely.

Unit 10 – Poetry

Sounds

Question types: literal 1, 2, 4; inferential 5; evaluative 8; deductive 3, 6, 7, 9, 10
Language focus: present participle (words ending in 'ing'), poetry structure.
1. The poet likes to hear cats purring.
2. Water makes a gushing sound.
3. Answers may vary – dripping; splashing; roaring.
4. Dogs make a barking sound.
5. Answers may vary – trees make a rustling sound because of leaves and branches moving in the wind.

6. Your own answer.

7. Answers may vary – you might hear a whistle blowing in the playground; on a games field; at a train station; at a swimming pool.

8. Your own answer.

9. Answers may vary – thunder can be a loud, frightening sound; it accompanies lightning.

10. crackling; roaring; banging; squeaking; whistling.

Unit 11 – Drama

The boy who cried 'Wolf'

Question types: literal 1, 2, 9; inferential 3, 5, 7; evaluative 8; deductive 4, 6
Language focus: following stage directions; dialogue.

1. There are four characters in the play.

2. The boy is at the top of a hill.

3. Answers may vary – the boy plays a trick on the people because he is bored; he thought it would be funny.

4. Answers may vary – when the people found out they had been tricked, they may have felt angry and annoyed.

5. The wolf wanted to eat the boy.

6. Answers may vary – when he saw the wolf he may have felt very frightened and worried.

7. The people didn't believe the boy because he had tricked them twice before.

8. Answers may vary – not to play tricks on people because they will not believe you when you really are in trouble.

9. Answers may vary – any stage directions in brackets may be chosen.

Unit 12 – Narrative

The little dog and the big, juicy bone

Question types: literal 1, 2, 5, 10; inferential 3, 4; evaluative 7–9; deductive 6
Language focus: direct speech.

1. The little dog was happy and proud because he had a big, juicy bone.

2. The little dog met a mouse first.

3. The little dog met five animals altogether, including the fish.

4. The dog said, 'No, you can't! It's my bone and I'm going to eat it all on my own.' (This is what he had said to the mouse and the rabbit.)

5. The rabbit asked his friend the fish to get the bone; the fish swam down to the bottom of the lake to get it.

6. No, the dog could see a reflection of his bone in the water.

7. The other animals would not help the little dog because the dog had refused to share his bone with them when they had asked if they could have some.

8. Yes, because they all share the bone.

9. Answers may vary – the message in this story is that you should be happy and grateful for what you already have; you should share things with people as they may return the favour.

10. 'That's a lovely bone,' said the tiny mouse.
'Please help me get my bone back,' he begged.
'Don't worry,' said the rabbit.

Unit 13 – Report

Planet Earth

Question types: literal 1, 2, 5, 7, 8; inferential 3; evaluative 6; deductive 4, 9
Language focus: putting facts together in a report.

1. There are nine planets in our Solar System.

2. All living things need water to live.

3. Earth is called 'The blue planet' because so much of the Earth is covered in water by oceans, seas, lakes and rivers.

4. An astronaut is a person who travels in space.

5. It takes 365 days for the Earth to move around the Sun.

Answers

6. We know that there are other planets because we are able to observe the sky and space using telescopes; we can use satellites; and space missions can tell us about other planets.

7. Sun; Earth.

8. false; false; true.

9. Your own answer.

Unit 14 –Narrative

The naughty kittens

Question types: literal 1, 3, 4, 7, 10; inferential 2, 5; evaluative 9; deductive 6, 8

Language focus: structuring a story; description of characters at the beginning of the story.

1. The two kittens are called Tilly and Tommy.

2. An introduction to the characters is given at the beginning of the story – what the kittens look like; what they are called; where they live.

3. They lived with their owner in a large house. 'Great,' thought Tilly and Tommy. 'CRASH!' went the china doll, all over the floor. Tommy and Tilly were now very tired.

4. 'CRASH!' tells you the sounds things made when they fell on the floor.

5. Answers may vary – the owner thought that the dog had got in to the house because everything was in a mess; things had been knocked over; she never thought her little kittens could be so naughty.

6. Answers may vary – needles, cotton, pins, scissors and so on may have fallen out of the sewing tin.

7. The kittens felt tired after they had finished playing.

8. Your own answer.

9. Answers may vary – when the owner opened the door she must have felt surprised and shocked.

10. Answers may vary – 'Now, have a nice sleep, you two,' she said. 'Oh dear! What a mess!' she cried. She smiled fondly at the two little kittens who were still asleep. She had brought them a special treat for tea.

Unit 15 – Explanation

Why is the Sun important?

Question types: literal 1, 2, 5; inferential 4; evaluative 8; deductive 3, 6, 7

Language focus: recall of information.

1. Words that tell us what the Sun is like are 'huge', 'hot' and 'bright'.

2. The Sun gives us light and heat.

3. Answers may vary – examples of things that can give us light are electricity, torches, candles and matches.

4. We can still see during the day even when the sky is cloudy because the sunlight is so powerful that it shines through the clouds.

5. live; chain, Sun; day.

6. Answers may vary – because the Earth is spinning on its own axis, when our part of the Earth is turned away from the Sun we do not receive any light.

7. Answers may vary – the sun can damage your eyes and skin; it can cause rivers to dry up and if the land is too dry, crops, animals and people can suffer; hot sun on dry land can cause fires.

8. Answers may vary – there would be no life on Earth.

Unit 16 – Argument

You should look after your teeth

Question types: literal 1–7; inferential 9; evaluative 8; deductive 10

Language focus: recognising the main points of an argument.

1. This argument tells you to look after your teeth.

2. You will have two sets of teeth in your lifetime.

3. Your first set of teeth is called milk teeth.

4. Adult teeth will grow when the milk teeth have fallen out.

5. You should clean your teeth twice a day (in the morning and before you go to bed).

6. Answers may vary – foods that are bad for your teeth are sweets, chocolate, biscuits and fizzy drinks, for example.

7. Sweet foods have sugar in them that makes your teeth rot.

8. Answers may vary – you should go to the dentist so that he or she can check, treat and clean your teeth, give you advice about how to look after your teeth and spot any problems in time.

9. Answers may vary – clean your teeth twice a day; don't eat too many foods which have sugar in them; visit the dentist regularly.

10. Your own answer – cakes, jam, custard.

Unit 17 – Poetry

In our playground

Question types: literal 1–3; inferential 6, 7; evaluative 4, 8, 9; deductive 5
Language focus: recognising the rhythm or beat in a poem.

1. The children are playing in the playground.

2. Answers may vary – they are running, laughing, joking, having fun, skipping, shouting names, playing different games, twirling and pointing.

3. 'Running' and 'skipping' tell you how the children are moving ('twirling' is also correct).

4. Answers may vary – probably yes, because the poet writes: 'And laugh and joke and have some fun'; also, the activities the children are doing all suggest that the children are happy.

5. Your own answer.

6. The whistle blowing and the bell ringing stops the children's fun.

7. Answers may vary – the playground is still and silent; playtime is over and all the children have gone into school.

8. The next line has four beats.

9. Each line has three beats.

Unit 18 – Narrative

Sally Ann – Princess of the Chip Kingdom

Question types: literal 1–3; inferential 4; evaluative 6; deductive 5, 7, 8
Language focus: proper nouns; discussion of fantasy stories; use of commas when listing items ('large ones, small ones...').

1. Answers may vary – Sally Ann was selfish and rude (children may give other answers using their own words).

2. Mr Chipit told Sally Ann she could be Princess of the Chip Kingdom.

3. There were large, small, brown, red and blue potatoes in the Chip Kingdom.

4. Chips are made from potatoes.

5. Answers may vary – she missed home; she had seen too many potatoes; and she had eaten too many chips.

6. No, she wasn't eating a healthy diet as she was eating only chips – you should have a varied diet.

7. Answers may vary – probably no because her time in the Chip Kingdom had weaned her off her love of chips.

8. Proper nouns – all the days of the week; May; Sally Ann; Mr Chipit; Chip Kingdom; Princess of the Chip Kingdom.

Unit 19 – Instruction

How to make cheese on toast

Question types: literal 1, 5; inferential 2; evaluative 4; deductive 3, 6–9
Language focus: numbered order of instructions; vocabulary associated with instruction ('recipe', 'list').

1. This recipe tells you how to make cheese on toast.

2. You would use the knife to spread the butter on the toast.

3. You would probably use margarine.

4. The numbers are put in so that you know in which order to follow the instructions.

Answers

5. Butter one side of the toast. Sprinkle grated cheese on top of the toast. Spread some sauce or pickle over the top of the melted cheese.

6. Answers may vary – you could use tomato sauce or other types such as brown sauce or piccalilli sauce.

7. The heat melts the cheese under the grill.

8. Answers may vary – beans; eggs; tomatoes; pâté; peanut butter.

9. You can also toast bread in a toaster.

Unit 20 – Explanation

Why do some animals sleep in winter?

Question types: literal 1, 2, 4, 6; inferential 5; evaluative 8; deductive 3, 7, 9
Language focus: new vocabulary ('hibernate'); writing an explanation.

1. Some animals hibernate in winter because the weather can be very cold; it is difficult to find food.

2. Its heart beats slowly and it breathes slowly.

3. Answers may vary – they could be attacked or eaten by other animals if they did not find a safe place.

4. Answers may vary – three animals which hibernate are dormice, hedgehogs and bears (the other animals that are mentioned in the passage are chipmunks and frogs; there are also other animals which hibernate).

5. An animal might wake up during hibernation to feed.

6. Animals stop hibernating in spring, when the weather becomes warmer.

7. Answers may vary – they might find a sheltered place under some leaves, perhaps under a pile of garden rubbish or under a woodpile.

8. Answers may vary – because food is scarce; snow may cover the ground; the ground becomes hard so animals cannot dig the earth for insects.

9. pond; mud; feed; place.

Unit 21 – Argument

Being able to swim can save your life

Question types: literal 1, 2, 9; inferential 4; evaluative 7; deductive 3, 5, 6, 8
Language focus: words which precede a reason in an argument ('if', 'because').

1. The main point of the argument is that being able to swim could save your life.

2. If you could not swim and you fell into deep water, you could drown.

3. Answers may vary – reservoirs; rivers; ponds; seas.

4. Answers may vary – it helps to keep you fit; it exercises your heart and other muscles in the body.

5. Answers may vary – no diving in the shallow end; no running along the poolside; no eating in the water.

6. Answers may vary – surface dives; sculling; floating; water games such as polo; snorkelling.

7. Answers may vary – because if you fell into deep water it is unlikely there would be any steps to help you climb out, so you need to know what to do.

8. because; unless; so; if.

9. You might learn front crawl, breaststroke and backstroke at school (butterfly is also a possibility for a more advanced swimmer).

Unit 22 – Argument

Exercise is good for you!

Question types: literal 1, 2, 4, 8; inferential 3, 5; evaluative 10; deductive 6, 7, 9
Language focus: summing up an argument.

1. stronger; 600; heart.

2. The main idea in this argument is that exercise is good for you.

3. Answers may vary – the muscles which help you to move about are in your legs and arms (but there are muscles all over your body).

4. If you do not exercise, your muscles with not be as strong and you will therefore not be as fit and healthy.

5. Answers may vary – swimming and any game in which you run about such as tennis or football.

6. Your own answer.

7. Answers may vary – examples of joints are the knee, elbow, shoulders, hips and fingers.

8. The author enourages people to exercise because it is good for them.

9. Answers may vary – you can exercise at home, in a gym, in a park or in a garden, for example.

10. Your pulse should get faster.

Unit 23 – Poetry

Time flies

Question types: literal 1, 4, 5; inferential 7; evaluative 6, 9; deductive 2, 3, 8

Language focus: poems can have a special message.

1. The poem is about time; the passing of time.

2. You would find the hour, minute (and perhaps the second) hands on a clock.

3. Answers may vary – we can use a watch (digital or analogue), a speaking clock or a sundial to tell the time.

4. The words that describe the sound that the clock is making are 'tick tock tick' and 'tock tick tock'.

5. Time seems to stand still when we are bored or sad or ill.

6. Make the most of your time; don't waste it as time flies and cannot be recaptured.

7. 'Don't idle away! Come on, be quick!' is the line which tells you not to be lazy.

8–9. Your own answers.

Unit 24 – Narrative

The strange plant

Question types: literal 1, 2, 7; inferential 3–5; evaluative 6; deductive 8, 9

Language focus: use of adjectives to describe plant attributes (colour, shape, size).

1. Samantha and Jake were playing in the garden when they found the plant.

2. Answers may vary – adjectives include 'long', 'blue', 'golden', 'red', 'yellow', 'beautiful', 'thin', 'long' and 'spiky'.

3. Jake and Samanta did not run away because they were curious.

4. Samantha thought it was a strange plant because she had looked at different plants in school but had never seen anything like this.

5. 'Weird' means the same as 'strange'.

6. Answers may vary – they may have felt astonished and curious.

7. When Jake tried to touch the plant, it made a strange sound and started shaking.

8–9. Your own answers.

Unit 25 – Narrative

The magic pencil

Question types: literal 2, 4, 10a; inferential 1, 3, 5; evaluative 6, 9; deductive 7, 8, 10b

Language focus: question marks.

1. The story takes place in school (in the classroom).

2. 'Hey ginger long legs,' said one unkind girl to Mark. Mark flicked the red hair from his face and didn't know what to say. He could feel his big blue eyes filling up with tears.

3. Mark was sad because he was hopeless at drawing and he did not know what to draw.

4. The two words that tell you how the magic pencil moved are 'shake' and 'twitch'.

5. The pencil was a magic one because it could move and draw a picture on its own.

6. Answers may vary – astonished; surprised; happy.

7–9. Your own answers.

10a. Answers may vary – any two from the following are correct: 'What are you

Answers

going to draw?'; 'What can I do?'; 'Have you got a bike or maybe a pet you can draw?'; 'However did you draw that?'
b. Your own answer.

Unit 26 – Poetry

On the beach
Question types: literal 1; inferential 3, 7; evaluative 5; deductive 2, 4, 6, 8, 9, 10
Language focus: setting out verse of a poem; rhyming words; discussion of conjunctives/prepositions in poetry (for example, then, with, and).
1. The sea makes a roaring noise.
2. Your own answer.
3. The weather is bad, because the descriptive words chosen depict bad weather such as 'howling wind', 'heavy rain', waves 'crashing' and 'dark sky'.
4. Your own answer.
5. Answers may vary – the children may have gone home because it is getting late; it's the end of the day; it's time for tea!
6. Answers may vary – the motion of the waves moving forwards and backwards gives the impression of somebody breathing in and out.
7. Answers may vary – capitals have been used for emphasis, to make the reader think the noise is really loud.
8. The poet is writing about winter and summer. Your own answer for the second part of the question.
9. Answers may vary – the sandcastles have been swept away by the incoming tide.
10. Answers may vary – 'making', 'taking'; 'bed', 'head'; 'day', 'away' and so on.

Unit 27 – Drama

In the rainforest
Question types: literal 1, 2, 5; inferential 3, 4, 9; evaluative 6; deductive 7, 8
Language focus: sound effects in a play.
1. Hanif and Megan are in a rainforest.
2. A parrot makes a squawking sound.
3. Megan speaks with a shaking voice because she is nervous and worried about animals she might find there.
4. Answers may vary – examples are 'Don't worry, it's only a parrot, it won't hurt you'; 'Be quiet, you'll scare it away'; 'It won't hurt you – that one's not poisonous'; and 'Look at that amazing tiger'.
5. Three animals that they see are a parrot, a snake and a hummingbird (they also see a monkey and a tiger).
6. The sound effects are important because people cannot see the play being performed, they can only listen to it.
7. If the rainforest were chopped down, the animals would lose their natural habitat and there would be a danger of them becoming extinct.
8. People chop rainforests down so that they can try to farm the land, and the wood can be used to make paper and furniture.
9. The sound effects needed in this play are: twigs breaking underfoot; leaves rustling; a parrot squawking; a snake hissing; water dripping on a leaf; a hummingbird fluttering its wings; a monkey swinging through branches; a tiger lapping up some water; possibly a waterfall; and wood being chopped.

Unit 28 – Narrative

A trip to the future
Question types: literal 1–5, 10; inferential 6, 7; evaluative 9; deductive 8
Language focus: importance of characters; exclamation marks.
1. Leon and Surinder are the characters in the story.
2. The children were looking at toy cars in a toyshop.
3. The big sign said 'Do not Touch!'
4. The colour of the light was green.
5. The children found an old rusty motorbike (it was a time machine).

6. Answers may vary – the buttons were for controlling the bike/time machine.

7. Surinder wanted to get off the bike because she felt frightened.

8. The children have found a motorbike/time machine in the toyshop; this is taking them to the future.

9. Answers may vary – surprised, excited, worried.

10. Answers may vary – select from: 'This is great!'; 'It's like one of those video games!'; 'I want to get off!'

Unit 29 – Explanation

How a guitar makes a sound

Question types: literal 1, 3, 4, 5; inferential 6; evaluative 7; deductive 2, 8, 9

Language focus: new vocabulary ('pluck', 'vibrate').

1. The strings on a guitar are made of steel or nylon.

2. Answers may vary – examples of other instruments that have strings are a violin, harp, viola, double bass, cello and piano.

3. You can make a sound on the guitar by plucking the strings with your fingers.

4. When the string is plucked it 'shakes' or 'vibrates'.

5. You can change the sound a guitar makes by making the strings longer or shorter; by moving the tuning pegs; or by pressing your fingers on the string.

6. Electric guitars are more powerful; they do not have a sound hole; they use electricity and a loudspeaker.

7. Yes, because when a note is played, a hammer hits a string.

8. You use a bow to play a violin.

9. Pluck – pick, pull sharply; vibrate – quiver, shake, move to and fro.

Unit 30 – Report

Dinosaurs

Question types: literal 1, 2, 5, 6, 9; inferential 8; evaluative 9; deductive 3, 4, 7, 10

Language focus: putting facts together in a report.

1. We know that dinosaurs lived millions of years ago because people have found old dinosaur bones (fossils) in the ground.

2. The report first tells us about Tyrannosaurus Rex (T-Rex).

3. Diplodocus had a very long neck so it could eat the leaves from tall trees.

4. A giraffe has a very long neck.

5. Triceratops had horns.

6. fossils; plant; millions.

7. Answers may vary – enormous; large; big; gigantic.

8. T-Rex got its food by sprinting after its prey.

9. Your own answer.

Unit 1 – Recount

First Day in Year 3

Question types: literal 1–4; inferential 5–7; evaluative 8, 9; deductive 10
Language focus: discuss personal recount features – orientation ('on Tuesday'); sequence of events; personal comment ('I think I'm going to like...'); proper nouns ('Ben', 'Mr Rigg').

1. The writer's friend was called Ben.
2. The new teacher's name was Mr Rigg.
3a. The class did some writing; b. Mr Rigg read a story.
4. His story was about a frightening encounter with a big snake.
5. He was the first male teacher that the writer had had.
6. Year 2 had more things around the walls.
7. The things that made the writer happy were: sitting next to Ben; Mr Rigg was really friendly; Mr Rigg read a great story.
8. Answers may vary – you feel lonely; you don't know anyone; you have no friends; you do not know where things are.
9. Answers may vary – the writer could be a boy (best friend is Ben) or a girl (finds it hard to call the teacher Mr Rigg).
10. Answers may vary – he wants to appear braver than he really is.

Unit 2 – Instruction

Making scrambled eggs

Question types: literal 1, 3, 4; inferential 2, 7; evaluative 6, 8; deductive 5, 9, 10
Language focus: instructions – verbs in imperative mood; structure of commands; sequenced, numbered steps in a process.

1. You need four eggs.
2. You would use a whisk or fork to beat the eggs.
3. You would use a medium-sized saucepan.
4. Toasting is mentioned in the recipe.
5. Butter or margarine is used so that the eggs will not stick to the pan.
6. You would sprinkle parsley on the scrambled eggs to make the dish look attractive and to add taste.
7. To feed four people you would need eight eggs.
8. Scrambled eggs are easy to chew and to digest.
9. Answers may vary – baking, frying, boiling, stewing, roasting and so on.
10. Squeeze toothpaste on to toothbrush. Brush teeth up and down. Don't forget gums. Rinse out mouth and rinse toothbrush.

Unit 3 – Drama

Trouble at home

Question types: literal 1–4; inferential 5–7; evaluative 9, 10; deductive 8, 11
Language focus: oral language features phrases, not complete sentences; non-standard English – omission of letters ('goin'', ''em'); slang ('Yeah') and colloquialisms ('broke').

1. The two characters in the play are Joshua and Luke.
2. Joshua's dad has just lost his job.
3. He looks for jobs in the paper every morning.
4. He is going for a job interview.
5. The stage directions tell us, 'He frowns'; he says that he hopes his dad finds a job soon.
6. The conversation is taking place in mid-afternoon.
7. The boys are discussing Joshua's family problems and his home life.
8. The company did not make enough money and had to close down.
9. Answers may vary – the problems might be lack of money; depression; loss of self-esteem and self-respect; frequent arguments at home; people losing their temper more easily.
10. Answers may vary – people look for new jobs in advertisements in newspapers or job agencies; by visiting the Job Centre; by writing letters to employers; asking around, getting information from friends and relatives.
11. Answers may vary – it is written in dialogue form; there are no speech marks;

names of speakers are in small capitals followed by a colon; it is made to sound like oral language with incomplete sentences, slang and so on.

Unit 4 – Drama

The Hare and the Tortoise

Question types: literal 1–3; inferential 4, 5, 6; evaluative 8, 9; deductive 7
Language focus: procedural writing in stage directions; layout of dialogue in a play; acting out the scene – facial expression and tone of voice; adjectives to describe characteristics.

1. The two main characters are Hare and Tortoise.
2. Hare lost the race because he went to sleep.
3. The message was 'slow and steady wins the race'.
4. Hare saying, 'No one has ever beaten me. Ever!' showed he was boastful.
5. The audience liked Tortoise more; they cheered and cried, 'Hooray for Tortoise!'
6. Hare: boastful, overconfident, scornful, fast, impatient, rude;
Tortoise: steady, slow, patient, determined, persistent, wise.
7. Your own answer.
8. Answers may vary – Hare is very quick and so confident in his own ability that he will probably not remember Tortoise's advice.
9. Your own answer.

Unit 5 – Report

Football

Question types: literal 1–4; inferential 5, 6; evaluative 7, 8; deductive 9, 10
Language focus: factual text in an information report uses technical vocabulary and sometimes includes explanations within the text; use of verbs in third person and continuous present tense ('The striker's job is to score goals').

1. Another name for football is 'soccer'.
2. A net is used behind the goalposts.
3. Yes, football is played by both girls and boys.
4. The most famous football event in the world is the World Cup.
5. The goalkeeper makes it difficult to score a goal.
6. It is the goalkeeper's job to stop the ball going into the net, so using his hands is allowed.
7. Answers may vary – football is one of the most popular games in the world and is often on TV; it is a game of skill, which girls and boys admire.
8. It is played in many countries around the world and is popular all over the globe.
9. 'Olympic sport' means a sport played at the Olympic Games.
10. inflated with air – filled with air; net – webbed material strung between the goalposts to catch the ball when it goes into it; goalkeeper – a player protecting the goal; striker – a player whose job is to score goals; defend – to stop the other team from scoring.

Unit 6 – Narrative

The Fox and the Crow

Question types: literal 1–5; inferential 6, 7; evaluative 9; deductive 8
Language focus: third-person narrative using the past tense, with direct speech using the first-person present tense ('I want', 'I know'); narrative structure of fables and traditional stories with moral teaching.

1. The crow had found a piece of cheese on the ground.
2. The crow flew on to a branch of a nearby tree.
3. The fox planned to get the cheese by getting the crow to open her mouth.
4. When the crow began to sing the cheese dropped out.
5. Don't trust people who flatter you.
6. The fox thought his plan would work because he knew the crow was vain.
7. She was flattered, and was thinking about how the fox thought she could sing well.
8 and 9. Your own answers.

Unit 7 – Argument

We should look after our trees

Question types: literal 1, 2; inferential 3, 7; evaluative 5, 6, 8, 9; deductive 4
Language focus: ordering ideas using words such as 'first', 'second', 'finally'; causal relationships shown by words such as 'because'; arguments often conclude with a recommendation; written in continuous present tense.

1. Answers may vary – points to cover include: trees maintain the right quality of air; they support the soil; they can be used as homes for animals and birds and give them food; they provide shade and shelter; they make the environment pleasing to look at.
2. They provide homes and food for birds and animals.
3. Trees are important in summer because they provide shade from the hot sun.
4. Answers may vary – birds and animals may eat the flowers, leaves, berries, fruit and sometimes the bark of the trees.
5. The main idea given in the argument is that we should look after our trees.
6. Answers may vary – all around the world forests are being cut down, so we need to protect those trees that are left and plant more of them.
7. Trees keep the air pure because they give off oxygen. The roots of trees hold the soil together. Trees provide homes for birds and animals. Trees keep us cool because they shade us from the hot sun. Trees are beautiful to look at.
8. Answers may vary – the balance of nature would be harmed; there would be no shade; no beautiful trees to look at; no habitat for birds and animals; soil erosion would take place.
9 and 10. Your own answers.

Unit 8 – Instruction

Tug of war

Question types: literal 1–5; inferential 6, 7; evaluative 8; deductive 9, 10
Language focus: instructions often omit articles for brevity ('hold rope' instead of 'hold the rope'); verbs are often imperatives; the process is explained by the use of a numbered list of steps.

1. These instructions tell you how to play a game of tug of war.
2. You need a long thick rope with a piece of cloth tied at the halfway mark, and a line on the ground.
3. Two teams of equal numbers and size are needed to play the game.
4. A team knows when to start when they hear 'Pull!'
5. To win, a team has to pull the other team over the line.
6. The teams should be of equal number and size to make the tug of war a fair contest.
7. A thin rope might break and would be hard to hold.
8. Answers may vary – strong or heavy people would be preferable.
9. Line up runners, each with book on head; begin race; tell runners who drop book to go back to start; give prize to runner who is first over line with book on head.
10. A team game means that a game is played by teams, not individuals; answers may vary for teams – possibly football, netball, cricket, rugby, basketball, hockey, volleyball.

Unit 9 – Narrative

King Midas and the golden touch

Question types: literal 1–4; inferential 5, 6; evaluative 7, 9; deductive 8
Language focus: narratives can use the third person in the past tense, with direct speech which uses past or future tense ('will starve'); proper names are capitalised ('King Midas', 'Marigold'); direct speech is placed within inverted commas; punctuation is placed inside inverted commas.

1. The name of the king was King Midas. His daughter was called Marigold.
2. The first wish he was granted was the golden touch; the second wish he was granted was that the golden touch was taken away.
3. A servant brought his breakfast to him. He was going to eat pancakes, fresh fruit and an egg.

4. The first problem was that his breakfast turned to gold.

5. The worst thing that happened to him in the story was his daughter turning to gold.

6. He didn't realise that his food and his daughter would turn to gold.

7. Magical things happen that would not occur in real life.

8. 'I have learned my lesson' means that you have realised where you went wrong, and now know not to make that mistake again.

9. Your own answer.

Unit 10 – Poetry

A lesson for young James

Question types: literal 1–3; inferential 4; evaluative 6; deductive 5, 7–9

Language focus: narrative poems tell a story; the rhyme scheme is abcb (the second and fourth lines rhyme).

1. The name of James's first teacher was Mrs King.

2. James was very spoiled when he first came to school.

3. Three words that he used a lot were 'Won't', 'No' and 'Yuk'.

4. James changed because Mrs King wouldn't put up with his behaviour.

5. They must have thought that he was very rude.

6. Your own answer.

7a. lost her cool – lost her temper; b. Just will not work with me – will have no effect on me.

8 and 9. Your own answers.

Unit 11 – Narrative

Katy's Dog

Question types: literal 1–3; inferential 4, 5; evaluative 10; deductive 6–9

Language focus: structure of a narrative – orientation (beginning), complication (middle), resolution (ending); includes direct speech; written in past tense; uses metaphor.

1. Katy's dog was called Dylan.

2. He had long legs, a short tail and long hair; his coat was a mixture of colours.

3. Two dogs tried to attack Katy in the park. Dylan stood in their way and fought them off.

4. She trusted him to look after Katy.

5. Usually he barked and ran to her.

6. Answers may vary – Dylan may have chased the dogs and got lost. Her father was right when he said that Dylan would find his way home.

7. He had been fighting and had probably fallen into some mud.

8. A tornado is a fierce and violent storm; Dylan became fierce if Katy was in danger.

9. Katy felt happy and relieved at the end of the story.

10. Your own answer.

Unit 12 – Recount

A letter to Grandma

Question types: literal 1–4; inferential 5, 6; evaluative 11; deductive 7–10

Language focus: features of a recount – orientation (when, where and how); verbs in past tense; use of first person.

1. The letter was sent from Jersey.

2. The flight left Manchester at 10 o'clock in the morning.

3. The flight attendant told the passengers about the plane.

4. Stephanie drank lemonade during the flight.

5. The rough air in the clouds (turbulence) made the plane bump about.

6. Stephanie thought her parents were frightened because they closed their eyes.

7. She may have been frightened too – she also closed her eyes.

8. Answers may vary – Stephanie had probably not flown before.

9. Your own answer.

10a. revved – made the engine run quickly; b. descending – going down.

11. Your own answer.

Answers

Unit 13 – Report

The fairy penguin

Question types: literal 1–4; inferential 5–7; evaluative 9; deductive 8, 10, 11
Language focus: adjectives usually describe objects or people ('dark blue', 'small'); use of verbs in continuous present tense; use of proper nouns ('fairy penguin').

1. The smallest penguins in the world are fairy penguins.
2. They live in the south of Australia and New Zealand.
3. The back of a fairy penguin is dark blue.
4. Fairy penguins eat small fish and squid.
5. Webbed feet would be important to help them swim.
6. They chase and catch fish and squid in the sea.
7. If penguins get covered in oil, it stops them swimming and they drown; it can also get into their stomachs and lungs.
8. Your own answer.
9. Answers may vary – to protect fairy penguins we should create sanctuaries, restrict fishing and prevent oil spillages.
10. 'Breeding grounds' are places where fairy penguins mate and have their young.
11. live, lay, hunt.

Unit 14 – Narrative

A close shave

Question types: literal 1–4; inferential 5; evaluative 9; deductive 6–8, 10
Language focus: narratives are usually structured – orientation, events, complication, resolution; use of third person and past tense; inclusion of direct speech, using present and future tense ('I'll').

1. Three people went fishing: the narrator, the narrator's father and Hannah.
2. They put the boat into the water at the slipway.
3. The slipway was on a river.
4. Four fish were caught.
5. The big, black clouds were the signs that a storm was coming.
6. Your own answer.
7. They travelled back in the coastguard launch because their own boat was immobilised; it would be safer.
8. If they hadn't had the mobile phone, they would have been caught in the storm and their boat might have capsized or sunk.
9. Answers may vary – she was probably worried, then relieved and glad that she had put the mobile phone in the bag.
10. Answers may vary – the story tells about a dangerous situation which could have turned out badly, but didn't.

Unit 15 – Explanation

Why the sea is salty

Question types: literal 1–4, 10; inferential 5, 6; evaluative 7; deductive 8, 9
Language focus: use of sequence adverbs ('first', 'next', 'then'); use of present continuous tense ('washes', 'flow'); use of generalised nouns.

1. Yes, salt dissolves in water.
2. Rivers carry the salt to the sea.
3. Millions of tonnes of salt are washed into the sea each year.
4. The Red Sea and the Dead Sea are easy to swim in.
5. Yes, the Red Sea is more salty than the Atlantic Ocean.
6. Yes, because more salt will be washed into the ocean.
7. Answers may vary – mud, earth, plants, fish, bones, rubbish and so on.
8. Answers may vary – sugar, honey, jelly cubes, instant coffee powder, gravy granules and so on.
9. Your own answer.
10. true; false; true.

Unit 16 – Argument

Going to school

Question types: literal 1, 3–6; inferential 2, 7, 8; evaluative 10, 11; deductive 9
Language focus: use of logical or causal phrases; use of the continuous present tense.

1. Children in the UK must start school at the age of five.
2. Children must attend school for eleven years.
3. When we first go to school we learn to read, to write and to work with numbers.
4. literacy; numeracy.
5. No, these skills are useful in our daily lives.
6. They will be helpful to us throughout our lives.
7. It teaches us that it is important to stay fit, strong and healthy.
8. Your own answer.
9. Answers may vary – reading, writing, numeracy, working co-operatively and keeping fit are all important things we learn at school.
10. Your own answer.
11. Answers may vary – there are many jobs for which numeracy skills are required, such as jobs in banks and accountancy.

Unit 17 – Poetry

Grasshoppers

Question types: literal 1–4; inferential 5, 6; evaluative 7, 8; deductive 9
Language focus: repetition for effect ('Do you... Do you...?'); use of rhyme ('do/too', 'hop/stop', 'fly/I'); the first word of each new line usually starts with a capital letter.

1. The poem is about a grasshopper.
2. The insect is green.
3. The poet creeps up on them, then stops.
4. No, the poet has never caught a grasshopper.
5. Their big back legs help them to jump high.
6. The part of the poem that reveals that the poet may be scared of grasshoppers is 'Creeping up/Till they hop?/Or do you stop?'
7. probably young; timid; afraid; interested in creatures.
8a. Grasshoppers are wild and green; they have big back legs; b. The poet is rather timid (he is very careful not to get too close to the grasshoppers); he is interested in grasshoppers and probably other wild creatures.
9a and b. Your own answers.

Unit 18 – Narrative

Catherine and the Carrot King

Question types: literal 1–4, 7; inferential 5, 6; evaluative 8; deductive 9, 10
Language focus: structure of a narrative for a fantasy (could not really happen and contains magical happenings); use of adverbs to establish when events happen.

1. No, Catherine did not like carrots – they took too long to chew and meant that she didn't get any playtime.
2. The Carrot King had a carrot-coloured coat, a carrot-coloured suit, pointed carrot-coloured shoes and a crown made of carrots.
3. There were carrots of all kinds – raw and cooked in different ways.
4. The task was that they had to eat all the carrots by midday.
5. These were the other children who hated carrots.
6. Answers may vary – he may want to persuade them to like carrots because he is king of the carrots or because carrots are good for you.
7. The two main characters are Catherine and the Carrot King.
8. Answers may vary – the reader knows that the passage is a fantasy because of details such as the Carrot King appearing with a 'Zing! Zap!', the way in which the Carrot King is described and the main event on which the story is based, which is taking children away in a carrotmobile and forcing them to eat carrots.
9. Answers may vary – she would probably be dressed in carrot-coloured clothes

and would wear a crown of carrots like the Carrot King.

10. Your own answer.

Unit 19 – Report

Learning to swim

Question types: literal 1–4; inferential 5–8; evaluative 11; deductive 9, 10
Language focus: use of continuous present tense; written in the third person; structured with an opening statement followed by facts to back it up.

1. Many children learn to swim when they are quite young.
2. The special swimming classes are held in the school holidays at local swimming pools.
3. Children learn to swim in shallow water.
4. To become a good, strong swimmer you need lots of lessons (and practice).
5. Answers may vary – to teach them not to be afraid; for a number of strokes correct breathing involves putting your head under the water.
6. Shallow water is more suitable so that they can touch the bottom and learn to swim without being frightened.
7. 'Doggy paddle' is a swimming stroke in which you swim like a dog, with your arms and legs bent.
8. Older children or adults who are strong swimmers swim in the deep end.
9. Answers may vary – it is good fun, it is good exercise and it could save your life one day.
10. Answers may vary – basic swimming is the ability to keep yourself afloat, while swimming really well means knowing a number of strokes and being a strong swimmer.
11. Answers may vary – the training would entail learning to be a good swimmer yourself; knowing lots of different strokes; being aware of safety rules and techniques.

Unit 20 – Explanation

How to find information in a book

Question types: literal 1–5; inferential 8, 9; evaluative 7; deductive 6, 10
Language focus: use of third person; verbs in simple present tense ('Most books have', 'the contents page gives'); use of adverbs of time ('information we need quickly') and place ('on the cover').

1. The title of the book is printed on the cover and the title page.
2. The contents page lists all the different subjects covered in the book and the pages where information can be found.
3. Any one selected from the following sections is correct: Invention of the steam train; The first steam trains; Travel by steam train; The end of the steam train era.
4. 'The end of the steam train era' would begin on page 41.
5. A section in a book is called a chapter.
6. Finding information in a book quickly would enable you to use the information when it was needed.
7. Yes, a contents page would be helpful because it would tell you where information can be found.
8. You would find the title and the author's name on a title page.
9. false; true; false; false; true.
10. Answers may vary – a. volcanoes; b. football; c. animals or pets.

Unit 21 – Argument

Things were better then

Question types: literal 1–4; inferential 5; evaluative 6, 7, 10; deductive 8, 9
Language focus: structure of an argument – opens with a statement of the writer's viewpoint followed by logical steps which back up the viewpoint, sums up with a conclusion based on the evidence presented; use of linking connectives ('First', 'Second', 'Lastly').

1. There were fewer people living in cities in our grandparents' day.
2. The air was cleaner.
3. There were not many cars, lorries, planes and factories.

4. Boys and girls tend to spend less time outdoors nowadays.
5. Answers may vary – there is too much traffic; roads are too busy; land is much more built up; there are not enough cycle tracks.
6. 'All of these things make me think that life was better for boys and girls in my grandparents' day.'
7. They give off gases containing tiny particles, and these gases make the air dirty.
8. Rubbish and industrial waste are dumped in our rivers and oceans; algae forms.
9. pollution – something that makes the air, water or land dirty; industrial waste – matter that is left over from factories; algae – a type of weed that pollutes the water.
10. Your own answer.

Unit 22 – Instruction

How to plant a tree
Question types: literal 1–3; inferential 4, 5; evaluative 6, 9, 10; deductive 7, 8
Language focus: omission of words ('Dig [a] hole'); use of commands or imperatives (Turn tree...'); lists written in sequences which may be numbered.
1. You need a tree, a spade and a watering can (fertiliser and a small stake are also correct answers).
2. Answers may vary – you dig a hole, place the tree in the hole and water the tree lightly.
3. You need water to moisten the hole.
4. The spade is used to dig the hole for the tree.
5. Answers may vary – the hole would need to be larger than the pot to ensure that the roots of the tree, and the attached soil, fit in the hole, and to allow you to fill the hole with earth, which will hold the tree firmly in place.
6. Packing the earth tightly around the roots would stop the tree from falling over.
7. A stake is a thin piece of wood used for holding the tree upright as it grows.
8. Compost is rich soil in which plants are grown; fertiliser is a food for plants.
9. This gives information on how many steps there are and in which order they come.
10. The labels help the reader to understand the instructions and ensure that the diagrams are clear.

Unit 23 – Poetry

See the robbers passing by
Question types: literal 1, 2; inferential 3; evaluative 4, 7; deductive 5, 6, 8, 9
Language focus: use of old-fashioned words; use of omission of words ('[He] Stole my watch and [he] stole my chain'); use of repetition for effect.
1. The robber stole a watch and a chain.
2. He must go to prison.
3. The words and phrases are 'robbers', 'My fair la-dy!' and 'watch and chain'.
4. A watch would have a chain if it was an old-fashioned pocket watch kept on a chain, rather than a watch fixed to a strap and worn around the wrist.
5. He would have to be tried and found guilty.
6. Your own answer.
7a. A highwayman lay in wait for travellers and then robbed them; b. He rode on horseback.
8. robber – thief; prison – jail.
9. Your own answer.

Unit 24 – Recount

A letter to a school friend
Question types: literal 1–4; inferential 5–7; evaluative 11; deductive 8–10
Language focus: letters as a type of recount; written in the first person, containing personal comment; layout of addresses and use of capitalisation.
1. Danielle was staying at the Alphorn Chalet, Rue St Antoine, Beauville, Switzerland.
2. Mum, Dad and Oliver are on holiday with Danielle.
3. It was too windy to ski.
4. She normally ate lunch at the chalet.

5. They took skiing lessons to help them to ski better.

6. Even good skiers can improve.

7. Yes, the tone of her letter was that she was enjoying her holiday, and looking forward to skiing the next day if the weather improved.

8. A chalet is a hut, traditionally made of wood, with a wide, overhanging roof.

9. A blizzard is a violent snowstorm.

10. Answers may vary – Switzerland, Austria, France, Italy, America and Canada are some of the countries.

11. Your own answer.

Unit 25 – Narrative

The genie

Question types: literal 1–3; inferential 4, 5; evaluative 6, 8, 10; deductive 7, 9

Language focus: written in the third person; past tense may contain direct speech in the first person, present or future tense; punctuation of direct speech – use of inverted commas (speech marks) around the words spoken.

1. The two boys were called Kirpal and Scott.

2. It was winter.

3. They decided to go to look for shelter at the train station.

4. The bottle was dirty and he couldn't read the label; he wanted to clean it.

5. The food was hot and tasty.

6. They must have felt astonished, possibly frightened.

7. The wind was freezing cold and blowing fiercely.

8. Answers may vary – the genie was wearing a 'glittering blue suit'.

9. They felt warm and happy.

10. Your own answer.

Unit 26 – Explanation

Why there is lightning then thunder

Question types: literal 1–4; inferential 5, 6; evaluative 7, 8; deductive 9

Language focus: use of third person and verbs in simple present tense ('Thunderstorms are', 'Sound travels'); initial orientation statement followed by points in a logical order; use of causal connectives ('because'), generalised nouns ('thunder', 'lightning') and action clauses ('damp air rises', 'light travels').

1. Lightning is a giant electric spark.

2. Thunder is the noise exploding air makes when it heats up and expands.

3. Light travels faster than sound.

4. A flash of lightning is a long way off if the thunder is heard much later than the lightning is seen.

5. The lightning would be very close.

6. The lightning is a long way away.

7. Run to a safe place indoors (a car is very safe). If you are in a wide, open space and there is nowhere to run to, lie flat on the ground. Try to make your surroundings higher than you are (for example, by sitting down on a river bank).

8. Answers may vary – rainstorms, sandstorms, hailstorms, snowstorms.

9. false; true; true.

Unit 27 – Argument

Travel teaches you many things

Question types: literal 2; inferential 3; evaluative 5, 6, 9; deductive 1, 4, 7, 8

Language focus: structure of an argument – opens with a statement of the writer's viewpoint, then presents logical steps with facts which back this up, sums up with a conclusion based on the evidence presented; use of repetition for effect ('You can... You can'); use of rhetorical questions for effect ('How different is your lifestyle, your language, the food you eat?').

1. The first, second and fifth statements are correct.

2. Correct answers are three from the following: homes, food, clothes, jobs, transport, leisure time, language, lifestyle.

3. It is important to ask questions so that you learn more and understand better.

4. 'Lifestyle' means the way in which people live.

5. Your own answer.

6. Answers may vary – 'Travel teaches you about other people and other places' is one correct answer.
7. Answers may vary – the writer sums up the argument in the final paragraph, so any statements taken from that section are correct.
8 and 9. Your own answers.

Unit 28 – Narrative

A narrow escape
Question types: literal 1–3; inferential 4, 5; evaluative 7; deductive 6
Language focus: structure of a narrative – opens by introducing the characters and the setting (time and place) followed by a complication involving an event or events, and finally an ending where everything is worked out; may be written in the past tense but may include dialogue in the present or future tense; use of different words for 'said' to avoid repetition ('yelled', 'gasped').
1. The adventure took place in the rapids of a rainforest river.
2. The experienced rafter was the instructor.
3. The raft was made out of rubber.
4. Answers may vary – he may have thought that there was a danger of Lucy going overboard as they rafted around the bend.
5. He probably feared that Lucy might have drowned.
6a. A rafter became a member of the Tadpole Club by falling over the side of a raft; b. Your own answer.
7. The crisis is when Lucy falls overboard and goes under the water.

Unit 29 – Poetry

Hare in summer
Question types: literal 1–4; inferential 5, 6; evaluative 11; deductive 7–10, 12
Language focus: poetic language compresses meaning; use of figurative language ('goggling eyes').
1. It is summer.
2. The strainer-post is making the shade.
3. The hare changes position to stay in the shade of the post as the sun moves.
4. The hare lifts his 'goggling eyes'.
5. 'weakly panting', 'goggling eyes', 'naked sun'.
6. The third phrase is correct.
7. He is hot and exhausted.
8. He has 'squatted there' to avoid the sun and sit in the shade.
9. Nothing covers the sun; there are no clouds.
10. A 'strainer-post' is a post in the ground to hold another post upright when the wire is tightened.
11. Your skin would start to burn and your body would lose water; if you did not find shade or water you would eventually die.
12. hare – 'there'; run – 'sun'; shade – 'made'; shifts – 'lifts'.

Unit 30 – Drama

The haunted house
Question types: literal 1, 2, 6; inferential 3, 4a; evaluative 4b; deductive 5, 7
Language focus: plays written for radio depend on good sound effects and different tones of voice to convey mood; layout of dialogue – speaker's name in capitals followed by a colon; stage directions usually in the present tense (in italics and inside brackets).
1. The play took place at night, probably just after dark.
2. They dived behind the couch and screamed.
3. Tanya was braver; she was ready to go inside the house and she switched on the torch at the end.
4a. Tanya persuades Joanne that it's an adventure; b. Your own answer.
5. They make the play more atmospheric; the audience cannot see what is happening so they must imagine the scene by hearing the sounds.
6. The ghost is only a cat.
7. Answers may vary – the stage directions reveal that the girls were frightened ('in a shaking voice', 'terrified', 'in a panic', 'The girls scream').

Answers

Unit 1 – Instruction

How to catch a train

Question types: literal 1–3; inferential 5; evaluative 4, 6, 7; deductive 8–10
Language focus: order of instructions; omission of articles ('Choose [the] date and [the] time'); use of verbs in imperative (command) form.

1. You might buy a single ticket or a return ticket.
2. You need to hold on to your ticket in case a railway official asks to check it.
3. The three pieces of information are the time the train leaves, the platform it leaves from and the stations where the train stops.
4. It is important to stand away from the edge so that you don't risk falling under the train.
5. You can prepare to leave the train and make sure you are near the door when your station is reached.
6. You should keep clear of the doorways so that you don't get caught in the doors and don't get in the way of people entering and leaving the train.
7. You should find a secure place to stand, well away from the doors, and preferably with something to hold on to.
8. Decide if you want single or return ticket. Check you have enough money with you. Ask for ticket to destination. Hand over money for ticket. Wait for ticket. Move to platform to catch train.
9. Your own answer.
10. Step 8 – Wait for the train. Do not stand too near the edge of the platform. Step 15 – Step out on to the platform and move away from the edge.

Unit 2 – Explanation

How a rainbow is made

Question types: literal 1, 2; inferential 3–5; evaluative 7; deductive 6, 8–10
Language focus: principal and subordinate clauses and their relationship; subordinate conjunctions beginning adverbial clauses ('When', 'If', 'because'); use of verbs in the present tense.

1. You might see a rainbow on a rainy day when the sun is shining.
2. The drops of water split the white light up into its different colours.
3. The seven colours are red, orange, yellow, green, blue, indigo and violet.
4. White light comes from the sun; it is the light we see.
5. You can't see a rainbow at night because there is no light.
6. Indigo and violet are shades of blue and purple.
7. Answers may vary – possibly reflected in glass, in a splash of oil mixed with water on the ground, on the skin of bubbles.
8. The child's drawing of a rainbow is required for this answer.
9. Answers may vary – for example, clouds gathering and becoming darker, and animals taking shelter, may indicate an approaching storm.
10. Your own answer.

Unit 3 – Narrative

Theseus slays the Minotaur

Question types: literal 1, 2; inferential 4–6; evaluative 7, 8; deductive 3
Language focus: proper nouns ('Minotaur', 'Crete', 'Ariadne') all start with a capital letter; use of unusual vocabulary ('lair', 'labyrinth', 'slew').

1a. It was a monstrous creature who was half man and half bull; b. It ate human flesh; c. It lived in a labyrinth, a maze of passageways under the palace of the king of Crete.
2. Theseus was the son of King Aegeus of Athens. He followed the thread back to the gate.
3. A map is needed for this answer for the child to find Athens and Crete.
4. Answers may vary – he decided to go and kill the Minotaur even though he didn't have to.
5. He killed the monster with his bare hands.
6. They wouldn't have to supply any more people for the Minotaur to eat.
7 and 8. Your own answers.

Unit 4 – Recount

Our trip to Shingle Cove

Question types: literal 1–4; inferential 5–7; evaluative 8; deductive 9, 10
Language focus: structure of a recount – when, what, where; verbs in past tense; use of adverbs and adverbial phrases of time ('Every morning', 'One day').

1. The writer went to Shingle Cove, a small town near the sea.
2. The children went to the beach for a swim.
3. They scrambled through some gorse and down a rocky track.
4. They would sit and look out over the sea and sometimes they played cards.
5. Answers may vary – she probably just enjoyed some time on her own.
6. It was on a slope – they went down a path to the beach and were able to sit and look out over the sea.
7. Answers may vary – the writer's friend Jody could be a boy or a girl.
8 and 9. Your own answers.
10. Answers may vary – weather, location, activities, company, good planning, good health and many others.

Unit 5 – Narrative

Lauren and the Flying Dog (part 1)

Question types: literal 1–4; inferential 5; evaluative 6, 7; deductive 8, 9
Language focus: structure of a narrative – orientation and complication; verbs used in third person, past tense in narrative, but first and second person present and future tense in dialogue; capital letters for proper nouns ('Sheeba', 'Lauren', 'Airedale').

1. It was a horrible night and Lauren was afraid there was going to be a storm.
2. Mum insisted that Sheeba go out into the garage.
3. Lauren was in bed.
4. They shot out through the window.
5. They live in Scotland.
6. Lauren probably would have been frightened. She would not have expected anyone to have been outside her window at that time of night.
7. She was only wearing her pyjamas, and also they had been travelling at great speed and in a northerly direction.
8. Contests involving different Scottish activities, including dancing and sports, take place at a Highland Games.
9. It is a dance.

Unit 6 – Instruction

How to grow tomatoes

Question types: literal 1–3; inferential 5; evaluative 4, 6, 7; deductive 8–10
Language focus: structure of an instruction; use of verbs in the imperative ('Plant', 'Water'); omission of articles ('Water [the] plants daily').

1. You need tomato plants, fertiliser and water (support canes, string and space in the garden to grow the plants are also correct answers).
2. You plant the tomatoes in the garden.
3. You need to water them every day.
4a. The plants would not grow very big and would have very little fruit; b. The plants would die.
5. The canes are needed to support the plants and to prevent them from falling over.
6. The tomatoes should be picked when they are ripe because that is when they taste best.
7. A tomato is red when it is ripe.
8. Answers may vary – sunshine is also necessary for tomatoes to grow.
9. Answers may vary – people spray tomatoes to keep insects and other pests away.
10. Sprays may contain poisons which can harm people.

Unit 7 – Poetry

Door

Question types: literal 1, 2, 4; inferential 3; evaluative 5, 6, 7; deductive 8, 9
Language focus: structure of poetry – breaking up sentences into lines of verse; use of punctuation and capitals; use of metaphor and simile for comparison ('flakes of rainbows', 'like fallen flowers').

1. The poet's grandmother's front door is being described in the poem.
2. The door was made of glass.
3. Answers may vary – the small reflections of light showed the colours of the rainbow.
4. They reminded the poet of fallen flowers.
5. Your own answer.
6. Answers may vary – the poet is probably grown up, looking back to a time in her childhood.
7. Your own answer.
8. Answers may vary – possibly in a church (stained glass).
9. Your own answer.

Unit 8 – Explanation

How we digest our food

Question types: literal 1–4; inferential 5; evaluative 7, 8; deductive 6, 9, 10
Language focus: structure of an explanation – general statement, then points that explain; use of adverbs of time ('First', 'finally').

1. When food is chewed it is mixed with saliva.
2. The chewed food goes into the stomach.
3. Bile comes from the liver.
4. Nutrients are building blocks of the body.
5. No, some food is left over; this is passed into the large intestine and then out of the body.
6. If you eat too much your digestive system might not be able to deal with all the extra food – this can make your stomach hurt or it can make you feel sick.
7. Answers may vary – to keep us healthy by eating a full range of nutrients.
8. Answers may vary – we need foods that provide proteins, carbohydrates, fats, mineral salts and essential vitamins, such as bread, meat and fish, cheese, vegetables and fruit.
9. 'Bloodstream' means the flow of blood around a person's body.
10. It provides a picture of what the explanation tells us, and this makes it easier to follow.

Unit 9 – Drama

The Hare with many friends

Question types: literal 1–4; inferential 5, 6; evaluative 7, 8; deductive 9
Language focus: contrast language of narrative and language used for dialogue; use of language to give clues to characters.

1. Hare was being chased by a pack of hounds.
2. The characters he thought of as friends were Bull, Goat, Ram and Calf.
3. He wanted Bull to charge at the hounds and frighten them with his horns.
4. Answers may vary – nobody else had been able to help him, and he didn't know who else to ask; also, the hounds were now getting very close.
5. Answers may vary – he was sure he could rely on his friends to help him.
6. Answers may vary – they didn't like Hare as much as he thought, they thought he was boastful and possibly that he needed to be taught a lesson, they couldn't be bothered to help him and they may have been afraid of the hounds themselves. His friends' replies were excuses, which weren't necessarily truthful.
7. Answers may vary – the reader may feel sorry for the hare because his friends let him down.
8. Answers may vary – Bull may have been the most useful in protecting the hare because of his horns and because he was the largest and most powerful animal.
9. The narrator keeps the story moving along and explains the action to the audience. In this play the narrator plays a very important part.

Unit 10 – Report

Sports day

Question types: literal 1–4; inferential 5, 6; evaluative 7; deductive 8–10
Language focus: features of an information report – facts, technical terms, action verbs.

1. Blue House won the trophy.
2. Ashi Khan scored the most points.
3. The champion boy athlete was Fergus Thomas.
4. Yellow House won the egg-and-spoon race and had the most fun.
5. Answers may vary – they probably did not take the day as seriously; they enjoyed winning the novelty races and didn't mind losing overall.
6. Nearly everyone in the school was there, and all the houses tried hard to win the trophy.
7. Your own answer.
8. Answers may vary – Blue House won, Ashi Khan was top girl, Fergus Thomas was top boy, Yellow House won the egg-and-spoon race and the sack race.
9. Your own answer.
10. Answers may vary – to be a top athlete you would need to live a healthy life, eat and sleep well, train regularly and be determined and committed. You would also need to have natural strength, speed and talent.

Unit 11 – Narrative

Lauren and the Flying Dog (part 2)

Question types: literal 1–3; inferential 4–6; evaluative 8; deductive 7, 9
Language focus: structure of a narrative – events after the complication (the resolution); past tense of verbs in narrative text, present or future tense in dialogue; use of language in dialogue, especially French words and accent.

1. Lauren was going to meet Fifi and Pierre in Paris.
2. The name of the café is L'Ironique.
3. She joined in with the can-can.
4. Lauren was wearing a kilt (over her pyjamas).
5. She had been dancing and was out of breath.
6. She is referring to the English Channel.
7a. A croissant is a bread-type roll, usually shaped like a crescent; b. It would probably be breakfast time.
8. Lauren wakes up at the end of the story; the adventure was a dream.
9. *cherie* – darling; *belle* -- beautiful; *magnifique* – wonderful.

Unit 12 – Argument

A varied diet is best

Question types: literal 1–3; inferential 4–6; evaluative 7, 8, 9; deductive 10
Language focus: features of an argument – point of view, supporting facts, summing up; use of technical terms ('carbohydrates', 'minerals').

1. They make the body grow.
2. Answers may vary – meat, fish, nuts, eggs and cheese are all rich in proteins.
3. We need to eat foods that contain vitamins and minerals to keep us fit and well.
4. No one food can supply all the things we need.
5. Yes, it would provide most things needed to keep the body healthy.
6. No, it is not healthy and contains too much fat and sugar.
7. You need to eat all kinds of food to have a balanced diet; your own answer for the second part of the question.
8. Your own answer.
9. Answers may vary – fresh fruit would be a healthy snack.
10. Answers may vary – people like the taste of the food even though they know that it is not good for them; convenience foods and junk foods are quicker and easier to prepare; people don't always understand about healthy eating.

Answers

Unit 13 – Argument

Team games are more fun

Question types: literal 1–3; inferential 4, 5; evaluative 6; deductive 7–9

Language focus: structure of an argument – points for and against.

1. Answers may vary – the writer thinks that team games are better than games you play yourself (you can play them with your friends, people have to co-operate as a team and they are good fun).

2. The players have to work together if they wish to win a team game.

3. Team games help people learn how to be part of a team and are also good fun (winning can be seen as a bonus).

4. Answers may vary – you have to think of others, share the play, give players who are weaker a fair chance.

5. Answers may vary – you feel proud, pleased, happy to have contributed to the team effort.

6. Answers may vary – playing team games would help you to make friends because you would get to know people with common interests, learn to work with them and consider their needs, and you would be able to have a lot of fun with the group.

7 and 8. Your own answers.

9. develops character – strengthens your sense of self and develops you as a person; b. team spirit – a spirit of friendship and achievement, the feeling you get from working and playing together as a team.

Unit 14 – Poetry

Too early

Question types: literal 1–3; inferential 4; evaluative 6, 9; deductive 5, 7, 8, 10

Language focus: features of poetry – use of rhyme, need for interesting content; use of wit and humour.

1. Early to bed and early to rise makes a man healthy, wealthy and wise.

2. Birds eat worms.

3. The earliest bird, the one who gets up first, is best fed.

4. No, worms would be eaten if they got up early.

5. The early bird gets the worm.

6 and 7. Your own answers.

8. prosper – do well, thrive, improve your position in the world; sup – dine, eat, have a meal.

9. No, it suggests that the worms would be better to stay in bed.

10. Your own answer.

Unit 15 – Explanation

Why an iceberg floats

Question types: literal 1, 2, 4; inferential 3, 6; evaluative 7; deductive 5, 8–10

Language focus: features of an explanation – opening statement; principal and subordinate clauses and their relationship; subordinate conjunctions ('because', 'so') beginning adverbial clauses of reason; use of verbs in the present tense.

1. Yes, an ice cube floats.

2. Ice is frozen water.

3. You make ice in a freezer.

4. Eight-ninths of an iceberg is submerged beneath the surface.

5. The wine would freeze, expand and push the cork out.

6. Answers may vary – the water turns into crystals of ice and expands.

7. The iceberg is compared to an ice cube. This is useful because everyone knows what an ice cube looks like.

8. false; true; true.

9a. 160 metres would be below the surface of the sea; 9b. The height of the iceberg would be 180 metres.

10. Icebergs are often very big, so if a ship hit one the ship would be damaged; much of the iceberg is under water, so it is often not easy to spot.

Unit 16 – Drama

The storm

Question types: literal 1–4; inferential 6; evaluative 7; deductive 5, 8
Language focus: use of stage directions; comparison of language used for dialogue and stage directions.

1. Matthew and Kirsty had been to the cinema.
2. When they were on their way home, the weather changed suddenly and they found themselves caught in the thunderstorm.
3. Matthew made the decision to shelter under the tall tree.
4. The old lady blew a whistle loudly.
5. Answers may vary – possibly to summon help if required, or to call a pet.
6. Her umbrella was turned inside out because the wind was blowing so hard.
7. They felt frightened, but thankful.
8. Your own answer.

Unit 17 – Report

The elephant

Question types: literal 1–4; inferential 5, 6; evaluative 8; deductive 7–9
Language focus: features of a report – general opening statement followed by detailed facts; use of adjectives.

1. Elephants live in Africa and the south of Asia.
2. African elephants are bigger and darker in colour. They also have sloping foreheads and very large ears.
3. The elephant uses its trunk for eating, drinking and for lifting things.
4. Elephants are hunted and killed for the ivory in their tusks.
5. They might be used to move heavy loads or to carry people.
6. It is hoped elephant numbers will increase now that plastics can be used instead of ivory, and wild elephants are protected in many parts of the world. This should help elephants avoid extinction.
7. Answers may vary – ivory is used for piano keys, for ornaments and decoration of various types.
8 and 9. Your own answers.

Unit 18 – Narrative

Androcles and the Lion

Question types: literal 1–3; inferential 4, 5; evaluative 8, 9; deductive 6, 7, 10
Language focus: structure of a narrative – finding the crisis; the use of moral in a fable.

1. Androcles saw a lion lying on the ground, moaning and groaning.
2. It had a thorn in its paw.
3. He pulled out the thorn and bandaged the paw.
4. The lion recognised Androcles as the man who had helped him.
5. No, the story is set in the past, probably in Roman times; clues include the words 'slave', 'emperor' and 'arena' and the fact that throwing a person to the lions was used as a punishment.
6. Answers may vary – the emperor came to watch what has happening to Androcles as a form of entertainment.
7. He could not believe that the lion had not attacked Androcles.
8. The crisis of the story was when the lion was about to eat Androcles.
9. If you help someone who is in trouble, then good will come back to you in the end.
10. filled with pity – felt very sorry; sprang to kill – leapt forward to kill (and eat).

Unit 19 – Recount

Flat Stanley

Question types: literal 1–4; inferential 6; evaluative 7; deductive 5, 8–10
Language focus: features of a recount – verbs in the past tense; humour in literature from improbable happenings.

1. The name of the book was *Flat Stanley*. The author was Jeff Brown.
2. A bulletin board fell on Stanley and made him flat.

3. He went to California for his holiday.

4. His best adventure was when he helped to capture a gang of art thieves.

5. Answers may vary – Mrs Lambchop is probably Stanley's mother.

6. The thieves would have thought he was a picture because he was flat. To look like a painting he would have needed to have kept very still.

7. Answers may vary – funny books, adventure books and fantasy stories are possibilities.

8. Answers may vary – in fact, his brother, Arthur, blows him up with a bicycle pump!

9. Answers may vary – he couldn't be squashed flat, be put in the post, flown as a kite and so on.

10. Your own answer.

Unit 20 – Narrative

The Amazing Tamara Mudpuddle

Question types: literal 1–3; inferential 4; evaluative 5, 6; deductive 7–9

Language focus: structure of a narrative – introduction, complication, resolution; verbs used in the past tense.

1. She rose, like a hot-air balloon, until her head bumped against the ceiling.

2. Her grandfather had brought it back from Tibet.

3. No, she was always doing unusual things.

4. No, the trekking trip is referred to as recent.

5. Answers may vary – Tamara is imaginative, adventurous, rather unusual.

6. Answers may vary – they are probably fairly normal parents, quite dull, in fact, when compared with Tamara.

7. Answers may vary – floating to the ceiling could only take place in a fantasy story.

8. Tibet is a country in Asia; 'trekking' means going on a long journey on foot, perhaps in surroundings that make the journey difficult.

9. Your own answer.

Unit 21 – Instruction

Catching a fish

Question types: literal 1–3; inferential 4; evaluative 7; deductive 5, 6, 8–10

Language focus: features of an instruction – materials, steps; verbs used in imperative mood ('Fix', 'Cast'); omission of articles ('Fix [the] bait on to [the] hook.').

1. Answers may vary – fishing line, hooks and landing net (a knife, weights, keep net and bait are also correct answers).

2. The bait is fixed to the hook.

3. You put the fish in the keep-net.

4. Answers may vary – you may have to wind in any loose line to stop it getting tangled or if you can feel a fish tugging.

5. You would use a weight to allow the bait on the hook to sink down below the surface of the water.

6. Answers may vary – because the fish might snap the line or escape from the hook.

7. If you caught a very small fish it would be best to throw it back.

8. Bait is something that attracts the fish because they think they can eat it.

9. 'Cast' means to throw out the line so that it floats in the water, at a distance from where you are standing.

10. Answers may vary – it is important to be very quiet because if you make too much noise you may frighten the fish away; patience is required because you may have to wait a long time for a fish to bite.

Unit 22 – Poetry

Big Black Bird

Question types: literal 1, 2, 4; inferential 3; evaluative 6, 7; deductive 5, 8, 9

Language focus: features of shape poetry; expression of emotion in poetry.

1. The bird's eyes are yellow.

2. The bird's beak is black.

3. The bird's yellow eyes, its size, its long legs and its black beak seem to worry the poet.

4. The poet's two excuses are that the bird might attack or it might fly away.

5. Answers may vary – it may be a blackbird, a crow or a raven.

6. Answers may vary – the poet is probably a child, as the bird seems very big and frightening.

7. The poet seems to be afraid of the bird, but is not keen to admit it outright.

8. In the second line of the poem the letter 'e' has been made to look like an eye; 'size', 'long', 'black', 'fly away' and 'distance' have been written so that the shape of the words matches their meaning; the block of colour for words like 'black' also helps to emphasise the meaning.

9. Your own answer.

Unit 23 – Explanation

Why some spiders have webs

Question types: literal 1–5; inferential 6, 9; evaluative 7, 8; deductive 10

Language focus: features of an explanation – need for reasons; verbs used in the present tense ('A spider's web is its home.').

1. It begins to build its web with a single strand of spider silk.

2. It is able to run along these strands.

3. The strands that run around the web are sticky.

4. It feels the movement made by the struggling victim.

5. It kills them and uses them as food.

6. The child's labelled diagram is required for this answer.

7. Answers may vary – this helps the reader to see that the spider's needs can be thought of as being similar to a human being's, and it helps the reader to relate more to the spider.

8. It would be a good comparison because, just like a net, the spider uses its web to catch food; also, webs and nets are similar in appearance because they are both woven.

9. true; false; false.

10. prey – the victim, the creature that is caught; pantry – a place to store food.

Unit 24 – Narrative/mime

The Lion and the Mouse

Question types: literal 1–3; inferential 4, 5; evaluative 6, 8; deductive 7

Language focus: features of mime – actions conveying meaning without words.

1. The lion caught the mouse because he was angry with the mouse for waking him up.

2. He promised that if the lion let him go he would return the favour.

3. The hunters went away to collect a cart to carry the lion home.

4 and 5. Answers may vary – select from choice of words.

6–8. Your own answers.

Unit 25 – Report

The earthworm

Question types: literal 1–5; inferential 6, 7; evaluative 8; deductive 9, 10

Language focus: features of a report – use of facts; verbs used in present tense.

1. The earthworm is long, round and pinkish brown in colour; it has no spine, legs or feet; it is made of rings, or segments, which are covered in hairs (also correct is that the earthworm has a blunt head).

2. Earthworms eat soil that contains decaying plant or animal matter.

3. They live underground.

4. A worm cast is the waste soil, digested by the worm, which is left in little heaps on top of the ground.

5. They enrich it with their waste, and they also loosen the soil, creating passages where air and water can enter it.

6. It would mean that the soil was fertile.

7. Answers may vary – it might become hard and infertile so that nothing would grow.

8. Your own answer.

Answers

10. Answers may vary – you could keep the soil moist by watering it, loose by digging it regularly and rich by adding decaying animal and plant matter.

Unit 26 – Narrative

Julie of the Wolves

Question types: literal 1–3, 5, 6; inferential 4, 7; evaluative 8, 9; deductive 10
Language focus: language of narration; role of the narrator; animal stories.

1. Miyax's father had become hungry on the hunting trip because he had seen no game – there had been nothing for him to kill and eat.

2. He had not explained to her how he had told the wolf that he needed food.

3. Miyax was trying to discover the sounds and movements that they made to express friendship.

4. She would then be able to tell the wolves that she was hungry and needed food.

5. They used signals to communicate.

6. She had managed to attract them by flicking her forefinger in the same way as they flicked their tails.

7. Answers may vary – Miyax's father had not returned from a seal-hunting trip; Miyax was starving.

8–10. Your own answers.

Unit 27 – Argument

Cats make good pets

Question types: literal 1–3; inferential 4; evaluative 5–8; deductive 9, 10
Language focus: argument in the form of a debate; points for and against; summing up and adjudication.

1. Cats make good pets because they are clean, easy to feed and like to be stroked and cuddled (they are also 'beautiful' in appearance).

2. Cats scratch and spit when they are angry, they aren't able to protect the house and do not come when they are called (you cannot take them for walks, they do not travel well and they kill small birds and animals are also correct answers).

3. They scratch and spit.

4. They purr.

5–10. Your own answers.

Unit 28 – Poetry

Me-moving

Question types: literal 1–3; inferential 4, 5; evaluative 6–8; deductive 9, 10
Language focus: features of action poetry – action verbs, length of line; use of rhyme and alliteration.

1. The title tells the reader that the poem is about the poet moving.

2. The poet darts, dashes, jigs, jumps, scampers, skates, scrambles, struts, strides, slips, slides and ambles.

3a. amble; b. gambol.

4. Answers may vary – 'slip' and 'slide', 'crawl' and 'creep', 'rove' and 'ramble'.

5. Answers may vary – examples of him moving slowly is that he ambles, crawls and creeps.

6. Three more groups of alliterative words in the poem are 'scamper', 'skate' and 'scramble'; 'strut' and 'stride'; and 'slip' and 'slide' ('leap' and 'lurch'; 'crawl' and 'creep'; 'rove', 'romp' and 'ramble'; 'turn' and 'trip'; and 'skid' and 'skip' are also correct answers).

7. You would not be able to crawl.

8. Your own answer.

9. amble – move along in a slow, relaxed way; gambol – skip or jump about.

10. Your own answer.

Unit 29 – Narrative

Tom

Question types: literal 1–5; inferential 7; evaluative 8, 10; deductive 6, 9
Language focus: structure of a narrative – orientation, complication, conclusion; use of present tense verbs in orientation, then past tense verbs in main text.
1. The ballet classes are held on Saturday mornings.
2. Tom had trainers on his feet.
3. He would have waited outside the cricket pavilion.
4. Tom is a good cricketer, he is good at batting, bowling and fielding, he plays every Saturday morning in summer with his team at the local cricket pitch.
5. He walks with his sister to her ballet school on his way to cricket.
6. Answers may vary – he may have been looking bored or perhaps he was in the way.
7. He joined in and had a go at everything they were doing; he didn't seem in a hurry to leave for his match – Jessica pointed to the clock to remind him of the time.
8. Answers may vary – he scored a century for his team; he batted, bowled and fielded very well.
9. barre – a horizontal, waist-height bar used for ballet exercises; splits – with the legs spread at right angles to the body; scored a century – made one hundred runs; took five wickets – responsible for dismissing five members of the opposing team; pavilion – a sports building used for changing or refreshments; *pas de chat* – a type of leap in ballet.
10. Answers may vary – probably no, because he might have thought it had spoiled his game.

Unit 30 – Drama

Brer Rabbit and the Tar Baby

Question types: literal 1–3; inferential 4, 5; evaluative 7, 8; deductive 6, 9
Language focus: dialogue in drama; interpretation of character and situation.
1. Brer Fox had been trying to catch Brer Rabbit.
2. He had no wood.
3. Brer Rabbit kept telling Brer Fox not to throw him into the blackberry bush.
4. No, he should have suspected that Brer Rabbit was trying to trick him.
5. Answers may vary – Brer Rabbit was quick-witted and good at talking his way out of things.
6a. Answers may vary – in a fierce, bold voice to the tar baby, then in a meek, pleading voice to Brer Fox, finally in a triumphant voice when he knows he has escaped; b. Answers may vary – probably quite slowly, thinking things through as he goes.
7 and 8. Your own answer.
9. trickster – a clever person, good at fooling others; Brer – brother, a term of address; pesky – annoying, a nuisance.

Unit 1 – Explanation

How bees 'talk'

Question types: literal 1–4; inferential 5; evaluative 6; deductive 7–9
Language focus: features of an explanation – facts, use of present tense; interpretation of a diagram.

1. Bees send messages to each other by using special movements or dances, and by releasing chemicals called pheromones.
2. Answers may vary – when they are looking for food, when the queen bee wants to attract drone bees to mate with her.
3. They fly off to find it.
4. The waggle dance tells the bees that food has been found a long way off.
5. If the queen bee did not produce an important pheromone, drone bees would not mate with her to produce young bees and bees could become extinct.
6. Yes, through 'talking' they communicate about food and mating.
7. Answers may vary – reference should be made to special movements or dances, and to the release of pheromones.
8. Answers may vary – probably because they live packed close together in the hive.
9. On the diagram, the arrow should be pointing straight ahead from where the leading bee is.

Unit 2 – Narrative

The greatest tightrope walker in the world (part 1)

Question types: literal 1–4; inferential 5, 6; evaluative 7; deductive 8, 9
Language focus: structure of narrative – orientation; use of past tense verbs in text – present tense verbs in reported speech.

1. Blondin was the greatest tightrope walker in the world.
2. He had learned his skills as a child in France.
3. He carried a twelve metre pole to help him balance.
4. He started to run.
5. Answers may vary – it seemed an amazing thing to be able to do; it was very dangerous; nobody had ever done it before.
6. He would almost certainly have been killed.
7. Answers may vary – he was very good at tightrope walking and wanted to show off his skills; he enjoyed a challenge; he enjoyed the admiration of the crowd; he may also have earned money from doing it.
8. daring – courageous, brave; taut – stretched tightly; at intervals – with a gap in between.
9. Your own answer.

Unit 3 – Recount

A letter from Mozart

Question types: literal 1–4; inferential 5, 6; evaluative 7, 8; deductive 9
Language focus: recount in letter format; features of a letter; use of verbs in present tense.

1a. The letter was written from Innsbruck; b. It was written in 1769.
2. The Italian for 'my dear little sister' is *cara sorella mia*.
3. It was too expensive for the whole family to travel.
4. Miss Bimbes was the family dog.
5. Mozart mentions, and asks about, the dog several times in his letter.
6. Mozart asks if Bimberl still howls and chases his tail when his sister sings a high B-flat.
7. Answers may vary – because she has certain features that resemble a horse; because he likes to tease and annoy her; because it is a family pet name.
8. Yes, because he takes time to write to her and says that he is missing her and their mother, and wishes they could have joined him and his father on the trip.
9. Answers may vary – Austria is probably very picturesque: he describes the Alps as glittering with ice, and tells us of the branches of the fir trees under lots of snow, a blue, blue sky and wonderful sunsets.

Unit 4 – Instruction

How to make a kite

Question types: literal 1–3; inferential 4; evaluative 8, 9; deductive 5–7
Language focus: structure of an instruction; use of imperative verbs in an instruction.

1. The two sticks should be tied in the shape of a cross.
2. The notches are cut at both ends of each stick.
3. Paper or strips of cloth should be tied on the string to complete the tail.
4. Notches are cut at the ends of the sticks to hold the binding string in place.
5. The tail will prevent the kite from tumbling over and over when it is flying.
6. A big ball of string will allow the kite to fly high in the sky.
7. Strong paper is needed so that the kite does not tear in the wind.
8. Answers may vary – for the feeling of achievement; because it is beautiful to watch; it can be relaxing; it is fun to do.
9. Your own answer.

Unit 5 – Report

Your skeleton

Question types: literal 1–4; inferential 5; evaluative 6, 9, 10; deductive 7, 8, 11
Language focus: structure of a report – generalised introduction followed by key facts; use of specialist words, often explained in the text; use of verbs in present tense.

1. There are 206 bones in your skeleton.
2. Bone marrow is a substance inside some of your bones that helps to make red blood cells.
3. Cartilage is hard tissue that bends when you push it.
4. There are 28 joints in each hand.
5. Answers may vary – the brain controls the body and, if it is damaged, this could cause serious problems; during your life your head is quite likely to take some knocks and bumps, so the brain needs a proper shield.
6. Answers may vary – possibly either the skull, rib cage or spine.
7. Another name for your backbone is the spine.
8. The spinal cord is protected by your backbone. This is the thick cord of nerves which carries important messages from your brain to different parts of your body.
9. If you think you have a broken arm, keep it steady (possibly with a splint) and have it examined by a doctor as soon as possible.
10. Answers may vary – perhaps because when people die, after a while only the skeleton remains, therefore they are associated with death, graveyards and so on.
11. organs – a part of the body which performs a specific job, for example heart, liver or lungs; calcium – the chemical from which bones are made; cartilage – harder material that helps shape parts of your body, for example nose or ears; rib cage – bones that protect your heart and lungs; ligaments – parts of the body that act like elastic bands to hold bones together.

Unit 6 – Poetry

A Remarkably Woolly Dog

Question types: literal 1–3; inferential 4, 5; evaluative 6; deductive 7, 8
Language focus: features of comic verse – play on words, exaggeration, slapstick humour, the unexpected; rhyming patterns in verse.

1. The poet was playing.
2. The poet descibes the dog as being remarkably woolly, with its tail, head and sides all looking the same.
3. The dog said to the poet, 'Am I coming or going or staying?'
4. Answers may vary – due to being so woolly, he could not see which way he was going or what he was doing; if he was spoken to at the wrong end, he could not hear what was being said to him.
5. He spoke to the dog's rear, rather than to his head.
6. Answers may vary – the silly situation; the poet's mistake; the play on words.
7. playing – 'straying', 'staying', 'saying'; head – 'said'; hear – 'rear'.

8. Oh, I see; I'm in a tender mood today and feel poetic, too; for fun I'll just dash off a line and send it off to you. I'm sorry you've been sick so long; don't be disconsolate but bear your ills with fortitude, and they won't seem so great.

Unit 7 – Explanation

How to fly a plane

Question types: literal 1–4; inferential 5; evaluative 6–8; deductive 9, 10
Language focus: nature and order of an explanation; use of action verbs; interpreting a diagram.

1. The controls you would find outside the plane are the elevators, the ailerons and the rudder.
2. The throttle controls the speed of the engine.
3. The wheel is pulled backwards during take-off.
4. The compass indicates direction.
5. The elevators move downwards when the pilot wants the plane to go lower.
6. Answers may vary – it is a specialised and complex job so the pilot must be confident in controlling the plane and must know what to do in any situation.
7 and 8. Your own answers.
9. Answers may vary – pilots need to receive information on the weather, on other planes that are near them and on when, and where, they may land.
10. Answers may vary – they would involve a different type of responsibility; smaller planes may be more affected by weather conditions and have a different number and type of controls; in a smaller plane there would be a greater sensation of flying and a greater feeling of exhilaration.

Unit 8 – Argument

Reading books is a good hobby

Question types: literal 1–3; inferential 4, 5; evaluative 6, 7; deductive 8, 9
Language focus: structure of an argument; use of sequential words ('First', 'The next...').

1. Answers may vary – reading can be done anywhere, you can stop and start easily.
2. Most school subjects depend on reading and, as you read, you learn more and more.
3. Answers may vary – the better you read, the faster you will be able to work on the computer; you need to be able to read the instructions that are given on the computer and possibly in computer manuals.
4. Answers may vary – you would see many words spelled correctly and seeing them written down in context is likely to help you remember them.
5. Answers may vary – because people have been doing it for a long time; it is not a modern hobby, as computer work is.
6. Answers may vary – probably no, because this would not leave you time to read or to do other activities. You would just be staring at a screen.
7. Your own answer.
8. You can become so involved in a book that you forget about everything else.
9. Your own answer.

Unit 9 – Narrative

The greatest tightrope walker in the world (part 2)

Question types: literal 1–4; inferential 5; evaluative 6–9; deductive 10
Language focus: structure of a narrative – complication; use of verbs in past tense in the narrative, but present/future tense in the dialogue; development of character.

1. Blondin carried out his new trick on 19th August 1859.
2. Blondin did not find anybody who was prepared to be carried across the tightrope.
3. The crowds were waiting on the cliffs.
4. Harry Colcord, Blondin's friend, finally agreed to go with him.
5. Answers may vary – because they enjoyed seeing somebody cross the tightrope; because other people told them about it; it was an amazing, daring new feat and they wanted to see whether he would be able to do it.

6. Your own answer.

7. Answers may vary – no, because he should have found a volunteer first; yes, because he felt confident enough to perform the task.

8. Harry Colcord's decision to go on Blondin's back.

9. Answers may vary – probably no, because he did not give Harry much choice; he made him feel uncomfortable; he asked him to do a really dangerous thing.

10. Answers may vary – Colcord agreed because he wanted to help his friend; he trusted Blondin; he wanted an adventure.

Unit 10 – Recount

When my cat died

Question types: literal 1–3; inferential 4; evaluative 5–7; deductive 8, 9
Language focus: features of a recount – adverbs and adverbial phrases of time ('Soon').

1. The writer had got his cat when he was three years old.

2. The writer's dad thought the cat should be put to sleep because she had been sick for a long time and was suffering.

3. The vet said that nothing more could be done to save her.

4. He gave her an injection.

5. It was the first night without her and he missed his cat being there.

6. Answers may vary – he was kind; he was gentle with the cat; he left them alone with the cat for a while.

7. Answers may vary – because he felt they were private details; they were too sad to recall; writing them down would make him remember and feel unhappy again.

8. resigned – to have got used to an idea, probably one you do not like very much; euthanasia – to give someone who is very ill a quick and painless death.

9. Answers may vary – yes, because he would have loved it just as much; no, because he might not have had it so long, or it might have been a less lovable type of animal, such as a goldfish.

Unit 11 – Narrative

Wrecked in the Antarctic (part 1)

Question types: literal 1–4; inferential 5, 6; evaluative 7, 8; deductive 9
Language focus: structure of a narrative – orientation, complication; third person, past tense verbs.

1. The Shackleton expedition set off in 1914.

2. Twenty-eight men set off.

3. Their ship became stuck in the ice pack and was eventually crushed.

4. They camped on an ice floe.

5. They did not have a radio.

6. Shackleton measured the movement of the ice floe with the navigation instruments. After 18th January the ice floe then began to move slightly faster due to the gale.

7. Answers may vary – probably no, because of the extreme conditions, the shortage of food and the danger of the ice floe breaking up.

8. Your own answer.

9. ice pack – the frozen surface of the sea; whaleboats – smaller boats, possibly lifeboats from the *Endurance*; ice floe – ice that has broken away from the ice pack and is floating freely; navigation instruments – tools used to help steer the ship.

Unit 12 – Instruction

Making a creepy crawly caterpillar

Question types: literal 1, 3, 4; inferential 2, 5; evaluative 6, 7; deductive 8–10
Language focus: omission of articles ('Cut [the] egg carton'); verbs in the imperative mood.

1. The egg carton should be cut in half, lengthways.

2. A short caterpillar will have one segment (with three separate egg sections).

3. Two shiny buttons are used to create the eyes.

4. Two pipe cleaners are used for antennae.

5 and 6. Your own answers.

7. Your own answer. For the second part of the question, answers may vary – it would be a suitable gift for a young child because it is attractive to look at, but the child would have to be old enough to know that it could be easily damaged.

8–10. Your own answers.

Unit 13 – Poetry

Snake

Question types: literal 1–4; inferential 5; evaluative 6, 7; deductive 8, 9

Language focus: features of poetry – use of original and creative images; use of the language of prose in verse form; use of line breaks to focus attention on the images created.

1. The poet is walking in some grass in the countryside.

2. The snake twisted and almost leaped up, before slithering away into the grass and disappearing.

3. It told other snakes about the encounter it had had in the grass.

4. The snake viewed the man as a 'monster' who was about seven feet tall.

5. Answers may vary – maybe both equally but in different ways.

6. Answers may vary – the poet felt startled, frightened, relieved he had not been bitten, fascinated, full of admiration for the snake's swift, graceful movements.

7 and 8. Your own answers.

9. Answers may vary – probably that they are seen as frightening, sneaky, slimy, something to be afraid of, while, in reality, they are shy rather than aggressive.

Unit 14 – Report

Sharks

Question types: literal 1–4; inferential 5, 6; evaluative 7, 8; deductive 9

Language focus: structure of a report – introduction followed by the facts; use of adjectives; use of technical terms.

1. There are 350 types of shark in the sea.

2. 20 types are dangerous to humans.

3. Sharks' skeletons are made of cartilage.

4. It does not have a swim bladder, like other fish, to keep it afloat.

5. Humans eat millions of tonnes of shark meat every year, while sharks rarely attack humans.

6. No, because a shark's teeth grow back if they are broken.

7. No, because sharks rarely come near British beaches.

8. Yes, because sharks are much more common in the coast around Australia.

9. cartilage – hard, but flexible tissue; sac – a bag-shaped bladder; murky – dark, gloomy, hard to see through.

Unit 15 – Argument

Computers or books?

Question types: literal 1–3; inferential 4; evaluative 5–8; deductive 9, 10

Language focus: structure of an argument – statement of position, supporting reasons, conclusions; arguments for and against.

1. All the information it contains could be found on a computer.

2. Computers can be better for research because information can be found quickly and easily.

3. Books only provide printed text and pictures, they cannot include moving pictures or sounds of any kind.

4. Answers may vary – probably more time will be spent on computers, especially as they become increasingly sophisticated and able to do more and more things.

5. Having information in several forms means that you can choose the type of information that suits your needs best; there may be more information available.

6. Answers may vary – to enjoy their surroundings or the weather, to get some fresh air.

7. Answers may vary – while travelling, in stations, trains, planes, in waiting rooms, at bus stops, and so on.

8. Answers may vary – a novel takes a long time to read and most people would prefer to do this somewhere comfortable, like in an armchair, or in bed; you are

enjoying a story, rather than seeking information; a computer is not portable and so is limited in the places where it can be taken.

9. A computer menu is a list displayed on a computer screen that tells you what information is available and where it can be retrieved.

10. Answers may vary – probably books, but the author recognises the need for both.

Unit 16 – Drama

Return of the Deadeye (part 1)
Question types: literal 1–4; inferential 5, 6; evaluative 7; deductive 8, 9
Language focus: presentation of a play reading; use of 'cowboy' language ('deputy', 'varmint').

1. Duke Floorwalker was the sheriff.
2. The heroes rode into Bodge City.
3. Princess Tequila was serving drinks in the bar.
4. Bart Wader was wearing an odd ten-gallon hat.
5. Answers may vary – something metallic, possibly a robot horse or some type of motorcycle or small spaceship.
6. Answers may vary – 'villainous-lookin' varmint', 'no-good, gun-totin' pillager', 'plunderer'.
7. Answers may vary – probably because Bart was a dangerous-looking man and the people in the bar knew that he was likely to cause trouble.
8. Answers may vary – 'Howdy pardners', 'I'll take a shot of deadeye', 'villainous-lookin' varmint', 'no-good, gun-totin'...' and 'sank the last drops of deadeye' are examples of correct answers.
9. Answers may vary – items may include a cowboy hat, a gun in a holster, a bandanna tied around his neck, a sheriff's badge.

Unit 17 – Narrative

The greatest tightrope walker in the world (final part)
Question types: literal 1–4; inferential 5, 6; evaluative 7, 8; deductive 9, 10
Language focus: structure of a narrative – conclusion; use of short sentences to heighten tension.

1. Blondin picked up his balancing pole before he stepped onto the tightrope.
2. Blondin stopped in the middle of the tightrope because Harry was too heavy and he was getting tired.
3. Harry's stomach was churning and he felt sick.
4. Blondin died in 1897 at his London home.
5. Answers may vary – because it might make him more afraid and therefore more likely to fall; he would feel sick and giddy.
6. Answers may vary – he probably thought that they were both going to fall and be killed.
7. Answers may vary – no, because he had had a truly terrifying experience when he was carried on Blondin's back.
8. Answers may vary – probably Colcord because he was not an experienced tightrope walker and had only agreed to be carried across the tightrope as a favour to his friend.
9 and 10. Your own answers.

Unit 18 – Instruction

How to help
Question types: literal 1–4; inferential 5; evaluative 6, 7; deductive 8, 9
Language focus: use of verbs in imperative mood ('Check', 'Get'); the need for materials and steps in an instruction.

1. You should only move an injured person if he or she is in danger.
2. If the patient is bleeding, you should press a pad against the wound to try to stem the bleeding.
3. A coat might be used to keep the patient warm.
4. The emergency number is 999.
5. Answers may vary – probably not, as the child is unlikely to be in immediate danger.

6. Answers may vary – stopping any bleeding and making sure the patient can breathe would be two important things to do.

7. If you rang the emergency number you would first need to say that you required an ambulance, then you would need to give as much information as you were able about where the accident had occurred, who the patient was and what sort of injuries he or she had sustained.

8. Answers may vary – yes, you would know techniques such as mouth-to-mouth resuscitation and cardiac massage; you would also know how to bandage wounds.

9. Answers may vary – bandages, cotton wool, antiseptic, scissors and sticking plasters would all be necessary items.

Unit 19 – Narrative

Beware Melanie Prosser

Question types: literal 1–4; inferential 5; evaluative 6–8; deductive 9, 10
Language focus: narrative technique – innovative beginning; use of colloquial language ('Showoff pig', 'smarmy').

1. Melanie Prosser is the school bully.

2. Her two friends are Sally-Ann Simpson and Vicky Farrant.

3. Lucy is in danger of being bullied.

4. The bullies have picked that day because it is Lucy's birthday.

5. Yes, because he is worried about her and warns her about Melanie Prosser. He puts kisses at the end of his note to her.

6. Answers may vary – he likes Lucy and wants to help her; he hates Melanie Prosser; he has untidy hair; he does not seem to write or spell very well; he is persistent. (Lucy requests that he stops sending her notes.)

7. The author starts with a note written by one of the characters; it makes you interested in the story straightaway (opinions on this may vary).

8. Answers may vary – hopefully yes!

9. Answers may vary – the author uses phrases such as 'Showoff pig', 'Be all smarmy smiles' and 'kick her fat teeth in'.

10. Your own answer.

Unit 20 – Poetry

Traffic Lights and *The Wild Bulls*

Question types: literal 1–3; inferential 4, 5; evaluative 6; deductive 7–9
Language focus: features of poetry – use of metaphor; blank verse.

1. The 'nobody-walk-across' light is red.

2. The 'yellow eye' gives the warning for 'beware'.

3. The poet thinks that the three lights look like eyes.

4. The poet is comparing a traffic light to a matador.

5. The wild bulls are the motor vehicles which are waiting for the traffic signal (the matador).

6. Bulls are said to charge at anything that is red.

7. *The Wild Bulls* is written in blank verse.

8. 'Circumspection' means warily, taking everything into account.

9. Your own answer.

Unit 21 – Instruction

Super Spuds

Question types: literal 1–3; inferential 4, 5; evaluative 6–8; deductive 9–11
Language focus: verbs in imperative mood ('Pour', 'Smear'); omission of articles ('Pour [the] breadcrumbs into one of the bowls'); using context for meaning.

1. The oven needs to be heated to 180° centigrade.

2. Any leftover olive oil should be drizzled over the potato wedges.

3. The wedges should bake in the oven for 40 minutes, or until golden brown.

4a. Olive oil is used on the potato wedges to make the breadcrumbs stick to them; b. It is used on the baking tray to prevent the wedges sticking to it.

5. You would need eight potatoes if you were cooking Super Spuds for eight people.

6. Remove the potato wedges and turn the oven off.

7–10. Your own answers.

11. smear – rub over, spread thinly; drizzle – trickle a small amount of liquid all over something; pre-heat – turn on the oven and allow it to reach a particular temperature before you start cooking; dip – lower something quickly into another substance (probably a liquid) to coat it.

Unit 22 – Report

Horses through time

Question types: literal 1–3; inferential 4, 5; evaluative 6; deductive 7, 8
Language focus: structure of a report – generalised introduction followed by facts; use of specialist terms, usually explained in the text.

1. The first horses were called Eohippus.
2. Diatryma is the name of the flightless birds that used to hunt Eohippus.
3. It looked more like a horse (it had a large middle toe) and it ate only grass.
4. Answers may vary – because the hoof is a distinctive feature of the horse, so its development is significant.
5. Answers may vary – to escape from predators such as Diatryma.
6. Merychippus is closest to the present day horse; it was bigger and walked on only one toe of each foot.
7. The toenails of humans are similar to the hoof of a modern horse.
8. Answers may vary – information has probably been gained through research, fossils and archaeological excavations.

Unit 23 – Explanation

How a violin works

Question types: literal 3, 4; inferential 1, 2, 5a; evaluative 5b; deductive 6–10
Language focus: nature and order of an explanation – begins with a general statement; use of verbs predominantly in the present tense.

1. Four types of string instrument are played in a symphony orchestra – the violin, viola, cello and double bass.
2. A bow is made from wood and strands of horsehair.
3. François Toute designed the modern bow.
4. When a string is plucked the sound is called pizzicato.
5a. The body and the finger board of a violin are made from wood; b. Answers may vary – probably not, as it would not vibrate in the same way.
6. Tightening a string makes the sound of that string higher.
7. Your own answer.
8. The double bass is the string instrument that plays the lowest notes.
9. devices – small machines or tools to do something; tension – how tight something is stretched; concave – curved.
10. A flute is a wind (or woodwind) instrument; a trumpet is a brass instrument; a drum is a percussion instrument.

Unit 24 – Narrative

Wrecked in the Antarctic (final part)

Question types: literal 2; inferential 1, 3–5; evaluative 6–8; deductive 9, 10
Language focus: structure of a narrative – orientation, complication, resolution and conclusion; use of third person, past tense verbs.

1. Shackleton and his crew left the ice floe on 10 April 1916.
2. It was four days before they sailed into open water.
3. The name of the first island on which they landed was Elephant Island.
4. There was a supply of food (seal meat) and fresh water.
5. They had landed on the wrong side of the island and still had a long walk to reach the whaling station.
6. Answers may vary – the men might have had to wait a very long time to be rescued, or they might even have died.
7. Answers may vary – he was a skilled and resourceful navigator and seaman.
8. Answers may vary – probably yes, because he made sensible decisions, took the major risks himself and saved all his crew.
9. Answers may vary – possibly because of its shape, or because it was home to elephant seals.

Unit 25 – Drama

Return of the Deadeye (final part)

Question types: literal 1, 3, 4; inferential 2, 5; evaluative 6, 7, 9, 10; deductive 8

Language focus: presentation of a play reading – movement, props, voice, sound effects; use of western language ('Deputy', 'Yer nothin'').

1. Bart Wader had a six-shooter laser gun.
2. He was hiding in the background behind an android spectator.
3. Duke Floorwalker called Bart a 'mangy son of a rusty robot'.
4. The universal sign of the intergalactic cowboy was three stamps with the right foot.
5. In this context 'bread basket' is a slang term for stomach.
6. Answers may vary – possibly when Bart Wader was accidentally tripped up by Starr Waugh.
7. No, he always seemed to be hiding when anything dangerous happened.
8. Answers may vary – a brave, tough, confident voice, probably with an American accent, could be used for the part of Duke Floorwalker.
9. Answers may vary – something to represent the bar, possibly hats and guns.
10. Answers may vary – punching, pointing the guns, pouring or drinking drinks, Bart writhing in agony when he is punched.

Unit 26 – Recount

The Brumby Drive

Question types: literal 1; inferential 2–4, 6, 8; evaluative 5, 7; deductive 9, 10

Language focus: use of past tense verbs in text, present/future verbs in reported speech; use of adverbs and adverbial phrases.

1. Thowra is the name of the silver brumby.
2. His mother's name was Bel Bel.
3. Thowra did not have the experience to know to kick the dog.
4. She neighed to him and nipped him gently.
5. Answers may vary – quite young because he had never seen a dog before; he was still being looked after closely by his mother; he panicked in a difficult situation.
6. The men were trying to round the brumbies up and capture them.
7. Dogs would bark and nip the horses' heels and, by so doing, head them in a particular direction.
8. Answers may vary – he was confused and frightened.
9. Answers may vary – they would be tamed and sold or possibly slaughtered for meat.
10. The story is set in New South Wales, Australia; map work is required for the second part of the question.

Unit 27 – Argument

The Olympic Games has lost its way

Question types: literal 1, 3; inferential 2; evaluative 4–6; deductive 7–9

Language focus: structure of an argument – a statement of position followed by supporting reasons, summing up and conclusion; limited use of adverbs and adjectives in an argument.

1. Amateur athletes were only allowed to win medals and trophies.
2. Some national teams allowed their athletes to devote themselves to their sport full-time.
3. Professional tennis players are now allowed to take part in the Olympics.
4. They would be able to use all their energy, commitment and time, training for their sport.
5–9. Your own answers.

Unit 28 – Poetry

Magpies

Question types: literal 1, 2; inferential 4, 8; evaluative 3, 5, 7, 10; deductive 6, 9

Language focus: features of poetry – use of rhyming and regular rhythm patterns; use of figurative language in the form of similes and metaphors.

1. The magpies are black and white.
2. The magpies remind the poet of 'certain gentlemen who seem most nonchalant and wise' – well-dressed and dignified gentlemen.
3. The poet describes the magpies as having 'hands in pockets' because of the colours on their wings and their shape.
4. No, they eat furiously.
5. Answers may vary – probably yes, as the tone of the poem seems affectionate and admiring.
6. Your own answer.
7. Answers may vary – the message in the poem may be that although the magpies do not always behave well, they are, at least, grateful for what they get; humans are often not so appreciative.
8. Answers may vary – for a short while they eat quickly but then sing appreciatively afterwards.
9. tilt – to tip over, to hold at an angle; stroll – to walk around in an unhurried fashion; nonchalant – in a relaxed, carefree manner.
10. Your own answer.

Unit 29 – Narrative

A name for a kitten
Question types: literal 1–3; inferential 4; evaluative 5, 6; deductive 7–9
Language focus: use of past tense verbs in narrative; punctuation of conversation.
1. The kitten was born at the King's palace.
2a. The first name given to the kitten was Sky; b. That name was chosen because the sky is above everything on Earth.
3. The name Cloud was rejected because clouds are blown about by the wind.
4. No, he changed his mind every time a new suggestion was made. He called his Council together to help him choose a name rather than selecting one himself.
5. Your own answer.
6. Answers may vary – probably to show that people who are considered the cleverest are not necessarily so and that they do not always give the best answers.
7. Answers may vary – possibly the Chief Councillor would advise the King on important matters; the Chief Magician would create magic to help or entertain the King; the General would be in charge of the King's armies; the Steward would manage the household.
8. Answers may vary – no, because the conversation seems unlikely though not impossible; yes, the moral is that the humblest person can be wise and that important people can be foolish.
9. Your own answer.

Unit 30 – Explanation

How our writing system works
Question types: literal 1–4; inferential 5; evaluative 6, 8; deductive 7
Language focus: nature and order of an explanation, beginning with a general statement followed by more detailed points; interpreting a diagram.
1. The first two letters of the Greek alphabet are alpha and beta.
2. The first people to use letters for writing were the Phoenicians.
3. We use about 44 sounds in our speech.
4. Approximately 80 percent of our spelling is quite straightforward.
5. Answers may vary – many words are often spelled differently to how they are pronounced; some letters have to be used more than once and in different combinations.
6. It was during Roman times that the alphabet began to resemble the one we have today.
7. Your own answer.
8. Yes – it would be much more complicated and would require more time and thought. It would also take up a lot more space. It is unlikely that there would be a common understanding of what was being expressed.

A letter from Ella

6 Cooper's Close
Little Drayton

28 January

Dear Mum

I am having a lovely time at Granny's but I do miss you and Dad and Patch. Granny and Grandpa are going to bring me home on Saturday. It was nice to talk to you yesterday. I can't wait to see my new baby sister. Granny helped me choose this card because we thought Susie might look like the baby in the picture.

It has snowed here. When I got up today everywhere was all white. Grandpa and I went outside to put out some food and water for the birds and we could see the marks their feet had made in the snow. I saw some very funny footprints. Grandpa said a rabbit had made them.

Grandpa is getting the sledge ready. We are going to take it up the hill. Granny says it's a good job I brought my wellies!

Granny says to tell you I am being very good.

Love,
Ella

Re-read the letter and answer the following questions.
(Use the back of the sheet for questions 5 and 6.)

1 Where is Ella staying? _____

_____

2 Why is Ella staying there? _____

_____

3 Who do you think Patch is? _____

_____

4 What had made everywhere white? _____

_____

5 What had the rabbit done?

6 Ella has written her letter to her mother on a card. What sort of card do you think it might be?

Caring for your dog

A dog will make a trusty friend if you look after it well. Remember! A healthy dog is a happy dog!

Your dog will rely on you to give it food and water. You will need two big dishes. Fill one dish with fresh cold water. Change the water every day. Make sure the dish is always clean and full.

A medium-sized dog needs two meals a day: a small breakfast before you go to school and its main meal when you come home.

Dogs are meat-eaters, so a third of the main meal should be meat and two-thirds should be broken biscuit. Mix it together and give it to your dog in the second dish. You can add vegetables and gravy from your own meals if there are any left over.

Crunching is good for your dog's teeth and gums. Give it some hard dog biscuits to crunch while you are at school. Chewing a marrow bone will help keep your dog's teeth clean.

Try to feed your dog at the same time each day.

Re-read the instructions and answer the following questions.

1 How many dishes will you need for your dog? _____

_____

2 Why should you give your dog meat to eat? _____

_____

3 Where could you get a marrow bone from? _____

_____

4 What would happen if you forgot to feed your dog? _____

_____

_____

5 Why should you change the water every day? _____

_____

6 What other items of equipment would you need for a dog? _____

_____

_____

Mr Lion's soup

SCENE 1

Mr Lion enters Brer Possum's Hotel. The waiters, Brer Coon, Brer Hare and Brer Hedgehog all look on as Brer Possum helps Mr Lion off with his coat and hat.

MR LION *(in a growly voice):* Give me the best table. I want some lunch.

BRER POSSUM: What will you have, Mr Lion, sir? *(He beckons the waiters who look nervous.)*

MR LION: Bring me some oxtail soup!

BRER POSSUM: Certainly, sir! Right away, sir!

(They all scurry off as Mr Lion sits at his table.)

SCENE 2

Enter Brer Hare with a bowl of soup.

MR LION: It smells good!

BRER HARE *(bravely):* It *is* good!

(The waiters and Brer Possum wait for Mr Lion to taste the soup.)

MR LION: I can't eat this soup!

BRER HARE: Is it too hot?

BRER COON: Has it too much pepper?

MR LION: I don't know. I can't eat the soup!

BRER HEDGEHOG: Is there too much onion?

BRER POSSUM: I'm sorry. There isn't a fly or a caterpillar in it is there?

MR LION: No! I can't eat it! I want to eat it but I can't! I HAVEN'T GOT A SPOON!

Re-read the play and answer the following questions. (Use the back of the sheet for questions 4 to 6.)

1 Where is Mr Lion? _____

_____

2 Why do the waiters look nervous? _____

_____

3 What sort of soup did Mr Lion want? _____

_____

4 What was wrong with the soup?

5 Had the table been set properly?

6 What would you have done if you had been Mr Lion?

Otto, the penguin chick

Otto was a penguin chick. He lived on his father's feet at the bottom of the world. That's what Leo said, anyway, that they lived at the bottom of the world. Leo was another penguin chick and he lived on *his* father's feet. That is how Otto met him. Their fathers Claudius and Nero were friends and when they stopped to talk to each other, beak to beak, Otto and Leo were almost beak to beak too. They had to shout a bit because Claudius and Nero were rather fat, like all the other penguins, so their tummies kept Otto and Leo rather far apart.

'How do you know we're at the bottom of the world?' Otto yelled across to Leo one morning.

'Your father told my father,' said Leo. 'Your father knows everything.'

Re-read the story and answer the following questions.

1 What sort of chick was Otto? _____

_____

2 Who was Leo? _____

_____

3 Where did the chicks think they lived? _____

_____

4 Who was looking after the chicks? _____

_____

_____

5 Who said the chicks lived at the bottom of the world?_____

_____

_____

6 Where do you think the chicks lived? _____

_____

_____

_____

The Cosy Café

The Cosy Café has a new manager and cook, Mr and Mrs Parsons.
They applied to be put in the local good food guide. Mrs Parker, the food
guide's inspector, went to the café to try the food. Here is her report.

The menu of the Cosy Café is quite small but it gives a choice of
three dishes for each course. The vegetable soup was hot and had
a good selection of vegetables in it, but it needed salt and pepper.
The main course chosen was roast chicken with a selection of
vegetables. The vegetables were freshly cooked and the chicken
had a tasty sauce. For dessert, the apple crumble was a little too
sweet and the custard was rather runny.

The price of the meal was reasonable for the quality of food
served. The café was busy but the staff managed to serve the
meals quickly and pleasantly.

Re-read the report and answer the following questions.

1 What is the name of the café? _____

_____

2 Why do you think Mr and Mrs Parsons wanted to have their café listed in the

local guide? _____

_____

3 How many dishes could you choose from for each course?

_____

4 How many courses could you have at a meal? _____

_____

5 Do you think the café will be put in the guide? _____

_____

_____

6 How can you tell the café was popular? _____

_____

_____

Pete's mouse

Pete was thinking about the actual words his mum or dad always used. 'You are not keeping a mouse in this house,' was what they said.

Suddenly he jumped up from his chair. Through the branches, he peered out across the lawn.

'OK, so I can't keep a mouse in *that* house,' he said excitedly, 'but what about in *this* house? Why not keep it here, in my tree-house? They would never know I had a mouse. I could make a nice cage for it and I could smuggle food up to it. We'd have a lovely time together, me and my secret mouse!'

Pete sat down again and took from the shelf a battered little booklet. It was called *Mice and How to Keep Them*. He had bought it secretly a long while ago. He had read it from cover to cover, over and over again.

Re-read the story and answer the following questions.

1 What wouldn't Pete's Mum and Dad let him do? _____

_____

2 Where was Pete in the story? _____

_____

3 What was his secret going to be? _____

_____

4 How did Pete know so much about mice? _____

_____

5 What would Pete need for a mouse? _____

_____

_____

6 What would be good about having a tree house? _____

_____

_____

_____

Your name, sir?

Long ago, most people in Britain had only one name each, their forename. Each village could have several people with the same name. There would be a few Williams, some Marys, a number of Johns and so on. This made it hard to know which John or Mary someone was talking about. To make it easier, people started to make up an extra name for each person. If there was a John with white hair, he might be called John White. Another John who lived in the woods might be called John Woods. If another John worked as a cook, he would be John Cook. John, the son of Richard could be called John Richardson.

These second names would be used by the whole family, so gradually everyone took a surname and passed it on from generation to generation.

There are four main surname types: these are names based on appearance, a place of living, an occupation and parentage. People like to trace back their surnames for a hobby.

Re-read the explanation and answer the following questions.

1 How many names did people have many years ago? _____

_____

2 Why did people decide to use a second name? _____

_____

3 How would William Hill have got his name? _____

_____

4 What name would the son of Robert be called? _____

_____

5 Is it likely that the same surnames would be used in other villages?

_____

_____

6 Do you think this is a good way to name people? _____

_____

_____

Collections

People have been collecting things for thousands of years. Sir Hans Sloane was a great collector, and when he died in the eighteenth century his collections were put together in the British Museum.

It is from special collections in museums that people can learn about their own countryside, about other areas of the country and other countries of the world.

If it were not for some people's love of exploring and collecting, there would be no museums. We would not be able to learn about life in other countries. Many of the collections are of ancient things. Not everyone can afford the time or money to explore and collect for themselves.

Some people think that ancient relics from other countries should be left in the countries in which they have been found. They think it is wrong that people from another country should 'steal' valuable articles and take them away. In the nineteenth century rich people visited the Pharaohs' tombs in Egypt. They took valuable things from the tombs and brought them back for their collections. Some people think that these treasures should be returned.

Re-read the argument and answer the following questions.

1 Where were the collections of Sir Hans Sloane put when he died? _____

_____

2 What is a good thing about museums? _____

_____

3 Do any children in your class have collections? What are they?_____

_____

4 What is wrong with going to other countries and bringing back treasures?

_____

5 What stops most people from exploring and collecting? _____

_____

6 Do you think valuable things from other countries should be returned?

_____

A toy telephone

This is a simple telephone that is quick to make. You will need two long, narrow tins and a long piece of string. The tins could be empty baked-beans tins, the 420g size.

If the tins are not empty, open them using a tin opener that doesn't leave a sharp edge around the top. Spoon the contents into a bowl and put aside. Then wash the tins out well.

Make a hole in the middle of the end of each tin by hammering a nail through it. Be careful you don't hit your fingers!

Thread the ends of the string through the hole in each tin. Tie a large knot at the ends of the string so that it stays inside the tins.

Let a friend hold one of the tins, and stretch the string so that it is quite tight.

Ask your friend to hold the open end of their tin to their ear.

Speak quietly into your tin and your friend will hear quite clearly what you say.

Re-read the instructions and answer the following questions.

1 What do you need to make the telephone? _____

_____

2 How will you make the holes in the tins? _____

_____

3 What could happen if the edges of the tins were sharp? _____

_____

4 How old do you think you need to be to make this telephone? _____

_____

5 When do you think this telephone could be useful? _____

_____

_____

_____

6 Why must the string be very tight for the telephone to work? _____

_____

Mice

I think mice
Are rather nice.

Their tails are long,
Their faces small,
They haven't any
Chins at all.
Their ears are pink,
Their teeth are white,
They run about
The house at night.
They nibble things
They shouldn't touch
And no one seems
To like them much.

But I think mice
Are nice.

Rose Fyleman

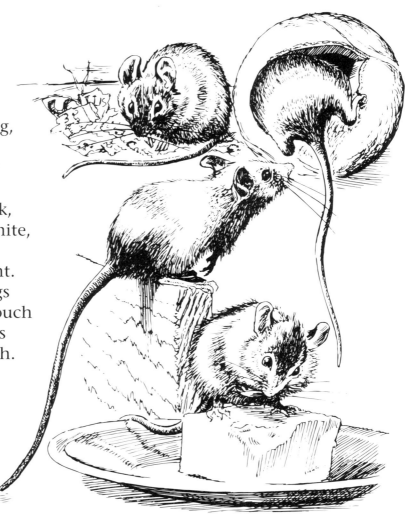

Re-read the poem and answer the following questions.

1 What does the writer think of mice? _____

_____

2 What do mice do at night? _____

_____

3 What do the mice do during the day? _____

_____

4 Find and write down the words that rhyme with **a)** small **b)** night **c)** touch.

_____

5 Does everyone like mice as much as the writer? _____

_____

6 What do you think of mice? _____

The first house

Stanley saw a field. 'Does anybody mind if I live here?' he asked.

'I don't mind if you don't snore,' said an animal who was going to sleep.

'I don't mind if you don't eat too much grass,' said an animal who was eating.

'I don't mind if you don't take up too much room,' said a very, very big animal. Stanley made himself at home. 'This is not bad,' he said.

But suddenly the wind blew and Stanley was cold. The rain fell and he was wet. 'This is worse than the cave,' said Stanley.

He made walls to keep out the wind. He made a roof to keep out the rain. He made a door, windows and chimney. He made a house!

'That's the first house I ever saw,' said a field mouse.

'It's the first one I ever made,' said Stanley. 'Won't you stay here and live with me?'

'I can't. I belong in the field. But I will come and visit you from time to time,' said the field mouse.

Re-read the story and answer the following questions.

1 What did Stanley want to do in the field he saw? _____

_____

2 How many animals were there in the field? _____

_____

3 Why did Stanley change his mind about living in the field with the animals?

_____

_____

4 Where had Stanley lived before he found the field? _____

_____

5 What made Stanley build his house? _____

_____

6 Why do you think Stanley wanted the mouse to live with him? _____

_____

Photocopiable

The pet survey

A survey is a way of collecting information. The information can be used to find out how many people like or do something. The results of a survey can be reported.

Most of the children in Year 2 at Dunston Primary School keep a pet. Four of the children decided to carry out a survey to see how many children in Years 2 and 3 kept a pet and which pet was the most popular.

They made a list of the animals that could be a pet. This list included dogs, cats, rabbits, guinea pigs, hamsters, budgerigars, goldfish and tortoises.

There are 59 children in Years 2 and 3. The information from the survey showed that 17 children kept a dog, 24 children kept a cat, 11 children kept a rabbit, 14 children kept a guinea pig, 39 children kept a goldfish, 12 children kept a budgie and 2 children kept a tortoise – 16 children kept pets that were not on the list and 12 children did not have a pet at all.

The children doing the survey found that a goldfish was the most popular pet and a tortoise was the least popular. They also found out that more children kept a pet in Year 3 than in Year 2.

Re-read the report and answer the following questions.

1 How many pets are listed in the survey? _____

_____

2 Which school do the children go to? _____

_____

3 Why does a tortoise seem to be the least popular pet? _____

_____

4 Why might a goldfish be the most popular pet? _____

_____

5 What sort of person would be good at looking after a pet? _____

_____

6 Which animals might you choose as a pet if you lived in a flat? _____

_____

The princess and the pea

Long ago, a prince lived with his father and mother in the family palace. The king and queen wanted their son to find a wife and live in a palace of his own. The prince didn't mind getting married, but he would only marry a real princess.

Early one evening, there was a terrible storm. The rain came down in torrents. In the middle of the storm, there was a knock at the gate. The old king went out to open it.

On the doorstep stood a soaking wet girl. She said she was a princess. The queen could see her dress was silk and she had a lovely pearl necklace, but to be sure that she was a real princess, the queen asked her to stay the night.

Before the princess went to bed, the queen popped a dried pea under the mattress, then she piled twenty more feather mattresses on top of it.

In the morning, the princess said she hadn't slept a wink all night because she was lying on something hard. It had made her black and blue all over. The queen knew then that she was a real princess. No ordinary person would have such tender skin.

Re-read the story and answer the following questions.

1 Who lived in the family palace? _____

_____

2 Who was the only person the prince would marry? _____

_____

3 Why was the girl on the doorstep soaking wet? _____

_____

4 What made the queen think the girl on the doorstep could be a real princess?

_____

5 What had happened to make the girl 'black and blue all over'? _____

_____

6 Do you think the prince would marry the girl? _____

_____

_____

Guinea pigs

Guinea pigs are sometimes called cavies, which comes from their Latin name *cavia*. Guinea pigs were first found in South America, where they were kept as pets by the Incas in Peru. They were brought to Europe over 400 years ago and people have kept them as pets ever since!

Guinea pigs are rodents like rats or mice. Rodents are animals that gnaw and chew. They have to gnaw because their teeth keep growing, and gnawing keeps them short.

Guinea pigs make very good pets. They are friendly and don't mind being picked up. In the wild, they live on open grassland, not in holes or burrows. When a baby guinea pig is born, it is all ready to run about and look after itself. Its eyes are open and it is covered with fur.

Guinea pigs like fresh greenstuff and fruit to eat. Some plants are poisonous to them, like buttercups and foxgloves, so you have to be careful. They need fresh water and straw in a warm, dry cage that is big enough for them to run about in.

Re-read the explanation and answer the following questions.

1 What is another name for guinea pigs? _____

_____

2 Why do baby guinea pigs need to be able to look after themselves?

_____

_____

3 Why must you be careful about giving guinea pigs plants from the garden?

_____

4 What would happen if guinea pigs had nothing to chew? _____

_____

5 What makes a guinea pig a good pet? _____

_____

6 Why do you think guinea pigs were brought to Europe from South America?

_____

_____

Children should earn their pocket money

It is a good idea for children to have pocket money. If children are asked to do little jobs to earn their pocket money, it helps them to understand what money is worth. Most parents have to earn their money, so it makes sense for the children to earn their pocket money in turn.

The children and their parents could work out a list of jobs to do. Younger children could do the easier jobs for less money. Then as they get older, the jobs they do could be harder and they could earn more money.

When the children become teenagers, they could be paid an allowance that would include their pocket money. They could then save up for clothes, books, outings with friends and other big items that they would like to have.

If children earned their pocket money, it would help them to feel independent. They would begin to understand that 'money doesn't grow on trees'!

Re-read the argument and answer the following questions.

1 Who gives the children pocket money? _____

_____

2 How do parents get their money for food and the home? _____

_____

3 Make a list of jobs children could do round the home. _____

_____

_____

4 At what age do you think children should start having pocket money?

_____

5 Do you agree with children earning their pocket money? _____

_____

6 What does the saying 'money doesn't grow on trees' mean? _____

_____

_____

Growing

When I grow up I'll be so kind,
Not yelling 'Now' or 'Do you MIND!'
    Or making what is called a scene,
    Like 'So you're back' or 'Where've you BEEN.'
Or 'Goodness, child, what is it NOW?'
Or saying 'STOP... that awful row,'
    Or 'There's a time and place to eat'
    And 'Wipe your nose' or 'Wipe your feet'.
I'll just let people go their way
And have an extra hour for play.
    No angry shouting 'NOW what's wrong?'
    It's just that growing takes so long.

Max Fatchen

Re-read the poem and answer the following questions.

1 What will the writer be like when he grows up? _____

_____

2 What are the writer's parents like? _____

_____

_____

3 What sort of child is the writer? _____

_____

4 What will the writer let people do when he is grown up?_____

_____

_____

5 Why is the writer told there is a time and place to eat?_____

_____

6 What makes your parents cross? _____

_____

The little girl who got out of bed the wrong side

There was once a little girl who got out of bed on the wrong side. Oh, how cross she was! Cross as two sticks! She made a terrible fuss getting dressed. She put her tights on back to front and she complained that her jersey was tickly. She put her feet into the wrong shoes.

When she came down to breakfast, things were even worse. Her porridge was too hot. The milk was too cold. And her banana had black specks in it.

'I shan't eat my horrid breakfast,' said the little girl.

Everyone in the house left her alone and hoped she would soon feel better.

During the morning, her mother was busy making the Christmas puddings. When she had the mixture ready in her big mixing bowl, it looked delicious and smelt even more delicious. She asked the little girl if she would like to give the puddings a stir and have a wish.

'You'd better wish to be a happy girl,' said her mother.

Re-read the story and answer the following questions.

1 What was the matter with the little girl? _____

_____

2 What was wrong with her jersey? _____

_____

3 What time of the year was it? _____

_____

4 What does it mean if you get out of bed on the wrong side? _____

_____

5 What would make the mixture smell delicious? _____

_____

6 What do you think the little girl will wish for? _____

_____

_____

Coming home

Mum's been ten days in hospital,
We missed her a lot;
It's seemed more like ten years,
But now guess what?
We've bought a prezzie,
Labelled it:
BEST MUM THERE EVER WAS;
We've cleaned the house
And garden up
Because... because... because...

She's coming home,
She's coming home,
SHE'S COMING HOME TODAY!
We're going to treat her
Like a queen.
I hope she'll be O.K.

Eric Finney

Re-read the poem and answer the following questions.

1 Where has the writer's mum been? _____

_____

2 Has the family managed without her? _____

_____

3 Why did they clean the house and tidy the garden? _____

_____

4 Has the time she has been in hospital passed quickly? _____

_____

5 Why are they giving mum a present? _____

_____

6 How will they treat her like a queen? _____

_____

Holidays

The word 'holiday' came from holy day. As a holy day was a day on which no work was done, the name came to mean a day when you relaxed and enjoyed yourself.

It is only since the Second World War that going on holiday has become so popular. Nowadays, most people expect and want to go away to relax and enjoy themselves. Taking a holiday in the United Kingdom helps the tourist trade. People get to know this country and can enjoy the customs in different places. Most holiday places are easy to get to on the same day by car, train or coach. There are no difficulties with money, food or language. People going on holiday in this country know, more or less, what to expect. Perhaps the main drawback is the weather which, even in summer, can be cold and wet.

Going on holiday abroad is exciting. If you haven't visited the country you have chosen before, you do not know exactly what it will be like. The food will be different, the people will speak a different language and the money they use will be different too. This makes it difficult to work out easily what everything will cost and could make the holiday expensive.

People generally like to go to a country where they know the weather will be good. Getting to their holiday could take a long time. There may be delays at the airports if they fly. If they want to go by train or coach, they have to cross the English Channel first and this can take time. If the crossing is rough, they could feel quite ill. Nowadays, the Channel can be crossed by going underneath it in the tunnel.

People who always go abroad for their holidays only know a little about the countries they visit and very little about their own country.

Re-read the argument and answer the following questions.

1 What does the word 'holiday' really mean?_____

_____

2 What is one of the main reasons for not having a holiday in the United

Kingdom? _____

_____

3 Did ordinary people expect to have long holidays a hundred years ago?

_____

4 Where would you have a holiday if you didn't like unusual food?

_____

_____

5 Would you go to Spain in the summer if you didn't like hot weather?

_____

6 How does living on an island like the United Kingdom make going abroad

difficult? _____

_____

7 How does it help holiday places in the United Kingdom if people have holidays

in this country? _____

_____

8 What would make it difficult if you were in trouble abroad?

_____

_____

9 Where would you like to visit for a holiday in the United Kingdom?

_____

10 Which do you think is best, holidays in the United Kingdom or holidays

abroad? _____

_____

Chalk and cheese

Even though Jo and Lily were sisters, they were very different.

'I wish *my* name was Jo,' Lily used to say. 'I don't like having the same name as a flower. "Jo" could be a boy's name.'

'My real name is Joanne,' said Jo. '*That* couldn't be a boy's name.'

Jo and Lily were like chalk and cheese. Jo was nine and small and dainty; Lily was seven, but tall for her age. They could have worn the same clothes if they'd wanted to, but Jo liked the colour pink, and Lily didn't. Jo liked frilly blouses and flowered dresses and pretty ankle socks trimmed with lace. Lily hated everything except jeans and dungarees, worn with a T-shirt in the summer and a jumper in the winter. Jo's shoes were black and shiny, and Lily thought they looked like dolls' shoes. Lily wore trainers with red and silver flashes on the heels. Whenever the sisters played together, they argued about what to do.

'Pirates!' Lily shouted.

'Tea parties!' said Jo.

'Tarzan!' Lily suggested.

'Mothers and babies,' said Jo.

Mostly they did what Jo said, because she was older, but Lily had her way as well.

'If we play tea parties,' she would say, 'I can be a Pirate Captain who comes to tea.'

Jo would sigh and agree. She even let Lily wear her eye-patch, because fighting with her sister could just go on and on, and then there was no time for the game.

Re-read the story and answer the following questions.

1 What are the names of the sisters? _____

_____

2 What is Jo short for ? _____

_____

3 Why didn't Lily like her name? _____

_____

4 What did the sisters always do when they played together? _____

_____

5 How can you tell the sisters are about the same size? _____

_____

6 Why are Jo and Lily said to be like chalk and cheese? _____

_____

_____

7 Do older sisters always have their own way? _____

_____

_____

8 Do you think their mother would find it difficult to take the girls shopping?

_____

_____

9 Why did Jo give in to Lily sometimes? _____

_____

10 What makes the sisters argue? _____

_____

_____

_____

_____

Jim and the beanstalk

Early one morning Jim woke up and saw an enormous plant growing outside his window. 'That's funny,' he said, 'it wasn't there yesterday. I'll see how high it goes,' and he began to climb up the plant. 'It certainly is a big plant,' he said, as he went into the clouds. When he reached the top of the plant, Jim saw a castle.

'I'm hungry,' he said. 'I'll ask at the castle for breakfast. I hope they have cornflakes.'

Jim ran to the castle and knocked on the door. He waited and waited, until the door was slowly opened by a very old giant.

'Aha!' said the Giant. 'A boy. A nice juicy boy. Three fried boys on a slice of toast – that's what I used to enjoy eating in the old days, but I've got no teeth now. Come in, boy, you're quite safe.'

The Giant shared his breakfast of beef and beer with Jim.

'Is your name Jack?' he asked.

'No,' said Jim, 'it's Jim.'

'Did you come up a beanstalk?' asked the Giant.

'I came up some sort of plant,' said Jim.

'It's that beanstalk again,' said the Giant. 'It came up once before. That pesky boy Jack stole some of my father's gold and took our golden harp and our golden hen and I've never really been happy since. And now I'm old, too. I can't even see to read my poetry books because the print is too small.'

'Haven't you got any glasses?' asked Jim.

'Only beer glasses,' said the Giant.

'I mean reading glasses,' said Jim. 'They go on your nose and ears.'

'It's my eyes I'm talking about!' roared the Giant, banging his fist on the table.

'These glasses are *for* your eyes,' said Jim, and he explained about glasses while the Giant listened carefully.

'Get 'em!' said the Giant fiercely when Jim had finished. 'Get 'em for me. I'll pay good gold.'

Re-read the story and answer the following questions.

1 What did Jim see out of his bedroom window? _____

_____

2 What sort of plant did Jim climb? _____

_____

3 Who do you think Jack was? _____

_____

4 Why was it safe for Jim to go in? _____

_____

5 Why didn't the Giant have any glasses for reading? _____

_____

6 Do you think Jim will be able to get some glasses for the Giant? _____

_____

7 Did Jim have what he wanted for breakfast? _____

_____

_____

8 Would you have climbed the plant? _____

_____

_____

9 How do you think the plant came to grow there? _____

_____

_____

_____

10 Why does the Giant want reading glasses? _____

_____

_____

_____

The glass eye

You can play a lot of tricks with a glass eye because you can take it out and pop it back again any time you like. You can bet your life Mrs Twit knew all the tricks.

One morning she took out her glass eye and dropped it into Mr Twit's mug of beer when he wasn't looking.

Mr Twit sat there drinking the beer slowly. The froth made a white ring on the hairs around his mouth. He wiped the white froth on to his sleeve and wiped his sleeve on his trousers.

'You're plotting something,' Mrs Twit said, keeping her back turned so he wouldn't see that she had taken out her glass eye. 'Whenever you go all quiet like that I know very well you're plotting something.'

Mrs Twit was right. Mr Twit was plotting away like mad. He was trying to think up a really nasty trick he could play on his wife that day.

'You'd better be careful,' Mrs Twit said, 'because when I see you starting to plot, I watch you like a wombat.'

'Oh, do shut up, you old hag,' Mr Twit said.

He went on drinking his beer, and his evil mind kept working away on the latest horrid trick he was going to play on the old woman.

Suddenly, as Mr Twit tipped the last drop of beer down his throat, he caught sight of Mrs Twit's awful glass eye staring up at him from the bottom of the mug. It made him jump.

'I told you I was watching you,' cackled Mrs Twit. 'I've got eyes everywhere so you'd better be careful.'

Re-read the story and answer the following questions.

1 What was one of Mrs Twit's eyes made of? _____

_____

2 What was Mr Twit drinking? _____

_____

3 What did Mr Twit find at the bottom of his mug? _____

_____

4 How good was Mrs Twit's eyesight? _____

_____

5 Why did Mrs Twit think that Mr Twit was plotting something?

_____

6 What did Mr Twit have on his face? _____

_____

7 Why would Mrs Twit watch Mr Twit like a wombat? _____

_____

8 Why did Mrs Twit say she had got eyes everywhere? _____

_____

9 What did the Twits like doing to each other? _____

_____

_____

10 What would it be like to live with the Twits? _____

_____

_____

_____

_____

_____

_____

The first oven

The people who first lived on the earth were frightened of fire just as the animals were. But when they learned to control it, the people came to see how useful fire could be. They were able to use it to keep warm, to light their homes at night and to scare wild animals away.

They discovered they could use fire to cook their food. This may have happened by accident! Someone may have dropped a piece of raw meat into the fire by mistake and then discovered that the heat cooked the meat. It must have tasted much nicer than raw meat! Perhaps everyone started putting their meat in the ashes of the fire now they knew that it tasted better and was easier to eat.

Even though the meat must have tasted better cooked, it would have been covered in gritty ashes and must have got burnt quite often. They thought hard about how to have their meat cooked without eating ashes as well.

The first oven people thought of was very simple. A pit was dug in the ground and lined with leaves. Some big stones were heated in a fire until they were very hot. Then the hot stones were placed in the pit with the food. The pit was covered with more leaves and the food was left to cook.

The person who thought of this idea for making an oven must have been very clever! He or she would have been famous among the people of the tribe. Other families would have been quick to make their own ovens so that they could have a hot meal of baked meat too. Some of the older members of the families may not have liked these modern ways. They may have prefered to eat their meat raw and stick to the old ways!

Re-read the explanation and answer the following questions.

1 What did people first use fire for? _____

_____

2 How did they cook their food? _____

_____

3 Why do you think animals are scared of fire? _____

_____

4 What was wrong with meat that had been cooked in a fire? _____

_____

5 Why was meat that was cooked in the pit oven better? _____

_____

_____

6 Why was the pit oven lined with leaves? _____

_____

7 What sort of things would be cooked in the pit oven? _____

_____

_____

8 How long do you think it would take to cook the food? _____

_____

9 Would the stones heated in the fire always be at the same temperature?

_____

_____

10 Who might use this way to cook food now? _____

_____

_____

_____

These are the clothes that my big brother wore

These are the clothes that my big brother wore,
And his elder brother,
And *his* brother before.
These are the short pants which reach to the floor,
For I'm much much shorter, than the brother before.

This is the hat, that he no longer wears,
For he has big brothers, and now he wears theirs,
And the socks I put on, are in non-matching pairs,
And the jumpers have sleeves full of patches and tears.

Yes, this is the sole of my big brother's shoe,
His big brother wore it, and *his* brother too,
And my Mum said 'My boy, I shall give it to you.
It's an honour to walk, in your big brother's shoe.'

These are the clothes that no rag man would buy,
With holes that have holes through which seagulls could fly,
But I wear them and wish it was not always I,
Who's the youngest young brother and the smallest small fry.

Clive Riche

Re-read the poem and answer the following questions.

1 Is the writer a boy or a girl? _____

_____

2 How many brothers has the writer got? _____

_____

3 What are the two main problems with the clothes? _____

_____

4 What are we told about the holes in the clothes? _____

_____

5 What do you think would really please the writer? _____

_____

6 Would there be any advantage in being the youngest brother?

_____

7 Why would the socks be in non-matching pairs? _____

_____

8 What can you tell about the sizes of the writer and his next brother at the

same age? _____ _____

_____

9 Why does the writer's mother think it is an honour for him to wear his

brother's shoes? _____

_____

10 Make a list of the clothes the writer has been told to wear. _____

_____

_____

_____

_____

A centipede

A centipede can run at great speed,
Because of his number of legs,
But when he hangs out his socks to dry,
It costs him a fortune in pegs.

A centipede likes to wear wellington boots,
But because of his centipede brain,
It takes such a time to sort out all the pairs
That he's never in time for the rain.

A centipede has one hundred legs,
But I'm glad I haven't because
When the front of a centipede gets where it's going
His back end is still where it was.

Julie Holder

Re-read the poem and answer the following questions.

1 How many legs does a centipede have?_____

_____

2 Why does it cost him a fortune in pegs to hang out his socks? _____

_____

3 How many pairs of wellington boots would a centipede need?

_____

4 Find the words that rhyme with **a)** legs **b)** brain.

_____

5 Why does the front of a centipede get where it's going before its back end has

left? _____

_____

6 What do you think the centipede does best? _____

_____

_____

My new school

My dad is a policeman. We did live in London but Dad got a transfer to a new job at a police station in Dorset. We moved in the summer holidays. It was sad leaving my friends at school but we have promised to write to each other.

I started my new school this week. The boys and other girls in my class are nice. One girl called Selina said I could play with her. She has got a lot of friends and she lives near my new house.

Selina has always lived in Dorset. It was funny when she asked me where I lived. She said, 'Where are you to?' and I didn't understand what she meant! It made us laugh! I told her about things people say in London like 'apples and pears' for stairs. Selina thought that was funny too!

Our teacher told us about the after-school clubs. I played the recorder at my last school so he said I could join the recorder group.

Mum says I can ask Selina round to play on Saturday and have tea. I am going to write to my friend Katharine to tell her all about it.

Re-read the recount and answer the following questions.

1 What job does the writer's dad do? _____

2 Where is his new job? _____

3 Do you think the writer is a girl or a boy? _____

4 What do you think the phrase 'Where are you to?' means? _____

_____

5 Do you think Selina will make a good friend? _____

_____

6 Do you think the writer will be happy at the new school? _____

_____

7 How will having Selina round for tea help the writer? _____

_____

8 Why is it a good thing that the writer can play the recorder? _____

_____

Treasure trove

SCENE 1

Ed and Will are kicking a football in the park. They are playing near the hedge. Will has kicked the ball over the hedge.

ED: Hey! That was a good shot!

WILL: We'll squeeze through the hedge – I hope we find the ball.

(The boys crawl through the hedge and look for the ball.)

WILL: Can you see it?

ED: Yes, look, it's stuck on a spike in this rabbit hole. Oh no, it's got a puncture now.

WILL: Look! There's a bag stuffed in the hole! What's in it?

ED: Wow! It's some silver plates and a dagger!

WILL: It's treasure trove – we'll be rich!

ED: We'd better take it to the police. We can't say 'finders keepers' with this lot!

SCENE 2

Down at the police station, the sergeant is looking at their find.

WILL: Is it treasure trove? It was just dumped in the hole.

SERGEANT: Well it could be – it was put there on purpose to be collected later. It would have to be solid silver though. It looks like the things stolen from the Browns. If it is, they will be glad to have it back. I expect they will give you a reward.

ED: Great! We'll be able to buy a new football!

Re-read the play and answer the following questions.

(Use the back of the sheet for questions 5 to 8.)

1 What were the two boys doing in the park? _____

_____

2 What had Will done? _____

_____

3 What punctured the football? _____

4 Why do you think the boys took their find to the police station?

_____

5 What two things would make their find treasure trove?

6 Do you think the Browns will give the boys a reward?

7 Do you think the boys were right to take their find to the police station?

8 What does 'solid silver' mean?

The first chick

'What are you doing?' Claudius complained one morning. 'If you bounce on my feet any more you'll plant me in the snow and I'll never move again. And stop waving your flippers about like that. It feels like a blizzard blowing up there.'

Otto didn't stop. 'I'm trying to fly,' he shouted. 'You said I'm a bird. Birds fly, don't they?'

'Penguins don't fly,' Claudius said. 'Now stop jumping on my feet and I'll tell you what penguins do.'

Otto stopped. He was getting tired anyway. 'What do penguins do?' he asked, a little breathlessly.

'They swim. That's like flying in the sea. They're very good at it too.'

Otto looked up at Claudius.

'I want to fly up high like that bird up there. It's going round and round in the sky, and I want to do that.'

'Well you can't, so don't start bouncing again. Anyway, what bird?' Claudius was looking up. 'Oh my goodness, a skua. Now stay close to me, Otto. Nasty things, skuas. They like chicks.'

Otto was puzzled. 'Are you nasty then, Claudius?'

'Am I...? Oh I see! I like chicks but not for dinner. A skua will dive down from the sky and steal a nice juicy penguin chick for its next meal.'

Re-read the story and answer the following questions.

(Use the back of the sheet for questions 4 to 8.)

1 What was Otto doing? _____

_____

2 What did Otto want to do? _____

_____

3 What do penguins use to swim with? _____

_____

4 Why was the skua flying in circles overhead?

5 Where do you think Claudius and Otto are?

6 What was puzzling Otto?

7 How will Claudius feel about seeing a skua flying overhead?

8 Do you think Otto is good at working things out for himself?

A birthday for Frances

It was the day before Frances's little sister Gloria's birthday. Mother and Gloria were sitting at the kitchen table, making place cards for the party. Frances was in the broom closet, singing:

'Happy Thursday to you,
Happy Thursday to you,
Happy Thursday, dear Alice,
Happy Thursday to you.'

'Who is Alice?' asked Mother.

'Alice is somebody that nobody can see,' said Frances. 'And that is why she does not have a birthday. So I am singing Happy Thursday to her.'

'Today is Friday,' said Mother.

'It is Thursday for Alice,' said Frances. 'Alice will not have h-r-n-d, and she will not have g-k-l-s. But we are singing together.'

'What are h-r-n-d and g-k-l-s?' asked Mother.

'Cake and candy. I thought you could spell,' said Frances.

'I am sure that Alice will have cake and candy on her birthday,' said Mother.

'But Alice does not have a birthday,' said Frances.

'Yes, she does,' said Mother. 'Even if nobody can see her, Alice has one birthday every year, and so do you. Your birthday is two months from now. Then you will be the birthday girl. But tomorrow is Gloria's birthday, and she will be the birthday girl.'

'That is how it is, Alice,' said Frances. 'Your birthday is always the one that is not now.'

Re-read the story and answer the following questions.
(Use the back of the sheet for questions 3 to 8.)

1 Who was sitting at the kitchen table? _____

_____

2 Where was Frances? _____

_____

3 Who is the oldest girl, Frances or Gloria?

4 Why doesn't Alice have a birthday?

5 Why can't anyone see Alice?

6 Why does Alice use the letters h-r-n-d and g-k-l-s to spell cake and candy?

7 Do you think this story is written for people in this country?

8 Do you think Frances often plays on her own?

Photocopiable

Fruit and cheese kebabs

These kebabs are fun to make for your friends when they come for tea.

You will need about 150g of firm cheese. You can use Cheddar cheese, Double Gloucester and Red Leicester cheese. The different cheeses will add colour to your kebabs.

You will also need a small bunch of green grapes and one of black grapes, a small tin of pineapple chunks, a small tin of mandarin oranges and a bundle of wooden kebab skewers or cocktail sticks.

Remember to wash your hands before you touch the food!

Drain the juice from the tins of fruit. (You can put this in a glass to drink.)

Cut the cheese into 2cm cubes. Wash the grapes and pat them dry with kitchen paper.

Thread the fruit and cheese cubes carefully on to the skewers. Decide what order looks the best and make all the skewers the same.

You can stick the end of each kebab into a hard cabbage cut in half. This looks good on a plate in the middle of the table for your friends to help themselves.

You can experiment with different fruits and vegetables that go well with cheese.

Re-read the instructions and answer the following questions.

(Use the back of the sheet for questions 3 to 8.)

1 Write out a shopping list of the things you need to make the kebabs.

_____

_____

2 What sequence of fruit and cheese do you think would look attractive?

_____

_____

3 Why do you need to use firm cheese?

4 What must you always do before touching food?

5 Which would make better kebabs – kebab skewers or cocktail sticks?

6 Write down three other things that you think could go on the kebabs

7 Why is it important to wash the grapes?

8 What would happen if you didn't drain the tinned fruit well or dry the grapes?

Crayoning

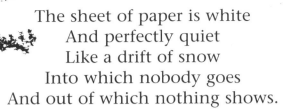

The sheet of paper is white
And perfectly quiet
Like a drift of snow
Into which nobody goes
And out of which nothing shows.

Then I crayon a sun to shine
And the sky's blue line,
A red house with a green door
And a chimney above it all
Out of which the black smoke pours.

In the garden is a mother
Hanging out clothes of every colour;
And flowers of every colour grow
Where once the paper
Was white as snow.

Stanley Cook

Re-read the poem and answer the following questions.
(Use the back of the sheet for questions 5 to 8)

1 How does the poem describe a sheet of paper? _____

_____

2 Write down two more words that would describe a sheet of paper.

_____

3 Whose clothes might you see hanging on the line? _____

_____

4 Write down the pair of words in each verse that rhyme.

_____

_____

5 Which pair of words sounds the same but doesn't look the same?
6 Why is the sheet of paper 'like a drift of snow into which nobody goes'?
7 What do you like about a clean sheet of paper?
8 What other things could the poem have in the garden?

The owl who was afraid of the dark

Plop was a baby Barn Owl, and he lived with his Mummy and Daddy at the top of a very tall tree in a field.

Plop was fat and fluffy.

He had a beautiful heart-shaped ruff.

He had enormous, round eyes.

He had very knackety knees.

In fact he was exactly the same as every baby Barn Owl that has ever been – except for one thing.

Plop was afraid of the dark.

'You *can't* be afraid of the dark,' said his Mummy. 'Owls are *never* afraid of the dark.'

'This one is,' Plop said.

'But owls are *night* birds,' she said.

Plop looked down at his toes. 'I don't want to be a night bird,' he mumbled. 'I want to be a day bird.'

'You *are* what you *are*,' said Mrs Barn Owl firmly.

'Yes, I know,' agreed Plop, 'and what I are is afraid of the dark.'

'Oh dear,' said Mrs Barn Owl. It was clear that she was going to need a lot of patience. She shut her eyes and tried to think how best she could help Plop not to be afraid. Plop waited.

His mother opened her eyes again. 'Plop, you are only afraid of the dark because you don't know about it.'

Re-read the story and answer the following questions.

(Use the back of the sheet for questions 4 to 8.)

1 What sort of bird was Plop? _____

_____

2 What made Plop different from other birds like him? _____

_____

3 Why are owls called night birds? _____

_____

4 Why will Mrs Barn Owl need a lot of patience?

5 Why does Plop want to be a day bird?

6 Do you think Plop's mother was right about why Plop was afraid of the dark?

7 Why wouldn't Plop know about the dark?

8 How will Plop get over his fear of the dark?

Dunston Primary School PTA

The Parent-Teacher Association for Dunston Primary School organises events to raise money for the school. Every year, the chairperson of the PTA writes a report about what they have been doing. This is the report for last year.

We have had a busy year and I am pleased to report that our events have raised the sum of £2117.

The year began with a jumble sale which raised £336. The Hallowe'en barn dance went well and 153 tickets were sold at £3 each. The refreshments and bar made another £187. The Christmas fête was in December and the school Christmas cards sold well. The total made was £420. The spring term began with a bingo evening. This raised £347 with the raffle. Sponsored swims and bicycle rides raised £302 and the sale of printed tea towels has brought in £66 so far.

The staff have asked if the PTA will buy a colour printer, a crash mat and a video recorder. Money for the Christmas play costumes and the children's party would be welcomed. We shall pay for a lifeguard for swimming as usual. Any money left over will be spent on library books. Thank you all for your hard work.

Re-read the report and answer the following questions.

(Use the back of the sheet for questions 5 to 8.)

1 What do the letters PTA stand for? _____

_____

2 How many events did the PTA organise during the year? _____

_____

3 What other events could the PTA have held? _____

_____

4 How much did the barn dance make altogether? _____

_____

5 Which event raised the most money?

6 Why is a lifeguard needed at swimming?

7 What sort of parent would belong to the PTA?

8 Has the money been well spent?

Ursula Bear

Ursula was so fond of bears that she thought about very little else, and she had a very special secret that hardly anybody knew about. She knew how to turn herself into a real live bear by means of a simple magic spell. She had found the spell in a book in the library and it really worked. Ursula had turned herself into a small brown bear for a whole day and a night and being a bear was wonderful, but it had got her into so much trouble that she thought she had better never do it again.

One Friday afternoon when Ursula was on her way home from her dancing lesson at Miss Jardine's, a large coloured poster in the window of the sweet shop caught her eye. It was a picture of two enormous polar bears, and as Ursula read the poster her eyes grew round.

'Bears!' breathed Ursula. 'Performing polar bears!' She ran all the way home without stopping once. The kitchen was full of the warm treacly smell of baking gingerbread and Aunt Prudence was there wearing a yellow apron and a smudge of flour on her nose. She blinked in surprise when she saw Ursula.

'Goodness, child! You look quite out of breath,' she said.

Re-read the story and answer the following questions.

(Use the back of the sheet for questions 5 to 8.)

1 What was Ursula so fond of? _____

_____

2 Where had Ursula been on Friday afternoon? _____

_____

3 Why would Ursula want to turn herself into a bear? _____

_____

4 What event could the poster be advertising? _____

_____

_____

5 What sort of person do you think Aunt Prudence was?

6 How did Aunt Prudence get flour on her nose?

7 What would stop Ursula using the spell again?

8 How difficult was it to turn into a bear?

Toothpaste

In the 1870s, people who cleaned their teeth used a tooth powder. The tooth powder was made of burnt eggshells, cuttlefish bone or coral that had been ground up to a fine powder.

The toothpaste we have today is made of ten or more different things. Some toothpaste is made of powdered chalk. The chalk is a little bit gritty. The grit helps to remove the layer left on our teeth by the food and drink we have had. This layer also has plaque in it. The bacteria in the plaque decays our teeth.

The powdered chalk is made into a paste by mixing it with water. The paste is then mixed with something to make it thick. A very tiny drop of detergent is added to make the toothpaste foamy, which helps to clean our teeth. To make the toothpaste taste nice, a little peppermint oil is mixed into it. Most toothpaste has fluoride in it. Fluoride helps to make the enamel on our teeth strong so they are not so easily decayed.

The toothpaste tubes are filled through the wide end. When the tube is full, the end is pressed flat and crimped to seal it.

Re-read the explanation and answer the following questions.
(Use the back of the sheet for questions 7 and 8.)

1 What was toothpaste made of in the 1870s? _____

_____

2 What might decay our teeth? _____

_____

3 How does the grit in toothpaste clean our teeth? _____

_____

4 Is toothpaste without any fluoride as good as toothpaste containing it?

_____

5 How would foam help to clean teeth? _____

_____

6 What other flavours could you use to make toothpaste taste nice?

_____

7 What do sticky sweets do to teeth?

8 Which part of a tooth is made of enamel?

Early to bed

Many children make a fuss when they are told to go to bed. This happens whether they are sent to bed early or late!

Resting in bed is important for growing children. Children have usually been very busy during the day. They run about when they are playing and doing sports at school. Resting in bed gives a child's body the chance to relax.

Relaxing is important for the body's bones and muscles. By the end of a busy day, the cells of young bones get squeezed together because they are not as hard as adult bones. Resting in bed lets the bones stretch out again. The muscles of the body become tired. Resting lets the muscles get their energy back.

Apart from the body, the brain has been working hard all day. This makes it tired. The best way for the brain to rest is by sleeping. Young children need about twelve hours sleep each night to keep healthy. As people get older, they need less sleep.

When people get tired, their brains don't work as well and accidents can happen. There is a lot of truth in the saying 'Early to bed, early to rise makes a man healthy, wealthy and wise'!

Re-read the argument and answer the following questions.

(Use the back of the sheet for questions 6 to 8.)

1 What do many children do when they are told to go to bed? _____

_____

2 How many hours sleep does a young child need? _____

_____

3 Why don't children like going to bed? _____

_____

4 What will make the brain tired? _____

_____

5 What sort of accident could happen if someone is tired? _____

_____

6 Does an adult skeleton need the same rest as a child's?

7 Do you think the saying 'Early to bed, early to rise' is true?

8 What time do you think you should be in bed?

John and Jim

I've got a secret friend
Who lives at home with me.
Even when we're talking
There's no one there to see.
   My name's John and his name's Jim.
   You can see me, but you can't see him.

I've got a secret friend
Who goes to school with me.
Even when we're walking
There's no one there to see.
   My name's John and his name's Jim.
   You can see me, but you can't see him.

I've got a secret friend
Who sits in class with me.
Even when we're writing
There's no one there to see.
   My name's John and his name's Jim.
   You can see me, but you can't see him.

I've got a secret friend
Who likes to box with me.
Even when we're fighting
There's no one there to see.
   My name's John and his name's Jim.
   You can see me, but you can't see him.

Barbara Ireson and *Christopher Rowe*

Re-read the poem and answer the following questions.

(Use the back of the sheet for all the questions.)

1 What is John's secret friend called?

2 Why is this friend kept secret by John?

3 How do you think they can box together?

4 Why can't the secret friend be seen?

5 Where does John's secret friend live?

6 What are the things the friends do together?

7 Which words in the poem rhyme with 'talking' and 'writing'?

8 Why do you think John has a secret friend?

The Twits

Once a week, on Wednesdays, the Twits had Bird Pie for supper. Mr Twit caught the birds and Mrs Twit cooked them.

Mr Twit was good at catching birds. On the day before Bird Pie day, he would put the ladder up against The Big Dead Tree and climb into the branches with a bucket of glue and a paint-brush. The glue he used was something called HUGTIGHT and it was stickier than any other glue in the world. He would paint it along the tops of all the branches and then go away.

As the sun went down, birds would fly in from all around to roost for the night in The Big Dead Tree. They didn't know, poor things, that the branches were all smeared with horrible HUGTIGHT. The moment they landed on a branch, their feet stuck and that was that.

The next morning, which was Bird Pie day, Mr Twit would climb up the ladder again and grab all the wretched birds that were stuck to the tree. It didn't matter what kind they were – song thrushes, blackbirds, sparrows, crows, little jenny wrens, robins, anything – they all went into the pot for Wednesday's Bird Pie supper.

Re-read the story and answer the following questions.

(Use the back of the sheet for questions 6 to 8.)

1 What did the Twits have for supper on Wednesdays? _____

_____

2 Which tree did Mr Twit climb into? _____

_____

3 On what day would Mr Twit put glue on the branches of the tree?

_____

4 Why would the birds roost in the Big Dead Tree? _____

_____

5 Do you think the birds would learn not to roost in the tree? _____

_____

6 What do you think gave Mr Twit the idea to put glue on the branches?

7 What would Mrs Twit have to do to the birds before she cooked them?

8 How do you think Mr Twit feels about wildlife?

The playground

A newspaper report tells us about things that have happened around the world. The reporters for local newspapers tell readers about things that have happened in their own area. Here is a report about a local playground.

Dunston County Council has improved the old playground next to the football ground by replacing the worn-out equipment and adding new pieces. This was made possible by a grant offer from the National Lottery Small Claims Board.

Children using the playground were asked what they would like. The old swings have been painted and six new swings have been added for toddlers to use. A new slide and playhouse have been built next to the sandpit and the roundabout has been painted. A new see-saw and rocking horse complete the play equipment. Rubber tiles have been put round each piece of equipment and the whole playground has been fenced in. A notice to say only children under 14 years can use the playground has been put on the gate.

The official opening of the playground was well attended by parents and children. When asked, Helen and Matthew Jones said they were very pleased with the new playground.

Re-read the report and answer the following questions.

(Use the back of the sheet for questions 5 to 8.)

1 What does a reporter for a local newspaper write about? _____

_____

2 What is next to the sandpit? _____

_____

3 Why should the playground be for children under 14 years only?

_____

4 What are the rubber tiles for? _____

_____

5 How safe do you think the playground will be?

6 How useful is this report to local people?

7 Who looks after the playground?

8 Where did the money for the playground come from?

The library

A library is a collection of books. If you have books at home, that is your own library. It will have the books that interest you.

Your school library has books that you all need for your school work. There are also story books for you to read and enjoy.

A public library has books for everyone to use and borrow. If your public library doesn't have a book you need, it can be borrowed from another public library for you.

Books can be divided into two big groups: there are fiction books, which are made-up stories, and there are non-fiction books, which are about things that are true.

Non-fiction books are divided into subject groups such as birds, sport, music and so on. Each subject has a different number. This is to help you find the book you need. These subject groups were worked out by an American librarian called Melvil Dewey in 1876. Books have been grouped like this in most libraries ever since. A 'Dewey number' is put on the spine of each non-fiction book and it has its own special place on the shelves.

Re-read the explanation and answer the following questions.

(Use the back of the sheet for questions 6 to 8.)

1 Who would use a public library? _____

_____

2 What is a collection of books called? _____

_____

3 Who put non-fiction books into the subject groups? _____

_____

4 Would a book about computers be fiction or non-fiction? _____

_____

5 What does a Dewey number tell you? _____

_____

6 How long have non-fiction books been grouped by subject?

7 Do you think it is a good idea to separate fiction books from non-fiction books in a library?

8 How useful do you think a public library is?

Saving wild flowers

Wild flowers are gradually disappearing from the countryside. Many farmers still use weedkillers or herbicides to make sure their crops are good. They think of wild flowers as weeds. Nowadays, people try to save the wild flowers that grow in meadows and hedgerows.

Part of a garden can be left as a wild garden. In this area, the common wild flowers will grow easily such as dandelions, daisies, sowthistles and buttercups. These are strong plants and they can grow almost anywhere. They are unlikely to become extinct.

Some of the more rare wild flowers will only grow in certain parts of the country. The pretty corn marigold likes sandy soil, and the lovely blue chicory likes chalky soil, so you find these plants growing well in the right place for them. But sickle hare's ear is very rare. It can only be found in one place – in the roadside grass near a village called Ongar.

Because the rarer wild flowers are so fussy about where they grow, it makes it difficult to grow them in your garden if they don't like the soil. The rarer wild plants that grow where you live may do well in your garden if you scatter some of the seeds. If everyone did this, we could be sure that our wild flowers would not disappear.

Re-read the argument and answer the following questions.

(Use the back of the sheet for questions 4 to 8.)

1 Which wild flowers are unlikely to disappear and become extinct?

_____

_____

2 What do some farmers think of the wild flowers growing in their crops?

_____

3 Why do you think wild flowers should be protected? _____

_____

4 What can someone with a garden do to help stop wild flowers from disappearing?

5 What makes it difficult to stop the rarer wild flowers from disappearing?

6 What problems could a gardener have with a wild garden area?

7 Who, apart from farmers, might be causing the wild flowers to disappear?

8 What could you do to find out which wild flowers grow best where you live?

First aid for a grazed knee

A graze can happen when a person slides along the ground as they fall and the top layer of skin is scraped away. If the fall happens outside, there may be dirt in the wound.

To give first aid to the person who is hurt, you will need a bowl of warm water, some cotton wool balls, a packet of sterile gauze and adhesive tape or adhesive dressings.

First, wash your hands before you start to give first aid. Then wet a ball of cotton wool in the water and gently bathe the grazed area to wash away any dirt or grit that is in the wound. Use a fresh piece of cotton wool each time you wipe the graze.

When all the dirt has been cleaned away, blot the wound with a piece of sterile gauze to mop up any water and blood.

If the graze is large, cover it with a sterile gauze dressing and fasten it in place with strips of adhesive tape. If the graze is small, use an adhesive dressing that is large enough to cover the wound.

It is important to keep the wound clean so that it does not become infected.

Re-read the instructions and answer the following questions.

(Use the back of the sheet for questions 5 to 10.)

1 How could you graze yourself? _____

_____

2 Why do you need to be gentle when bathing a graze? _____

_____

3 What do you need to give first aid to someone with a graze? _____

_____

_____

4 What might you be doing to get grazed? _____

_____

5 How do you think the person feels who is giving the first aid?

6 Why is it useful to know about first aid?

7 Which phrase means 'sterile'? **a)** brand new **b)** germ free **c)** scratchy.

8 What might happen if the graze isn't properly cleaned?

9 What other accidents can happen around the home?

10 What should you do if a really bad accident happened?

Photocopiable

The witches' ride

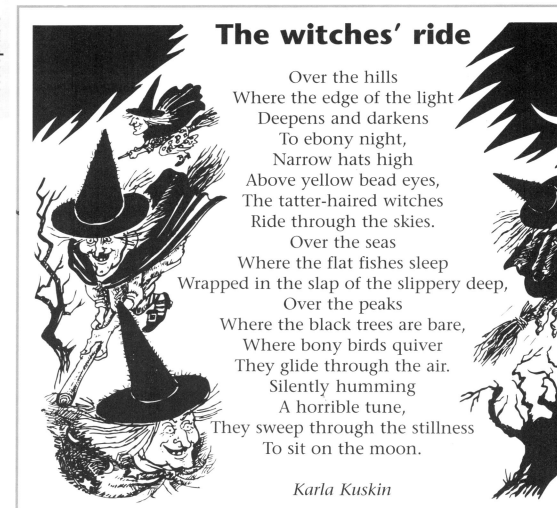

Over the hills
Where the edge of the light
Deepens and darkens
To ebony night,
Narrow hats high
Above yellow bead eyes,
The tatter-haired witches
Ride through the skies.
Over the seas
Where the flat fishes sleep
Wrapped in the slap of the slippery deep,
Over the peaks
Where the black trees are bare,
Where bony birds quiver
They glide through the air.
Silently humming
A horrible tune,
They sweep through the stillness
To sit on the moon.

Karla Kuskin

Re-read the poem and answer the following questions.
(Use the back of the sheet for questions 4 to 10.)

1 Who is the poem about? _____

_____

2 What are the witches doing? _____

_____

3 What time of the day is it in the poem? _____

_____

4 Describe how you think the witches look.
5 Where are the witches going?
6 What do you think the witches are riding on?
7 Why is the word 'ebony' used to describe the night?
8 Write down the pairs of words that rhyme.
9 What do you think is the 'slippery deep'?
10 What might be horrible about the tune the witches hummed?

Water

Water has no taste at all,
    Water has no smell;
Water's in the waterfall,
    In pump, and tap, and well.

Water's every where about;
    Water's in the rain,
In the bath, the pond, and out
    At sea it's there again.

Water comes into my eyes
    And down my cheeks in tears,
When Mother cries, 'Go back and try
    To wash behind those ears.'

John R Crossland

Re-read the poem and answer the following questions.
(Use the back of the sheet for questions 6 to 10.)

1 Write a list of the places in which the poem says water is found.

_____

2 Write down two other places in which water can be found.

_____

3 Why do you think the writer cries when he is told to wash behind his ears?

_____

4 How does the poem describe what water is like? _____

_____

5 Write down two more things that would describe water.

_____

6 'Smell' and 'well' rhyme. Write down four more pairs of words that rhyme.

7 What do you use water for in your home?

8 Why has the poet's mother said, 'Wash behind those ears'?

9 Where else is water used in the towns and country?

10 Make a list of animals that live in water.

No roses for Harry

Harry was a white dog with black spots. On his birthday, he got a present from Grandma. It was a woollen sweater with roses on it. Harry didn't like it the moment he saw it. He didn't like the roses.

When he tried it on, he felt cosy and snug. But he still didn't like the roses. He thought it was the silliest sweater he'd ever seen.

The next day when Harry went into town with the children, he wore his new sweater. When people saw it, they laughed. When dogs saw it ,they barked. Harry made up his mind then and there to lose Grandma's present.

When they went into a big store to shop, the children took off his sweater and let him carry it. This was just what Harry wanted. First he tried to lose it in the pet department – but a man found it and gave it back. Then he tried to lose it in the grocery department – but a lady found it and gave it back. He tried to lose it in the flower department – but a little boy found it and gave it back. The children didn't let Harry carry it any more. They made him wear it. As they started home, Harry was beginning to think he'd never lose it.

When he got home, his friends were waiting to play with him. But Harry didn't feel like playing so they left him alone. As he sat wondering what to do, Harry noticed a loose stitch in his sweater. He pulled at the wool – just a little at first – then a bit more – and a little bit more. Harry didn't know it, but a bird was watching.

In a minute, Harry had pulled out quite a long piece of the wool. The end of it lay on the grass behind him. Suddenly the bird flew down. Quick as a flash she took the end of the wool in her beak and flew away with it! It all happened before Harry could even blink. The sweater began to disappear right before Harry's eyes.

Re-read the story and answer the following questions.

1 What did Harry look like? _____

_____

2 Who gave Harry a woollen sweater? _____

_____

3 Why didn't Harry like the roses? _____

_____

4 What was good about the sweater? _____

_____

5 Why was it so difficult to lose the sweater in the shop? _____

_____

6 Why did the children make Harry wear the sweater when they came out of the

shop? _____

_____

7 Why didn't Harry feel like playing with his friends? _____

_____

_____

8 What would happen when the bird flew away with the end of the wool?

_____

_____

9 Do you think Harry meant the bird to take the end of the wool?

_____

10 What sort of sweater would suit Harry better? _____

_____

_____

_____

_____

Water

Some of our houses use a lot of water. Most people have washing machines to wash their clothes, and many people now have dishwashers to do all the washing up. These machines use gallons of water. We also use a lot of water when we have showers, baths and flush lavatories.

All the water we use in our homes and schools comes from rainwater in the first place. The rain that falls fills the rivers and lakes. Rainwater trickles down through the ground and fills wells and underground springs. With all the water we use in our homes, we need plenty of rain!

We need water to drink as well as for our machines. The water in the rivers or lakes is not clean or safe enough to drink. The water that comes to our houses has to be cleaned and made safe for us to drink and use for cooking.

To make water safe, it is pumped from the rivers or lakes and kept in a reservoir. A reservoir is a specially made lake. The water goes into the reservoir through a screen. This screen is like a net and traps all the leaves, twigs and branches that may be floating in the water.

The water then trickles down through layers of sand and gravel. Any tiny plants and bits that are still in the water are left behind. The water that trickles through is now quite clean. Chlorine is added to kill any germs that may be in the water. Now the water is safe for us to drink.

Re-read the explanation and answer the following questions.

1 What do we use water for in our houses? _____

_____

_____

2 Where does the water we use come from in the first place? _____

_____

3 What else do we use water for? _____

_____

_____

4 What would happen if it didn't rain? _____

_____

5 What else might be in the river water apart from twigs, leaves and branches?

_____

_____

6 What might happen to us if we drank water with germs in it?

_____

7 Do you think we need to use water that is fit to drink for our showers, baths

and lavatories? _____

_____

8 What would we need to do to sea water to be able to use it? _____

_____

9 Is the water in your house clear and nice to drink? _____

_____

10 What is a reservoir used for? _____

_____

_____

_____

Dental hygiene

Our teeth are one of the most important organs in our bodies. They grind up the food we eat so that we can swallow it easily. If you have ever swallowed a lump of food by mistake you will know how it can hurt! Grinding up the food also helps us to digest it.

Our 'milk teeth' are our first teeth. A baby usually gets its first tooth before it is one year old. These 'milk teeth' are replaced by our permanent or second teeth. You often see boys and girls of six or seven years old with their front teeth missing. These seem to be the first to come and the first to fall out!

It is important to take great care of your teeth. If they are not cleaned regularly, the food left on them becomes acid. The acid will make the teeth go bad and decay. This means that the enamel on the outside of your teeth develops holes as the decay works through. This will make your teeth ache and hurt badly.

Brushing your teeth gets rid of the little bits of food left on them. It is best to brush your teeth after every meal. Your teeth should be brushed up from the gums to the top of the teeth, not from side to side. This is to make sure the food stuck between your teeth is cleaned out.

It is difficult to brush your teeth after a midday meal if you are at school all day, but you can wash your mouth out with water – this is better than doing nothing. The most important time to clean your teeth is before you go to bed when you have finished eating for the day.

Parents can help children get into the habit of cleaning their teeth. When a baby's first milk teeth appear, a parent should gently brush the teeth with a soft brush specially made for babies. If you take good care of your teeth by keeping them clean and going to the dentist, your teeth will last a lifetime.

Re-read the argument and answer the following questions.

1 What are a baby's first teeth called? _____

_____

2 What will happen if teeth are not kept clean? _____

_____

_____

3 Why are our teeth important to us? _____

_____

_____

4 How does rinsing your teeth help if you can't brush them? _____

_____

5 Do you think you need to brush your teeth after each meal? _____

_____

6 Why is it difficult to brush your teeth at school? _____

_____

7 What would happen if a tooth decayed? _____

_____

_____

8 Do you think looking after your teeth is a good thing? _____

_____

_____

9 Why do you think the first teeth are called 'milk teeth'? _____

_____

_____

10 Why would brushing your teeth from side to side not be good enough to

clean your teeth? _____

_____

Charlie and the Chocolate Factory

Charlie Bucket stared around the gigantic room in which he now found himself. The place was like a witch's kitchen! All about him black metal pots were boiling and bubbling on huge stoves, and kettles were hissing and pans were sizzling, and strange iron machines were clanking and spluttering, and there were pipes running all over the ceiling and walls, and the whole place was filled with smoke and steam and delicious rich smells.

Mr Wonka himself had suddenly become even more excited than usual, and anyone could see that this was the room he loved best of all. He was hopping about among the saucepans and the machines like a child among his Christmas presents, not knowing which thing to look at first. He lifted the lid from a huge pot and took a sniff; then he rushed over and dipped a finger into a barrel of sticky yellow stuff and had a taste; then he skipped across to one of the machines and turned half a dozen knobs this way and that; then he peered anxiously through the glass door of a gigantic oven, rubbing his hands and cackling with delight at what he saw inside. Then he ran over to another machine, a small shiny affair that kept going *phut-phut-phut-phut-phut*, and every time it went *phut*, a large green marble dropped out of it into a basket on the floor. At least it looked like a marble.

'Everlasting Gobstoppers!' cried Mr Wonka proudly. 'They're completely new! I am inventing them for children who are given very little pocket money. You can put an Everlasting Gobstopper in your mouth and you can suck it and suck it and suck it and suck it and it will *never* get any smaller!'

'It's like gum!' cried Violet Beauregarde.

'It is *not* like gum,' Mr Wonka said, 'Gum is for chewing, and if you tried chewing one of these Gobstoppers here you'd break your teeth off! And they *never* get any smaller! They *never* disappear! *NEVER!* At least I don't think they do. There's one of them being tested this very moment in the Testing Room next door...'

Re-read the story and answer the following questions.

1 What was the room like that Charlie Bucket found himself in? _____

_____

2 Why had Mr Wonka become so excited? _____

_____

3 What was making the delicious rich smells? _____

_____

4 Why was Mr Wonka hopping about among the saucepans and machines?

_____

_____

5 Why did Violet Beauregarde think that an Everlasting Gobstopper was like

chewing gum? _____

_____

6 Why would children with very little pocket money like Everlasting

Gobstoppers? _____

_____

7 How long would you expect an Everlasting Gobstopper to last? _____

_____

8 Could Mr Wonka be called an inventor? _____

_____

_____

9 Was Charlie surprised at the gigantic room? _____

_____

_____

10 Why did the Everlasting Gobstopper look like a marble? _____

_____

_____

Bones

Bones is good with children,
He goes with us everywhere;
The beach, the park, the swimming-pool,
He comes to look us up at school –
He's stopped the Dodgems at the Fair.

Bones is good with children,
He does the same things as us;
Won't wipe his feet, won't shut the gate,
Goes off all day, then trails home late,
To *'Bad'*, and bed, and fuss...

Bones is good with children,
He gets muddy and then he pongs
Of earth and burn and wood and pond,
The hills and all the moors beyond –
When it rains he rolls his eyes and longs

To be out with the children
And gets himself soaked through,
Slide down the banks on tea-trays,
Chase sticks, and join our football-frays –
I think he'll even come with you:

'Cos Bones is good with children!

Brian Lee

Re-read the poem and answer the following questions.

(Use the back of the sheet for all the questions.)

1 What or who is Bones?

2 Who is Bones good with?

3 What did Bones stop at the fair?

4 Where do you think Bones lives, in the town or in the country?

5 Does Bones make a good companion for children?

6 What does Bones do when the children are at school?

7 What happens when Bones comes in late without wiping his feet?

8 Who do you think says 'Bad' to Bones?

9 Is Bones trustworthy and friendly?

10 How do you think Bones got his name?

Battleships

This is a game for two players. All you need are four pieces of squared paper (12 squares by 12 squares to make 144 squares) and a pencil.

Each player has two pieces of paper. On each piece of paper label the twelve squares along the top, A to L, and the twelve squares down the side, 1 to 12. These pieces of paper represent the ocean.

On one of his pieces of paper, each player marks out six ships on his grid, for example one battleship, two destroyers and three submarines. Five squares can be used for a battleship, three squares for a destroyer and one square for a submarine. The fleet can be arranged anywhere on the ocean – just make sure your opponent can't see where your ships are!

The second piece of paper is used as a spare grid to record a player's 'shots'. One player starts the game by firing the first shot (saying, for example, 'I am firing at H8'), naming a square that might be occupied by a ship in his opponent's fleet. He then marks down the shot he made on his spare piece of paper so that he doesn't aim at that square again and waste a shot.

The other player then has to tell him whether he has made a 'hit', and crosses off the square if a 'hit' has been made. He does not need to tell his opponent which of his ships has been damaged. Then the second player has a turn to fire his 'gun' in the same way. The game continues with each player taking it in turns to have a 'shot'.

A ship is 'sunk' when each square of the ship has been hit by the other player. The winner is the first player to sink the whole of his opponent's fleet.

Re-read the instructions and answer the following questions. (Use the back of the sheet for questions 6 to 10.)

1 How many players does the game need? _____

_____

2 What sort of paper do you need? _____

_____

3 What other ships could you have in your fleet? _____

_____

4 What are the letters and numbers for? _____

_____

5 When might you play this game? _____

_____

6 What could you do if you didn't have any squared paper?

7 Is this an easy game to play?

8 Could more than two people play the game at a time?

9 What changes to the rules could you have to make the game quicker?

10 What skills do you need to play the game successfully?

The water cycle

After it has stopped raining, the ground is soaking wet and puddles of water are left in dips and hollows on the roads and paths. Gradually, the ground dries up and the puddles disappear. The water has evaporated and has turned into water vapour. This is made up of very tiny droplets of water like those in steam but even smaller. You can't see it but the water vapour is in the air. The warmer the air, the more water vapour it can hold.

Water from the rivers and sea evaporates in the same way all the time. The water vapour in the air rises up into the sky. As the temperature of the air gets colder, the water vapour turns into tiny droplets of water again and wispy clouds are formed.

The droplets of water in the clouds join together and these drops get bigger and bigger. The clouds get thicker and bigger and turn grey. The water drops get so heavy that they start to fall as rain. In the winter if the air is very cold, the water vapour in the clouds forms ice crystals and these fall to earth as snow. Hail is formed when raindrops freeze as they fall through the air.

When the rainwater falls on the earth, it trickles through the ground and runs into the rivers, lakes and sea. Water is continually evaporating from all these places, turning into water vapour and rising up through the air to form clouds high up in the sky, only to fall again as rain. In this way, the water we have on earth just goes round and round in the water cycle.

Re-read the explanation and answer the following questions.

(Use the back of the sheet for questions 8 to 10.)

1 What happens to the water in the puddles left by the rain? _____

_____

2 What are the clouds made of? _____

_____

3 Why do wet clothes dry when they are hung up outside? _____

_____

4 Why do clouds turn grey? _____

_____

5 Do you think the Stone Age people could have used the same water as us?

_____

6 How would you need to dress if the clouds were grey when you went outside?

_____

7 How is snow formed? _____

_____

8 How important do you think rain is to us?

9 Do you think the amount of water in the world has always been the same?

10 Draw a diagram to show how the water cycle works.

Swimming lessons

We live by a canal. My friends and I love going there. Sometimes we try catching fish and sometimes we throw stones at bits of wood that are floating in the water. My mum was very worried about me falling in and drowning because I couldn't swim so she made me go to swimming lessons.

I didn't really like going much at first. The water was quite cold at the swimming pool and I didn't like getting my face wet. I'm used to it now and it's good fun. There are 12 boys and girls in my class. We all started off wearing armbands, and after having a go at doggy paddle, our teacher taught us how to do the breaststroke. It was quite difficult to begin with, trying to make our arms and legs work properly together. Luckily our armbands stopped us from sinking!

I went to swimming every week on Saturday morning. I made friends with another boy in the class. He's good at swimming – our teacher says he's a 'natural'. After a few lessons, we had to try swimming without our armbands. My friend could do it easily and swam a whole width. I kept sinking at first and I got really fed up. Then all of a sudden, I could do it! I was able to swim! I shall never forget the day I first swam a length! I was given my 25-metre badge. My mum has sewn the badge on my swimming trunks – it looks good! My mum says she is very proud of me and she doesn't mind me going down to the canal now.

Re-read the recount and answer the following questions.
(Use the back of the sheet for questions 9 and 10.)

1 Where did the writer live? _____

_____

2 Why did the writer have to learn to swim? _____

_____

3 What makes a canal a dangerous place? _____

_____

4 Why did the writer like going to the canal? _____

_____

5 Why was learning the breaststroke difficult? _____

_____

6 Why did the swimming teacher call the writer's friend a 'natural'?

_____

7 How many metres long is the swimming pool? _____

_____

8 How do you think the writer felt after first swimming a length?

_____

9 Is the writer a boy or a girl?

10 Could any of the children swim before they had swimming lessons?

Cam Jansen and the mystery of the UFO

Cam put her books and lunch box down. 'It's cold,' she said.

Cam fastened the top button of her coat. She pulled down the knitted cap she was wearing until it covered the tops of her ears.

'And it's getting dark,' Eric said. 'I'm not going to find anything to photograph now. Let's go home.'

Eric put the camera back in its case. 'I'm never around when anything happens,' he complained. 'And I'll bet if I *am* around, either I won't have my camera or I'll have run out of film.'

'Or,' Cam said, 'you'll forget to take the lens cap off!'

Cam and Eric often spent time together. They were in the same class at school and lived next door to each other.

'If it wasn't for your hair,' Cam's mother often teased, 'I'd think you and Eric were twins.'

Cam had what people called bright red hair, even though it was more orange than red. Eric's hair was dark brown.

Cam and Eric started walking home. They walked past a row of small shops at the edge of a shopping mall. Then they stopped at the corner and waited for the traffic lights to change.

Meow.

Cam and Eric looked up. A grey-and-white kitten was high up in a tree. The branch she was standing on was shaking. The kitten took a step towards the end of the branch. The branch shook even more.

Meow.

'I think she wants to come down,' Eric said, 'but she doesn't know how to.'

Cam opened her lunch box. 'I have a bit of tuna fish sandwich in here. Maybe I can get the kitten to come down.'

Cam reached up and put a piece of tuna fish on the part of the branch closest to the trunk. The kitten saw the food and turned round carefully. The branch shook, but the kitten didn't fall. She walked down the branch and ate the tuna fish. Cam reached out for the kitten.

Eric was holding his camera. 'Smile,' he said, and he took a picture just as the kitten jumped into Cam's arms.

'I'll call the picture "Local Girl Saves Untamed Feline".'

Narrative

Re-read the story and answer the following questions.

1   What time of day was it? _____

_____

2   What was Eric wanting to do? _____

_____

3   What did Cam and Eric see high up in a tree? _____

_____

4   What did Cam put on the branch? _____

_____

5   Do you think Cam is the girl's real name? _____

_____

6   Why did Cam think that tuna fish would get the kitten down? _____

_____

7   How do you think the kitten came to be in the tree? _____

_____

_____

8   Why didn't the kitten fall when the branch shook? _____

_____

_____

9   What do you think Eric will do with his picture? _____

_____

_____

10   Why couldn't Cam and Eric be twins? _____

_____

_____

_____

_____

_____

The story of Giant Kippernose

Once there was a giant called Kippernose. He lived on a lonely farm in the mountains. He was not fierce. Indeed he was as kind and as gentle as a giant could be. He liked children, and was fond of animals. He was good at telling stories. His favourite foods were ice-cream, cakes, lollipops and sausages. He would help anyone, large or small. And yet he had no friends. When he went to the town to do his shopping, everyone ran away from him. Busy streets emptied in a trice. Everyone ran home, bolted their doors and closed all their windows, even on hot summer days.

Kippernose shouted, 'Don't run away! I'll not hurt you! Please don't run away, I like little people. I've only come to do my shopping. Please come out. I'll tell you a good story about a dragon and a mermaid.'

But it was no use. The town stayed silent and empty; the doors and windows stayed firmly closed. Poor Kippernose wanted so much to have someone to talk to. He felt so lonely that he often sat down in the town square and cried his heart out. You would think someone would take pity on him, but no one ever did. He simply couldn't understand it. He even tried going to another town, far across the mountains, but just the same thing happened.

'Has all the world gone mad?' said Kippernose to himself, and took his solitary way home.

The truth was that the people were not afraid of Kippernose, and they had not gone mad either. The truth *was*... that Kippernose had not had a single bath in a hundred years, or more!

Re-read the story and answer the following questions.

(Use the back of the sheet for questions 6 to 10.)

1 What was the giant called? _____

2 What were his favourite foods? _____
_____

3 Why did the giant want someone to talk to? _____
_____

4 Do you think all giants are like Kippernose? _____
_____

5 What did the giant think would please the people? _____
_____

6 What would happen if someone didn't have a bath for a hundred years or more?

7 Why wouldn't anyone take pity on the giant?

8 Does 'in a trice' mean quickly or slowly?

9 What did Kippernose think made the people run away?

10 Do you think someone should tell Kippernose what is wrong?

Making an aquarium

To make an aquarium you will need a straight-sided glass tank, rounded pebbles or gravel, three or four larger stones, rainwater or pond water, and pond weed from a shop or pond.

First, carefully wash and dry the glass tank. Wash the pebbles or gravel. Scrub the stones well to remove any soil or dirt.

Collect some rain or pond water in a clean bucket. Do not use tap water.

Put a layer of pebbles, gravel or a mixture of both in the bottom of the tank. (A layer of about 3cm would be about right.) The layer does not need to be completely level. It could slope a little down to the front of the tank. This makes it easier to remove any uneaten pieces of food. Arrange the larger stones to look natural, as if they were in a pond or stream.

Gently fill the tank three-quarters full with the rainwater or pond water using a jug.

Put in the pond weed. This is usually strands of Canadian pond weed. You can trap the ends of the strands under the larger stones. The pond weed puts oxygen into the water and aerates it.

Leave the tank for a day to settle, and for the water to come up to room temperature.

Stock the aquarium with three or four water snails. They will keep the tank clean by removing any rubbish on the bottom of the tank and by eating the green algae that grows on the glass sides.

Put in two or three goldfish. Make sure the water in which you brought them home from the shop is at the same temperature as the water in the tank.

Place the aquarium in a cool, shady place.

Feed the fish once or twice a week with a pinch of fish food or tiny amounts of uncooked porridge oats.

Re-read the instructions and answer the following questions.
(Use the back of the sheet for all the questions.)

1 What sort of tank will you need?

2 What kind of water should you use?

3 Why is it best not to use tap water?

4 Where could you get water snails from?

5 Why do you need water snails in the aquarium?

6 Why should the tank be in a cool, shady place?

7 How does pond weed aerate the water?

8 How else could you make the aquarium look attractive?

9 Why does the water in which you brought the goldfish home need to be at the same temperature as the water in the aquarium?

10 How often will you need to change the water in the aquarium?

Thirty-two lengths

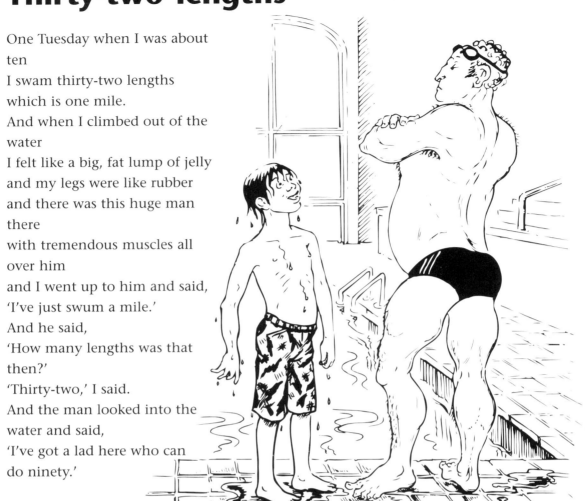

One Tuesday when I was about
ten
I swam thirty-two lengths
which is one mile.
And when I climbed out of the
water
I felt like a big, fat lump of jelly
and my legs were like rubber
and there was this huge man
there
with tremendous muscles all
over him
and I went up to him and said,
'I've just swum a mile.'
And he said,
'How many lengths was that
then?'
'Thirty-two,' I said.
And the man looked into the
water and said,
'I've got a lad here who can
do ninety.'

Michael Rosen

Re-read the poem and answer the following questions.

(Use the back of the sheet for questions 5 to 10.)

1   How old was the boy when he swam a mile? _____
_____

2   On which day did he swim a mile? _____

3   How many lengths would half a mile be? _____
_____

4   Why did the boy tell the man about swimming a mile? _____
_____

5   What made the boy feel like a lump of jelly?

6   How can you tell the man was very big?

7   How do you think the boy felt after talking to the man?

8   Did the man think the boy had done well?

9   Why do you think the man was proud of the boy who could do ninety lengths?

10   What sort of swimmer would be able to swim thirty-two lengths?

Ice-caps

Ice-caps are huge areas of ice in the polar regions of the world. The polar regions are at the North and South Poles of the world. These regions are as far as they can be from the equator, which circles the earth (the equator is where the sun is at its hottest).

It is so cold at the North and South Poles that the seas there are frozen. The ice-cap at the South Pole, Antarctica, has formed over a large island of solid land. At the North Pole, the Arctic is a huge ocean that has frozen solid into one big sheet of ice floating on the top of the sea, making a vast island of ice. The ice here is only a few metres thick. The ice over the land of the Antarctic can be as much as two kilometres thick.

The climate in the Arctic is very, very cold. The temperature is always below freezing or so little above it that the ice never melts away. In the summer, the edges of the Arctic ice sheet slowly melt in the warmth of the sun. Huge chunks of ice break away and float out to sea. These chunks of ice are icebergs. Some of the very big icebergs float right away into mid-ocean and they are a serious danger to ships.

If all the ice in the polar regions melted, the water from the ice would raise the level of the oceans in the world by 75 metres!

Re-read the explanation and answer the following questions.
(Use the back of the sheet for questions 9 and 10.)

1 Where are the polar regions? _____

_____

2 What has happened to the sea at the North and South Poles? _____

_____

3 Why is it so cold in the polar regions? _____

_____

4 What causes chunks of ice to break off the ice-cap in the Arctic? _____

_____

5 What sort of clothes would you need to wear to visit the Arctic? _____

_____

6 What would happen to the land of the world if all the ice at the ice-caps melted?

_____

7 How are icebergs dangerous to ships? _____

_____

8 When would be the best time to visit the North Pole? _____

_____

9 What would happen if you fell into the sea at the polar regions?

10 What could an explorer use for water in the Arctic?

The strange creature

SCENE 1

A lady is talking to a reporter at the office of the Daily Bugle. She is very upset.

LADY: It was huge, I tell you, and making a loud hissing noise. It was staring at me with its wild eyes!

REPORTER: Now calm down, Madam. Tell me exactly what happened.

LADY: Well, I was walking by Poddle Wood with Ralph – he's my dog – when it stuck its head out over the tops of the bushes!

REPORTER: What stuck its head out?

LADY: This awful creature! I thought I would die of fright!

REPORTER: Can you describe it, Madam?

LADY: Well, it was huge, like I said. About as big as a double-decker bus. It was making a horrible, hissing noise and rustling. I am sure it was getting ready to attack me! You'd better come and see!

SCENE 2

At the edge of Poddle Wood.

LADY: Yes, this is the place – I recognise the bushes. *(A man in flying kit is suddenly seen staggering out of the bushes.)* Oh look! Who is that man? And what has happened to the creature?

REPORTER: Hey, sir! Have you seen a huge, hissing creature in the bushes?

MAN: That was my hot-air balloon. I came down in the wood by accident and my balloon tore on the trees as it fell through. Where am I?

LADY: You'd better come with me, young man, you could do with a cup of tea.

REPORTER: Hang on! I'll just get a picture for my paper.

Re-read the play and answer the following questions.
(Use the back of the sheet for questions 4 to 10.)

1 Who is the lady talking to at the Daily Bugle? _____

_____

2 Where had she been walking? _____

_____

3 Why was the lady so upset? _____

_____

4 Do you think Poddle Wood is a long way from the Daily Bugle office?

5 Do you think the reporter believed her story?

6 What was the hissing noise the lady heard?

7 Why do you think the balloon came down in the wood?

8 Why did the lady think the man needed a cup of tea?

9 Why did the lady go to the Daily Bugle?

10 Describe what you think the balloon looked like when it was flying.

The Garden Produce Show

The local Garden Produce Show was held on 11 August and it was a great success as usual. The hall was a blaze of colour and there was a record number of entries. The high standard of the produce made the judging very difficult.

The show was held for the first time in the new community centre that was opened earlier in the year. There were classes for every kind of fruit, flower and vegetable as well as classes for children to enter with their vegetable animals and miniature gardens. The tasty tomato growing and cake making classes introduced last year proved popular once more.

Mr Cooper won first prize again for his enormous onion grown from seed. It weighed a record 3.5 kilograms. The first prize for the longest runner bean had to be shared between Mrs Green and her next-door neighbour, Mr Todd. Mrs Green thought the prize should have been hers. She was surprised to learn that Mr Todd had grown any beans to enter, as he had never been interested in gardening.

The Dibble twins won first prize for their joint entry of a truly magnificent vegetable dragon. People were amazed that children who were only five years old could have done so well. The judge said their parents must have given them a lot of encouragement. Daisy Smith's miniature garden was the best of the class. Her miniature garden was arranged around a small, thatched cottage she had made.

Mr Nutt won first prize for his excellent fruit cake, while Tommy Botter took first prize for his shortbread. Mrs Green won first prize with her apple chutney as usual.

The prizes were presented by the president of the Garden Club, Mr Plant, who congratulated all the people who entered and thanked the judges for carrying out their difficult task.

Re-read the report and answer the following questions.

(Use the back of the sheet for questions 4 to 10.)

1   Where was the Garden Produce Show held? _____

_____

2   Who won first prize for a vegetable animal? _____

_____

3   Which classes had been held for the first time the year before? _____

_____

4   Where did Mrs Green suspect Mr Todd had got his runner bean from?

5   Write down five other vegetables that you think could have been entered.

6   Has the show been held in the community centre before?

7   Do you think the Dibble twins made their vegetable animal all by themselves?

8   Do you think Mr Cooper expected to win a prize with his onion?

9   What do you think made the 'blaze of colour'?

10   Was it a surprise to anyone that Mrs Green's chutney won first prize?

Harry's Mad

One immediate benefit to Harry was in the matter of homework. It did not take him long to realise that it was a much pleasanter business with Madison around.

One evening the parrot had flown upstairs to find the boy chewing his pencil and staring at an empty page.

'I'm stuck, Mad,' Harry said.

Madison hopped on to Harry's shoulder and peered down at the open book.

'What have we here?' he said.

'English.'

'English!' cried Madison in ringing tones. 'The flower of languages, the noblest speech of all, the mother tongue that Shakespeare spake!'

'Spake?'

'Spake. Whatta we gotta do?'

'It's parts of speech,' Harry said. 'You've got to say which word's a noun and all that. In these sentences. Like this one – 'John fell off the wall and broke his left leg.'

'Tough on John,' said Madison, 'but not difficult to answer. Here's what you've got: proper noun; – verb; – preposition; – definite article; – noun; – conjunction; – verb; – pronoun; – adjective; – noun. Get it?'

'No,' said Harry.

But by the time that Madison had explained it and dictated it with the words all correctly spelled, Harry had learned quite a lot.

'You've got these all right, Harry,' his teacher said next day in a puzzled voice. 'Your dad help you?'

'No,' said Harry. 'A little bird told me.'

Re-read the story and answer the following questions.
(Use the back of the sheet for questions 4 to 10.)

1 What is the name of the parrot? _____

_____

2 Why was Harry chewing his pencil? _____

_____

3 What subject had Harry got for homework? _____

_____

4 Why couldn't Harry do his homework?

5 Which room do you think Harry did his homework in?

6 How can you tell Madison is good at English?

7 Did the parrot help Harry to understand what he was doing?

8 Why was Harry's teacher puzzled?

9 Do you think Harry is good at English?

10 How much help is the parrot to Harry?

Homework

Many teachers and parents think that giving children school work to do at home is a good thing. Older children at secondary school need to do homework to be able to learn enough to pass exams. There isn't enough time in the lessons to do all the things they need to know or finish off the work they have started.

If children are given homework from about the age of seven, it gets them into the habit of working at home, so that they are used to doing it by the time they go to their secondary school. Homework helps parents to understand what their children are learning at school. It gives them the chance to help their children if they need it and take an interest in what they are doing.

If the children can't do their homework because they don't understand it, the teachers will get to know this and they will be able to give them extra help. Doing school work at home helps children to learn to concentrate and work on their own. This is a great advantage when the children are older and go to college or university.

People who are against homework say children are too tired after a day at school to work at home and they need time to play. It can be difficult sometimes in a crowded house to find somewhere quiet to do the work. Other members of the family may want to watch television and younger members of the family may be noisy. Busy parents may not have time to help their children if they need it and this could cause problems. If children have to do homework, there is no time to play or watch TV before they go to bed. Some children make a fuss about doing homework and parents have a job to get them to do it, so it can all end in tears.

Re-read the argument and answer the following questions.
(Use the back of the sheet for questions 4 to 10.)

1 Why do older children need to do school work at home? _____

_____

2 Do all teachers and parents think homework is a good thing? _____

_____

3 How does homework help parents? _____

_____

4 Why could it be difficult to find a quiet place to do the homework?

5 Why would children make a fuss about doing homework?

6 What are some of the things younger children could do for homework?

7 Do you think it is a good idea to do homework?

8 Why do young children need to get into the habit of doing homework?

9 Why is it an advantage to be able to concentrate and work on your own when you are older?

10 When is the best time for you to do homework?

How to find information in a book

Information books are non-fiction and contain facts about different subjects. They are all grouped together in the public library or school library. Information books have a number on their spines. This number tells you what subject group each book is in. The books are put on the shelves in numerical order so that you can find the one you want quickly.

When you want to find information, first find out what number the subject you need will have by looking it up in a subject catalogue. Look through the books in the library with this number and read the titles. The titles will give you a hint of what the books are about. Choose the book you think will have the information you need.

Look at the contents page at the beginning of the book and read the chapter headings to see if your subject is included. If it is, make a list of 'key words' for your subject and look for these in the index at the back of the book to see if any of your key words are listed. If they are, make a note of the page numbers where the information can be found.

Skim through the book to see if there are any illustrations, charts or diagrams that may be useful for your work.

If you are satisfied that the book has the information you need, start your work by looking on the pages you found in the chapter headings or index. Read through the information and make notes about what you have found out.

When you have made all the notes you need, write your piece of work in your own words using your notes to help you.

Re-read the instructions and answer the following questions.
(Use the back of the sheet for questions 6 to 10.)

1   What do information books have on their spines in the school or public library?

_____

2   How will you find the number for the subject you need?

_____

3   How could the title of a book give a hint of what the book is about?

_____

4   What are 'key words'?   _____

_____

5   What would be three key words for information about how to look after a dog?

_____

6   How is the index of the book useful?

7   Is a library a good place to go for information?

8   What skills do you need to be able to use information books?

9   Will you find made-up adventure stories in the non-fiction section?

10   Where will you find out what the chapters are called in the book?

Grammar

The teacher said:
A noun is a naming word.
What is the naming word in the sentence:
'He named the ship *Lusitania*'?
'Named,' said George.
Wrong, it's 'ship'.
Oh, said George.

The teacher said:
A verb is a doing word.
What is the doing word in the sentence:
'I like doing homework'?
'Doing,' said George.
Wrong, it's 'like'.
Oh, said George.

The teacher said:
An adjective is a describing word.
What is the describing word in the sentence:
'Describing sunsets is boring'?
'Describing,' said George.
Wrong, it's 'boring'.
I know it is, said George.

Michael Rosen

Re-read the poem and answer the following questions.

(Use the back of the sheet for questions 6 to 10.)

1 Who is the teacher talking to? _____

2 What is a noun? _____

3 What is a verb? _____

4 Would the word 'enormous' be a verb, a noun or an adjective? _____

_____

5 Is George enjoying the lesson? _____

_____

6 Why does George get all the answers wrong?

7 Do you think the teacher is good at teaching grammar?

8 Why is a noun called a naming word?

9 How many words can you think of to describe a sunset?

10 What do you like or not like about this poem?

Canal locks

Canals are man-made waterways that have been used for thousands of years. Until the 1500s, canals could only be built across flat land. When canal locks were invented, canals could be built across hills too. The locks made it possible for boats to sail over the hills by lifting them up in a series of steps from one level to another.

Locks are gates built across rivers to connect two different levels of water. Boats cannot travel up a waterfall to go from a lower to a higher stretch of river, but they can go through a lock. Locks are also used on rivers and canals to control the water level. The locks act as dams on rivers to prevent the water running too swiftly to the sea.

A lock is a small area of the waterway with gates at both ends. The sides and the bottom of the lock are made of bricks or concrete. There are sluices in the lock gates and these help to control the flow of water. A sluice is like a serving hatch which you sometimes see in the wall between a kitchen and dining room. A square is cut from the wood of the lock gate and the gap is covered by a sliding door. When the sliding door or shutter is covering the square hole in the gate, no water can get through. But when the shutter is lifted the water flows through the hole.

If a boat is going from a higher level of a canal to a lower level, the water in the lock has to be at the same level as the water in the canal at the higher level. The lock gates are opened and the boat enters the lock. The lock gates are closed behind the boat so the boat is now shut in the lock.

Now the water level in the lock has to be made the same as the lower level of the canal. To do this, the sluices are opened in the lock gates in front of the boat and the water flows out of the lock through the sluices. The water in the lock gets lower and lower until it is at the same level as the lower part of the canal. The lock gates in front of the boat are opened and the boat can go ahead out of the lock and go on its journey.

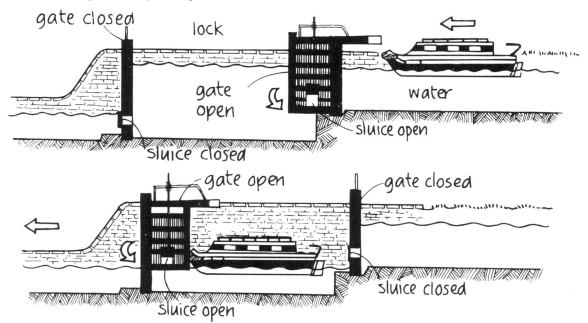

Re-read the explanation and answer the following questions.

1 When were locks invented? _____

_____

2 What were boats able to do after locks were invented? _____

_____

_____

3 What is the difference between a river and a canal? _____

_____

_____

4 What is used to make the sides and the bottom of the lock? _____

_____

5 How do sluices control the flow of water? _____

_____

_____

6 Why does a boat have to wait in a canal? _____

_____

7 How useful are canals today? _____

_____

_____

8 What heavy cargoes do you think could be moved by the canal boats?

_____

_____

9 Why do you think canals were invented? _____

_____

_____

_____

10 Write out the steps needed for a boat to go from a lower level of a canal to a higher

level. _____

_____

_____

_____

11 Does water flow along a canal as it does in a river? _____

_____

_____

12 Do you think canals are a quick way to travel? _____

_____

_____

_____

The rescue

SCENE 1

A boy and girl are sitting on a grassy canal bank with their fishing nets and jam jars. A canal boat is coming down the canal in the distance.

JACK: There don't seem to be many fish about today. How are you doing?

TINA: I've only got one little one. I don't know what it is.

JACK: Let's have a look – well, it's got spikes on its back so I think it is a stickleback. Hey! Look at that canal boat coming. I wonder why that lady is waving her arms about?

TINA: Never mind the boat! What's this floating along? Oh! It's a little dog! Can we get it to the side with our fishing nets?

(The children manage to get the dog to the side and lift it out.)

TINA: It's only a puppy – poor little thing!

JACK: It must belong to that lady on the boat.

SCENE 2

The children are aboard the boat having lemonade and biscuits. The lady is fussing over her dog.

LADY: How clever of you to save little Toby! He fell off the boat when it bumped into the lock gate. I was so afraid he would drown.

TINA: Mum made Jack and me have swimming lessons when we came to live near the canal. She wouldn't let us come fishing till we could swim. But little Toby can swim without any lessons!

LADY: Is that your house by the bridge? We'll tie up here and I'll ask your mum if you can come on the boat to the next lock as a thank you for saving Toby.

SCENE 3

Tina and Jack are aboard the canal boat sitting on the deck with Toby. The boat is approaching a lock.

JACK: Heave to! The lock gate is just ahead!

LADY: Stop the engine, Fred! Well! That's a bit of luck! The lock is full of water so we can go straight in when we've opened the gates.

(Fred and the lady jump ashore and open the gates.)

FRED: Okay! All aboard! Let's get the boat into the lock and close the gates again.

(Fred and the lady get the boat into the lock and close the gates.)

LADY: Open the sluices, Fred! We'll have to wait now for the water to go down, so that we can go through the other gates.

TINA: This is fun! We are going down. It's like being in a very slow lift!

JACK: We must be low enough now.

FRED: Open the gates, Fred!

(Fred opens the gates and the boat glides through.)

LADY: Here you are children, this is where you get off!

TINA AND JACK: Thank you for the ride, it's been really good!

Re-read the play and answer the following questions.

1 What are Jack and Tina doing by the canal? _____

_____

2 What sort of fish has Tina caught? _____

_____

3 Why was the lady waving her arms about? _____

_____

4 How did Toby come to be in the water? _____

_____

5 Why did the lady go to the children's mum? _____

_____

_____

6 Why wouldn't the children's mum let them go fishing before they could swim?

_____

_____

7 Have the children always lived near the canal? _____

_____

_____

8 How do you think the lady felt when her dog was saved? _____

_____

_____

9 Why did the lady ask Fred to stop the engine? _____

_____

_____

10 Why was it lucky that the lock was full of water? _____

_____

_____

11 Why did Fred have to open the sluices? _____

_____

_____

12 What would be good about a trip on a canal boat? _____

_____

_____

_____

_____

_____

_____

The Ashton Cricket Club

The cricket club has had quite a good year. The club has won more away matches than last year and all but one of the home matches.

The First XI finished the season in fourth place in the Sunday League, Division Two. This was a good effort. Seven games were won, six lost and five games were rained off. Tom Kipper scored a maiden century in a match against Bigton and Ted Potter scored 109 not out when the team played at home against Stockbury.

The Second XI played twelve games. They won six and lost six. They were luckier with the weather than the First XI. Two of the batsmen had outstanding seasons. Bob Flick scored a total of 467 runs including two centuries. Jack Hobble scored a total of 455 runs, again including two centuries. Jack has made a remarkable recovery from breaking his leg at the Christmas party.

The Ashton junior team had a successful season. There are some promising batsmen and bowlers in the team. Michelle Carter made a very good wicket keeper and had several good catches. The three other girls on the team scored most of the runs for the season. Four members of the junior team, two boys and two girls, will attend the cricket coaching course at the Indoor Cricket Centre in November. This will improve the level of coaching for the juniors. New members for the junior team would be welcome.

Mr Sparrow, the club's umpire, retired at the end of the season. He has umpired the matches for 43 years and it was only his failing eyesight that forced him to retire. He was made a life member of the club at his retirement party, and presented with a pair of binoculars. Mr Sparrow presented a set of new wickets to the club.

Mr Leather, Mayor of Ashton and keen supporter, has given the cricket club a new silver cup for the most promising junior. A presentation evening will be held in the cricket club on Saturday, 15 November. The prizes will be presented by the president of the club, Mr Legg. The catering committee will provide the food and the Cricketer's Arms will provide the licensed bar. Tickets are £13.50 each (£7.50 for juniors) from Mrs Hall, the cricket club secretary.

Re-read the report and answer the following questions.

1 What was the name of the cricket club? _____

2 Who was the president of the club? _____
_____

3 How many teams did the club have? _____
_____

4 What is an 'away' match? _____
_____

5 How many runs did Tom Kipper score against Bigton? _____
_____

6 How will the coaching course help the junior team? _____
_____
_____

7 Why did Mr Sparrow's eyesight force him to retire? _____
_____
_____

8 On which day of the week were the matches played? _____
_____

9 How many runs are there in a century? _____
_____

10 Who do you think will get the cup for the most promising junior?
_____
_____

11 What skills do you need to be good at cricket? _____
_____
_____
_____
_____
_____
_____

12 Who enjoys cricket matches the most, the players or the people watching?
_____
_____
_____
_____

Dreams

The Big Friendly Giant was seated at the great table in his cave and he was doing his homework.

Sophie sat cross-legged on the table-top near by, watching him at work.

The glass jar containing the one and only good dream they had caught that day stood between them.

The BFG, with great care and patience, was printing something on a piece of paper with an enormous pencil.

'What are you writing?' Sophie asked him.

'Every dream is having its special label on the bottle,' the BFG said. 'How else could I be finding the one I am wanting in a hurry?'

'But can you really and truly tell what sort of a dream it's going to be simply by listening to it?' Sophie asked.

'I can,' the BFG said, not looking up.

'But *how*? Is it by the way it hums and buzzes?'

'You is less or more right,' the BFG said. 'Every dream in the world is making a different sort of buzzy-hum music. And these grand swashboggling ears of mine is able to read that music.'

'By music, do you mean tunes?'

'I is not meaning tunes.'

'Then what *do* you mean?'

'Human beans is having their own music, right or left?'

'Right,' Sophie said. 'Lots of music.'

'And sometimes human beans is very overcome when they is hearing wonderous music. They is getting shivers down their spindels. Right or left?'

'Right,' Sophie said.

'So the music is saying something to them. It is sending a message. I do not think the human beans is knowing what that message is, but they is loving it just the same.'

'That's about right,' Sophie said.

'But because of these jumpsquiffling ears of mine,' the BFG said, 'I is not only able to *hear* the music that dreams are making but I is *understanding* it also.'

'What do you mean *understanding* it?' Sophie said.

'I can read it,' the BFG said. 'It talks to me. It is like a langwitch.'

'I find that just a little hard to believe,' Sophie said.

'I'll bet you is also finding it hard to believe in quogwinkles,' the BFG said, 'and how they is visiting us from the stars.'

'Of course I don't believe that,' Sophie said.

The BFG regarded her gravely with those huge eyes of his. 'I hope you will forgive me,' he said, 'if I tell you that human beans is thinking they is very clever, but they is not. They is nearly all of them notmuchers and squeakpips.'

Re-read the story and answer the following questions.

1 What was the Big Friendly Giant doing? _____

_____

2 Who was watching him at work? _____

_____

3 What was in the glass jar? _____

_____

4 What does the BFG collect? _____

_____

5 Do you think Sophie is afraid of the Giant? _____

_____

6 What are 'human beans'? _____

_____

7 What is special about the Giant's ears? _____

_____

_____

8 What does the Giant think of humans? _____

_____

_____

9 Do you think the Giant speaks good English? Give some examples.

_____

_____

_____

_____

_____

10 What do you think a 'spindel' is? _____

_____

11 Is the Giant good at keeping things in order? _____

_____

_____

12 What do you think the Giant will do with all the dreams he collects? _____

_____

_____

_____

_____

_____

_____

_____

Cinderella

I guess you think you know this story.
You don't. The real one's much more gory.
The phoney one, the one you know,
Was cooked up years and years ago,
And made to sound all soft and sappy
Just to keep the children happy.
Mind you, they got the first bit right,
The bit where, in the dead of night,
The Ugly Sisters, jewels and all,
Departed for the Palace Ball,
While darling little Cinderella
Was locked up in a slimy cellar,
Where rats who wanted things to eat,
Began to nibble at her feet.
She bellowed 'Help!' and 'Let me out!'
The Magic Fairy heard her shout.
Appearing in a blaze of light,
She said, 'My dear, are you all right?'
'*All right*?' cried Cindy. Can't you see
'I feel as rotten as can be!'
She beat her fist against the wall,
And shouted, 'Get me to the Ball!
'There is a Disco at the Palace!
'The rest have gone and I am jalous!
'I want a dress! I want a coach!
'And earrings and a diamond brooch!
'And silver slippers, two of those!
'And lovely nylon panty-hose!
'Done up like that I'll guarantee
'The handsome Prince will fall for me!'
The Fairy said, 'Hang on a tick.'
She gave her wand a mighty flick
And quickly, in no time at all,
Cindy was at the Palace Ball!
It made the Ugly Sisters wince
To see her dancing with the Prince.
She held him very tight and pressed
herself against his manly chest.
The Prince himself was turned to pulp,
All *he* could do was gasp and gulp.

Roald Dahl

Re-read the rhyme and answer the following questions.

1 Where was Cinderella? _____
_____

2 Where had the Ugly Sisters gone? _____
_____

3 What were the rats doing? _____
_____

4 Who was the Magic Fairy in the old story of Cinderella? _____
_____

5 Why is the word 'jalous' used? What should it be? _____
_____
_____

6 Did Cindy go to the Palace in a coach? _____
_____

7 Why did the Ugly Sisters wince when they saw Cindy dancing with the Prince?
_____
_____

8 Why did Cindy want to dress up? _____
_____

9 Why could the Prince only gasp and gulp? _____
_____
_____

10 What sort of person do you think Cindy is in this story? _____
_____
_____

11 What is different about this version of Cinderella? _____
_____
_____
_____
_____
_____

12 Were the Ugly Sisters fair to Cindy? _____
_____
_____
_____

The Beatles

The Beatles were a pop group whose fame swept the world in the 1960s. 'Beatlemania' broke out wherever the Beatles went. Teenage girls would fight in the streets for seats at their concerts. During the concerts they screamed for joy, or fainted because the heat and excitement were too much for them!

Some tried to scramble onto the stage to get as near to the four young men as they possibly could. There were often guards to hold the girls back, but when a concert came to an end they were hard to control. Girls surged to the front for a final chance to snatch at the Beatles' hair or clothes.

The Beatles grew very rich as thousands of copies of their records were sold every day. One had the title 'A Hard Day's Night'. This summed up what the Beatles' lives were like. Often, they spent a hard day getting microphones ready and practising songs. Then at night came the time that mattered most – the concert, the getaway in a flashy car and finally sleep in a posh hotel.

The Beatles were not used to wealth and comfort. They had grown up during the 1940s in rather rough parts of Liverpool, when food and other things were scarce. This was because the Second World War was raging when they were very young. For years the boys never met at all. They went to school in different parts of the city; but although they were taught music, they had to learn for themselves that playing drums and guitars is fun. Starkey's bedroom was full of drums. The other boys played guitars and sang. By the time they were 20 their music-making had brought them together. Richard Starkey had already changed his name to 'Ringo Starr' – it sounded better, and it went with all the rings he wore. They all agreed that 'The Beatles' would be a good name for the group. Their music would certainly have lots of beat!

The years of Beatlemania came to an sudden end when the Beatles quarrelled. The group split up in 1971; but all four Beatles have made records separately since then, while Ringo Starr has also appeared in several films.

Re-read the recount and answer the following questions.

1 How many young men were in the Beatles group? _____

_____

2 What was Ringo Starr really called? _____

_____

3 When did the Beatles' fame sweep the world? _____

_____

4 Why did the girls get so excited at the concerts? _____

_____

_____

5 What was the boys' life like when they were very young? _____

_____

_____

_____

6 Why didn't the boys meet until they were 20 years old? _____

_____

_____

7 How did the Beatles get so rich? _____

_____

_____

_____

8 Do you think 'The Beatles' was a good name for them? _____

_____

_____

9 Had the boys always liked music? _____

_____

_____

10 What kind of place is a 'posh hotel'? _____

_____

_____

_____

11 Did the boys have to work hard for their fame? _____

_____

_____

12 Why did the girls want to snatch at the Beatles' hair and clothes?

_____

_____

_____

The cave

He'd never seen anything like the collection of bits and pieces, odds and ends, bric-à-brac and old brock, that this Stig creature had lying about his den. There were stones and bones, fossils and bottles, skins and tins, stacks of sticks and hanks of string. There were motor-car tyres and hats from old scarecrows, nuts and bolts and bobbles from brass bedsteads. There was a coal scuttle full of dead electric light bulbs and a basin with rusty screws and nails in it. There was a pile of bracken and newspapers that looked as if it were used for a bed. The place looked as if it had never been given a tidy-up.

'I wish I lived here,' said Barney.

Stig seemed to understand that Barney was approving of his home and his face lit up. He took on the air of a householder showing a visitor round his property, and began pointing out some of the things he seemed particularly proud of.

First, the plumbing. Where the water dripped through a crack in the roof of the cave he had wedged the mud-guard of a bicycle. The water ran along this, through the tube of a vacuum-cleaner, and into a big can with writing on it. By the side of this was a plastic football carefully cut in half, and Stig dipped up some water and offered it to Barney. Barney had swallowed a mouthful before he made out the writing on the can: it said WEEDKILLER. However, the water only tasted of rust and rubber.

It was dark in the back of the cave. Stig went to the front where the ashes of a fire were smoking faintly, blew on them, picked up a book that lay beside his bed, tore out a page and rolled it up, lit it at the fire, and carried it to a lamp set in a niche in the wall. As it flared up Barney could see it was in fact an old teapot, filled with some kind of oil, and with a bootlace hanging out of it for a wick.

Re-read the story and answer the following questions.

(Use the back of the sheet for all the questions.)

1 Who was looking round the den?

2 Who did the den belong to?

3 What was the bed made of?

4 Why did Barney wish he lived there?

5 Why did Stig's face light up?

6 Does Stig rely on the rain for water?

7 How do you think Stig cooked his food?

8 What does Stig use his book for?

9 Why was the fire at the front of the cave?

10 Do you think Stig has lived in his den for a long time?

11 How did Stig feel about his den?

12 What do you think Barney's house is like?

Easy pizza

This is good for tea and quite easy to make. If you are hungry you may need to make two for each person. You need to allow time for it to cook in the oven.

For each pizza you will need: one thick slice of brown or white bread, about 25g butter or margarine, one thick slice of Cheddar cheese, one tomato, one teaspoon of tomato purée or ketchup, one chopped anchovy fillet (optional), two sliced black olives (optional), a dusting of pepper and a pinch of dried oregano or thyme.

Heat the oven to 180°C (350°F, Gas Mark 4). Melt the butter or margarine in a medium-sized pan. Cut the crusts off the slice of bread. Turn the bread slice in the melted butter so that the top, base and sides are coated. Put the bread slice on a baking sheet. Cover the bread with the cheese and spread thinly with tomato purée. Slice the tomato and arrange the slices on top of the cheese and tomato purée. Sprinkle the chopped anchovy and olive slices on top if used. Dust with pepper and herbs. Bake on the middle shelf of the oven for 20–25 minutes.

When the cheese is bubbling and the pizza is nicely browned, use oven gloves to take out the baking sheet. Serve the pizza on a warmed plate. Add a sprig of parsley to garnish. Eat it while it's hot!

Re-read the instructions and answer the following questions.
(Use the back of the sheet for questions 8 to 10.)

1 Write out a shopping list for the things you need to make Easy Pizza for four people.

_____

_____

2 Why do you need to melt the butter or margarine? _____

_____

3 Could you use just the black olives if you didn't like anchovies? _____

_____

4 Do you think your friends would like Easy Pizza if they came for tea?

_____

5 What else could you serve with Easy Pizza? _____

_____

6 What is the difference between Easy Pizza and an ordinary pizza? _____

_____

7 What is a garnish for? _____

_____

8 Why do you need to use oven gloves?

9 What sort of cheese does the recipe need?

10 Why is the bread covered with melted butter?

Zoos

Zoos are places where a collection of animals is displayed. People can go to a zoo to see wild animals from the many different countries of the world. They see animals they may not be able to see any other way apart from in pictures in books or on television.

To some people, keeping wild animals caged up in zoos is cruel. They argue that the animals should be free to roam in their natural surroundings and climate. Although it may seem cruel to keep wild animals in captivity, the advantage for the animals is that they are well cared for. Veterinary surgeons are available to help them if they become ill. The zoo keepers love the animals in their care and see that they are well fed with the food that suits them and properly cared for.

When the animals produce babies, these too are well cared for by the zoo keepers and, of course, in a zoo the babies can't be hunted and killed for food by other animals. Scientists are able to study the animals and find out as much as they can about them. This is far more difficult and costly to do in the animals' natural habitats.

Perhaps one of the greatest advantages of a zoo is that the animals are saved from extinction. Animals in the wild are hunted for sport. Animals such as tigers and lions are hunted for their skins, elephants have been hunted for their ivory tusks and rhinoceroses have been hunted for their horns. Many other animals are hunted because some people believe they can cure illnesses. Keeping animals in zoos ensures that their species will not die out and become extinct.

Re-read the argument and answer the following questions.
(Use the back of the sheet for questions 6 to 10.)

1   What is a zoo? _____

_____

2   Why do people go to zoos? _____

_____

3   Why do some people think zoos are cruel? _____

_____

4   What is one of the greatest advantages of a zoo? _____

_____

5   What danger is there for baby animals in the wild? _____

_____

6   What could you learn from seeing an animal in the zoo?

7   Do you think zoos are a good place to keep animals?

8   What would some animals find difficult about our climate?

9   Would you like to be a zoo keeper?

10   What happens if an animal becomes extinct?

Arthur, King of Britain

Kay found that in the excitement of setting out for his first jousting, he had forgotten his sword and left it in the inn where they had lodged the night before. 'Quickly, brother,' he said to Arthur, 'ride back to our lodging and fetch me my sword.'

Arthur made haste to do as he was bidden, but when he came to the inn he found the door locked and everyone gone to watch the tourneying. 'I cannot disappoint Kay,' he thought. 'But what shall I do?' Then he remembered the sword which was set in the anvil before the great church, and said to himself, 'My brother Kay shall not be without a sword today. I will pull out the sword from the anvil and take it to him.' He rode swiftly to the churchyard, and seeing no one about, he went to the sword, took hold of the hilt and gave a pull at it. Immediately it came easily out of the anvil. Well pleased, Arthur hastened back to the tourney-ground and gave the sword to Kay.

As soon as Kay saw the sword, he knew it for the one which had been set in the anvil, and he went to his father and said, 'Here is the sword from the anvil, father. Am I then king of Britain?'

'How did you come by it?' asked Ector, astonished.

'Arthur gave it to me.'

Ector sent for Arthur and asked him, 'How did you come by this sword?'

'I pulled it out of the anvil before the church, so that Kay might have a sword.'

'Did any man see you?'

'There was no one there to see me,' said Arthur. 'Have I done wrong?'

Ector looked at Arthur and said slowly, 'Do you know that because of this you must be king of Britain?'

Re-read the story and answer the following questions.
(Use the back of the sheet for questions 4 to 10.)

1   What had Kay forgotten? _____

_____

2   Who went to fetch Kay's sword? _____

_____

3   What happens at a tourneying? _____

_____

4   Where did Arthur find the sword?

5   Who do you think is the eldest brother, Kay or Arthur?

6   Why do you think Ector was astonished?

7   Was it important that Arthur should be seen taking the sword from the anvil?

8   What made Arthur king of Britain?

9   Why did Kay think he was king?

10   What did Arthur think of his brother Kay?

Douglas Bader

Douglas Bader was a famous pilot in the Royal Air Force. On 14 December 1931, when he was just 21 years old, he had a terrible crash on take-off as his plane became airborne. He woke up two days later to find he had lost both his legs. The doctors thought he would never walk again.

Douglas Bader was determined to walk and fly again. He began to practise walking on artificial legs. He stumbled and fell many times but he didn't give up. In a few months he could walk and drive and was ready to fly again.

No one thought he was fit to fly, but Bader pestered everyone until they gave in. The Second World War had started and he flew on bombing missions. In 1941, the Germans shot down his plane and took him prisoner. They knew how famous Bader was, and because one of his special legs had been damaged, they sent to England for a new one.

Helping Bader to walk again was not such a good idea for the Germans because he turned out to be very good at escaping. He even escaped from the hospital he was sent to first of all by making a rope of sheets and sliding down from the window! He was recaptured and sent to a high security camp but he escaped from there as well. After capturing him again, he was sent to Colditz where the most difficult prisoners were held. When he came home after the war, he was a hero.

Re-read the recount and answer the following questions.
(Use the back of the sheet for questions 8 to 10.)

1   What did Douglas Bader do in the Royal Air Force? _____

_____

2   What happened to his plane on take-off? _____

_____

3   What happened to Douglas Bader's legs? _____

_____

4   Why didn't anyone think he would be able to fly again? _____

_____

5   What sort of person do you think Douglas Bader was? _____

_____

6   In what year was he born? _____

_____

7   What sort of place do you think Colditz was? _____

_____

8   What did the Germans think of Bader?

9   What would he have done if he had escaped to England?

10   Was it easy for Bader to learn to walk again?

The silent spinney

What's that rustling behind me?
Only a cat.
Thank goodness for that,
For I'm afraid of the darkness,
And these tall trees
Are silent and black,
And if ever I get out of here, mate,
I can tell you I'm not coming back.

There's a dark shadow out in the roadway,
See if there's someone behind that tree,
For I'm afraid of the darkness
And it might jump out at me.

My sisters are scared stiff of spiders,
My mother is frightened of mice,
But I'm afraid of the darkness,
I'm not coming this way twice.

Seamus Redmond

Re-read the poem and answer the following questions.

(Use the back of the sheet for questions 7 to 10.)

1 What did the writer hear? _____

_____

2 What is the writer frightened of? _____

_____

3 Is the writer a girl or a boy? _____

_____

4 Does the writer usually go that way? _____

_____

5 Why do you think the writer chose to go that way? _____

_____

6 What does the writer think the shadow is? _____

_____

7 What is frightening about the trees?

8 Would the writer's sisters be afraid of the dark?

9 What is a spinney?

10 Is the writer afraid of spiders and mice?

How to make a scarecrow

A scarecrow is fun to make and a welcome addition to the smallest garden. The instructions given are for a male scarecrow but you could just as easily make a female scarecrow by using a skirt instead of the trousers. In fact, a skirt flapping in the wind may be a better deterrent for birds than the more usual trousers!

To make the scarecrow, you will need two straight pieces of wood, one about 2 metres long and one about 1 metre. Place the shorter piece of wood across the longer piece, about 30cm from the end. Nail or tie the sticks firmly in place. The shorter length is for the scarecrow's arms.

Make a head by taking a piece of material, 1 metre square, and using a filling of straw or old rags. It should be about the same size and shape as a football. Bunch the material under the ball shape and fasten it firmly with string. Push the head down on to the short head-end of the long stick. Now you have the basis of your scarecrow.

Paint or glue a pair of eyes, a nose and a mouth to make a face on the head. Staple or glue lengths of straw or old wool on the head for hair. Put an old hat or cap on the head.

Pack an old pair of trousers with straw or rags and tie the trouser ends. Tie the trousers to the long stick, about 60cm below the arms. Put an old shirt and jacket on the scarecrow. Fasten a scarf round the neck. You can add gloves to the ends of the arms and old shoes to the ends of the trousers. Now dress your scarecrow to your liking.

Re-read the instructions and answer the following questions.
(Use the back of the sheet for questions 6 to 10.)

1   What do you need to make the frame of the scarecrow? _____
_____

2   What do you need for the head? _____
_____

3   What sort of gardener would want a scarecrow? _____
_____

4   How will you stand the scarecrow in the ground? _____
_____

5   What would be the advantage of packing the scarecrow parts with straw rather than with rags? _____
_____

6   How would you dress your scarecrow?

7   In what sort of garden would you expect to see a scarecrow?

8   Who would a scarecrow be a good present for?

9   Why would anyone want to scare crows or other birds away?

10   Draw a set of diagrams to show the steps for making a scarecrow.

Photocopiable

Hazard Hill

Mrs Spinks, the spokesperson for the action group to improve the road at Church Hill, Splatborn, reported their progress at the monthly meeting held at the library last night.

Mrs Spinks and seven members of the action group collected 874 names in an effort to get the road at Church Hill made safer. Sixteen people including four children have been injured there in the past three years. People living in the area nearby call it Hazard Hill.

Many people in the area have been asked what could be done to improve the road. Experts on road construction insist that the surface of the road is good and in excellent condition. It has been suggested that the bend at the bottom of the hill could be straightened. The estimated cost would be £5600. If this work goes ahead, the number of accidents should be reduced.

Most of the people in the area want a stricter speed limit. They say that motorists use the road like a racetrack. Some of the people think a notice warning motorists of the danger would help. Others say the overhanging trees should be cut back as these cast shadows on the road. A few people thought footpaths would make the road safer for pedestrians. Many of the people questioned said the road should be widened.

Mrs Spinks is going to see the chairperson for the county council next week. With all the evidence she has, she hopes to convince the county council that action must be taken.

Re-read the report and answer the following questions.
(Use the back of the sheet for questions 7 to 10.)

1 Who is the spokesperson for the action group? _____
_____

2 Why did members of the action group collect a list of names? _____
_____

3 What do the experts say? _____
_____

4 Where is the danger spot on the road? _____
_____

5 Would straightening the road make it completely safe? _____
_____

6 Is Church Hill in the town centre of Splatborn? _____
_____

7 What danger would a notice warn motorists about?

8 When would the overhanging trees cause the most problems?

9 Do you think Mrs Spinks will be successful?

10 Which of the options do you think would be the most effective?

Washday blues

In the first part of the nineteenth century there were no such things as washing machines. People who could afford it sent their dirty clothes to a laundry or employed a washerwoman. Most people had to do their own washing. Families were often larger in those days so there was a great deal of washing to do.

The dirty laundry was brought down to the scullery and the clothes were sorted into different piles: whites and cottons, coloureds and linens, and woollens. The whites and cottons could be put into the copper boiler and boiled in soapy water. The coloureds and linens were soaked in a tub of soapy water to loosen the dirt. Very dirty clothes were soaked in lime and water.

There were no rubber gloves to protect the housewives' hands so the water was as hot as they could bear it. They would use a 'dolly' to pound the dirt out of the clothes as they soaked in the tub. They used a washboard by rubbing the clothes against the ridged surface of the board. Instead of using soap powder, they used soda crystals and hard, yellow soap.

After the clothes had been washed, they had to be rinsed to get out all the soapy water. They were then put through a mangle that pressed most of the water out of the clothes. After this, the clothes were hung outside to dry. If it was raining, they were hung on racks indoors. The next job was to iron it all and air it ready to wear, but that was another day's work!

Re-read the explanation and answer the following questions.
(Use the back of the sheet for questions 8 to 10.)

1 What did a laundry do? _____

_____

2 How did most people get their washing done? _____

_____

3 Why was there often more washing to do in the early nineteenth century?

_____

4 What would the housewives' hands look like after they had been in water all day?

_____

5 Why didn't the housewives use soap powder? _____

_____

6 How do you think the housewives felt at the end of washday? _____

_____

7 Why did the dirty clothes need to be sorted into different piles? _____

_____

8 What would the house be like on a washday in the winter?

9 How would the water be heated in the copper boiler?

10 What effect do you think the invention of electricity had on washdays?

The Chief Rabbit

In the darkness and warmth of the burrow Hazel suddenly woke, struggling and kicking with his back legs. Something was attacking him. There was no smell of ferret or weasel. No instinct told him to run. His head cleared and he realized that he was alone except for Fiver. It was Fiver who was clambering over him, clawing and grabbing like a rabbit trying to climb a wire fence in a panic.

'Fiver! Fiver, wake up, you silly fellow! It's Hazel. You'll hurt me in a moment. Wake up!'

He held him down. Fiver struggled and woke.

'Oh, Hazel! I was dreaming. It was dreadful. You were there. We were sitting on water, going down a great, deep stream, and then I realized we were on a board – like that board in the field – all white and covered with black lines. There were other rabbits there – bucks and does. But when I looked down, I saw the board was all made of bones and wire; and I screamed and you said, "Swim – everybody swim"; and then I was looking for you everywhere and trying to drag you out of a hole in the bank. I found you, but you said, "The Chief Rabbit must go alone," and you floated away down a dark tunnel of water.'

'Well, you've hurt my ribs, anyway. Tunnel of water, indeed! What rubbish! Can we go back to sleep now?'

'Hazel – the danger, the bad thing. It hasn't gone away. It's here – all round us. Don't tell me to forget about it and go to sleep. We've got to go away before it's too late.'

Re-read the story and answer the following questions.
(Use the back of the sheet for questions 7 to 10.)

1 What sort of creatures are Hazel and Fiver? _____

_____

2 Who had woken Hazel? _____

_____

3 What was the matter with Fiver? _____

_____

4 Where are Hazel and Fiver? _____

_____

5 What were the black lines that covered the white board? _____

_____

6 Who is the Chief Rabbit? _____

_____

7 What do you think the danger is?

8 What did the bucks and does have to do in Fiver's dream?

9 Where did Hazel go in the dream?

10 Will Hazel take any notice of Fiver?

Shoot the messenger!

On playground duty, while sipping her tea,
Miss Martin told us stories.

'Long ago,' she said, 'If he brought bad news,
they used to shoot the messenger.

This bringer of bad tidings,
message hidden, horse hard-ridden
would burst upon the scene
with news of some huge defeat
in battle.

And the first response would be,
pretend it hadn't happened,
make out they hadn't heard,
shoot the messenger,
forget his words.'

We listened, open-mouthed.
Miss Martin was smart,
her story must be true.

'Now,' she said, 'I've a job for someone.

Who wants to go to the staffroom
to tell the teachers
it's end of break?'

Brian Moses

Re-read the poem and answer the following questions.

1 Why was Miss Martin in the playground? _____

_____

2 What sort of news would get the messenger shot? _____

_____

3 Why did they shoot the messenger? _____

_____

_____

4 Why did the children believe Miss Martin? _____

_____

_____

5 Were the children surprised at Miss Martin's story? _____

_____

6 How long ago do you think messengers got shot? _____

_____

7 Would anyone want to tell the teachers that break was over? _____

_____

8 Will the teachers be pleased with the news that break is over? _____

_____

9 Where had the messenger come from? _____

_____

10 Was it fair to shoot the messenger? _____

_____

_____

_____

_____

_____

_____

The Bakerloo flea

Not long ago I was in a pub round the Elephant and Castle, and I got talking to a woman, an oldish woman. And we were talking about this and that, and she said she used to be a cleaner down the Underground... They sweep out between the lines on one station, and then, in a gang of about six or seven, walk on to the next station along the lines in the tunnels.

Anyway this woman (I don't know her name), she says to me:

'Did you ever hear talk of the Bakerloo flea?'

'Bakerloo flea?' I said. 'No, no, never.'

'Well,' she said, 'you know there are rats down there – down the Underground? Hundreds of 'em. And the thing is,' she said, 'is that some of them have grown enormous. Huge great big things.'

'I've heard of them,' I said. 'Super rats.'

'Right,' she says. 'Now you tell me,' she says, 'what lives on rats? Fleas, right? Fleas. So – the bigger the rats the bigger the fleas. Stands to reason. These rats, they feed on all the old garbage that people throw down on the lines. It's amazing what people throw away, you know.'

She told me they found a steak down there once, lipstick, a bowler hat, beads, a box of eggs and hundreds and hundreds of sweets – especially Maltesers and those balls of bubble gum you get out of slot machines.

Anyway, the rats eat these, get big, and it seems that one day they were working the Bakerloo Line – Elephant and Castle to Finchley Road – and just before Baker Street one of the women in the gang was looking ahead, and she screamed out:

'Look – look – what's that?' Up in front was a great, grey, spiky thing with huge hairy legs and big jaws. It was as big as a big dog – bigger.

Re-read the story and answer the following questions.

(Use the back of the sheet for questions 3 to 10.)

1 Where was the writer when he started talking to the woman? _____

_____

2 What did the woman used to do? _____

_____

3 What did she tell him about?

4 What was unusual about the rats?

5 Why did the fleas get bigger?

6 What is the Underground?

7 What is garbage?

8 Which town is the story set in?

9 Do you think the lady is making up the story?

10 What other garbage could be on the lines?

How to make a papier mâché toby jug

To make a papier mâché toby jug you will need a clean jam jar, a length of thin wire, newspaper, two large bowls, a packet of wallpaper paste and water.

First prepare your jar by twisting one end of the wire round the top of the jug and the other end round the bottom. Leave a loop of wire between the top and bottom to form the handle.

Tear the newspaper into narrow strips and put the pieces into one of the bowls.

Pour water on the newspaper strips to soak them and make them thoroughly wet. Squeeze the paper as dry as possible and put it into the second bowl.

Sprinkle a cupful of wallpaper paste over the paper and mix it well with your fingers. Add a little water at a time until the paper is a sticky pulp. If it does not feel sticky, add a little more paste.

Layer the jam jar with strips of the sticky paper, winding the strips round the wire handle and moulding strips over the top edge of the jar. Keep adding strips until you have covered the surface of the jar and the handle with a thick layer of paper.

Mould a pouring lip on the rim of the jug opposite the handle. Model a nose on the jug below the pouring lip.

Leave the jug in a warm, dry place for a week to dry out. Paint a face round the nose on your jug and hair on the handle-side of the jug. When the paint is dry, varnish the jug.

Re-read the instructions and answer the following questions.

(Use the back of the sheet for questions 7 to 10.)

1 What is papier mâché made of? _____

_____

2 How does tearing the paper into narrow strips help? _____

_____

3 What makes the paper become a sticky pulp? _____

_____

4 What do you do to the paper strips before you add the wallpaper paste?

_____

5 Why do you need to mix the papier mâché with your fingers? _____

_____

6 How thick do you need to make the papier mâché layer? _____

_____

7 Why do you need to let the papier mâché dry out before you paint the jug?

8 Why is it a good idea to varnish the painted jug?

9 Do you think the finished jug would make a good present?

10 Where would be a good place to make the jug?

A Devon disaster

Some of the worst floods Devon had ever experienced took place in August 1952. The first two weeks of the month had been unusually wet with a record rainfall. Exmoor, the large area of moorland above the small seaport of Lynmouth, had taken as much water as it could hold. The whole area was soaked to saturation point.

Two streams running down from Exmoor, the East Lyn and the West Lyn, meet at Lynmouth. They join and run as one stream into the harbour and out into the sea. With the amount of rain falling, these streams quickly became flooded and were in danger of bursting their banks.

The town of Lynmouth was at its busiest and full of holidaymakers. These holidaymakers and the people of Lynmouth were in for the most terrifying night of their lives.

On the evening of 15 August at about 8.30pm, the rainfall became torrential and an exceptionally fierce thunderstorm developed. The sky became so black that lights had to be put on in the village.

As darkness fell, the stream became a raging torrent and at 9 o'clock the lights failed. In complete darkness, except for the light of flickering candles, the people could hear the roar of the flood and the crashing of houses as they fell and were swept away. All the boats in the harbour were smashed or washed out to sea. The harbour wall and its tower vanished. Trees, bridges and rocks weighing as much as 30 tonnes, animals and people were all washed away. Furniture and motor cars were smashed to pieces and carried out to sea.

When morning came, the rain had stopped and the survivors went out to look at the damage. The streets were filled with the debris of the flood. Huge boulders of rock, fallen trees and the twisted remains of cars and furniture made the streets impassable. Thirty-four people had died and many were lost at sea. Six bridges had been smashed, 93 houses flattened or so badly damaged as to be useless, and 132 motor cars had been carried away to sea.

Over 114 000 tonnes of debris had to be moved to restore order. Plans had to be made and work carried out to put right the damage and make sure that such a flood could never happen again. The work cost almost a million pounds but this did not take into account the personal cost to the people of Lynmouth who had lost family members, homes and possessions. The whole country had a powerful reminder of the force of nature and the havoc it can wreak.

Re-read the report and answer the following questions.

1 On which date did the Lynmouth flood happen? _____

_____

2 What is the name of the moor above Lynmouth? _____

_____

3 Which two rivers meet at Lynmouth? _____

_____

4 How had the rain at the beginning of August added to the effect of the storm?

_____

_____

5 Why did the lights fail? _____

_____

6 How do you think the people felt when they were plunged into darkness?

_____

_____

7 Where would many young children have been when the storm struck?

_____

8 Do you think the people were prepared for the disaster? _____

_____

9 How would the boats in the harbour get smashed? _____

_____

10 How could the rest of the country help the people of Lynmouth? _____

_____

_____

_____

11 Why did the town have more people there than usual? _____

_____

12 What would you have done to help the children of Lynmouth? _____

_____

_____

13 What would make it difficult for rescue workers to reach the injured people?

_____

_____

14 Where would the safest place be in the Lynmouth area on the night of the disaster?

_____

_____

15 How many families lost their homes?

_____

Waging a war on waste

Recycling our waste has become an important issue in recent times. Many of the things we use in our everyday life such as oil, coal and metals are found in the earth, but the earth is not continually making new supplies of these things for future use. For many years we have behaved as if there were plenty of everything for ever but now we have come to realise this is not so.

The population of the world increases each year and this puts greater and greater demands on our natural resources. People living now have a responsibility to care about the environment we leave for our children and grandchildren. It is essential that we find ways of making our demands on the environment more manageable.

One of the problems we have to attend to is to reduce the amount of waste we create. We can all help with this. For many years, our rubbish has been collected and buried. Before we had refuse collectors taking away our rubbish, people buried it in their own gardens. Now the rubbish is taken to places such as old quarries, gravel pits or natural hollows in the countryside and buried there. With the amount of rubbish each household has, you can imagine how quickly these landfill spaces are being used up!

Many of the county councils in the country are encouraging people to think 'green'. They are wanting everyone to have a new attitude to waste, first of all by cutting down on the amount each household produces and then by thinking of the rubbish that is produced as a reusable resource. To reuse the rubbish it needs to be recycled. About 50 per cent of the rubbish we create is recyclable.

The benefits of recycling are much greater than simply not needing so much landfill space. Recycling makes precious raw materials available for use again. Making new things from recycled materials uses less energy. Using raw fruit and vegetable trimmings for compost can improve the garden soil.

There are four main ways to win the war on waste:

1 Avoid buying things with a lot of packaging and choose things that are packed in something that can be recycled (for example, milk in plastic containers or returnable glass bottles).

2 Think about what you put in the bin. Recycling is suitable for all but about 18 per cent of your rubbish.

3 Try to recycle the rest of your rubbish. Paper, glass, cans, clothing and textiles, and, in some places, plastic bottles can all be recycled.

4 Vegetable and garden rubbish can be composted by allowing it to rot to make it rich and peat-like in just a few months. This compost will benefit your garden and help your plants to grow.

Re-read the argument and answer the following questions.

1 What has become an important issue? _____

_____

2 What is happening to the population of the world? _____

_____

3 What happens to the rubbish collected from our houses? _____

_____

4 Why are the county councils worried about the amount of rubbish households leave out? _____

_____

5 Would people living in flats want to make compost? _____

_____

6 Do you think it is worth the effort to take recyclable rubbish to the recycling banks?

_____

_____

7 Do you think we make more rubbish now than people did 100 years ago?

_____

8 Would it be a good idea to start burying our own rubbish again?

_____

9 Make a list of the kind of things you put in your rubbish bin. _____

_____

_____

10 What are some of the things you buy that have a lot of packaging?

_____

_____

11 If oil, coal and metals are not being made by the earth now, what will happen when they are all used up? _____

_____

12 What difference does a growing population make to the world? ____

_____

13 What is recycled paper made from? _____

_____

14 About how much of our rubbish could be recycled? _____

_____

15 What would happen if no rubbish were recycled? _____

_____

_____

_____

The Watchers

Everyone at Kirby House went on the trip to Alton Towers. They went in a coach belonging to the local Round Table – it was their annual treat. Alton Towers was less than twenty miles away and you could get there on an ordinary bus and be dropped off right outside. Some of the older kids were boasting how many times they'd been before.

On the way there Mrs Rogers gave them the lecture they had all heard at least twenty times. They were to go round in pairs, no one was to go on the lake without a grown-up. They were to head for a certain meeting-point if they were in trouble, and were to meet at half past twelve for their packed lunch.

'You smaller ones, of course, won't be allowed on some of the rides without a grown-up. I shan't be going on them – I've no head for heights at all – but ask Mr Clarke or Mr Foster. You'll all be given a map when we go in, so there's no need for anyone to get lost.'

'Wish *she* would,' Josh muttered.

Then they were there, and it was amazing, a whole new world in that wooded valley. From the Monorail, bringing them from the coach-park, they could see it spread on all sides – the Haunted House, the Log Flume, the Big Top and Octopus. There were acres of space – places to get lost, escape. Katy had not really been looking forward to the day ahead. She remembered a fairground ride she had once been forced to go on because her friends had wanted to.

'Go on!' they had said. 'Not chicken, are you?'

She had not wanted to be chicken, but she soon found that she was. She could still remember the sheer terror of it, the speed and sickening lurches, the certainty that she would die.

'Let's you and me stick together,' she said to Josh, and was half-ashamed of her motives. He was only nine, small for his age and was a cast iron excuse for just going on the tamer rides.

They were off the Monorail and streaming towards the turnstiles, whooping and yelling.

'You two, you come along with me.' It was Mrs Rogers. She already had one of the smaller kids in tow. 'Katy, did you hear me? Chips?'

'Chips' meant Josh – a lot of them called him that and he hated it. He stopped and turned, and Katy held her breath. He couldn't throw one of his tantrums, not now, with the day hardly begun! He was scowling all right, glaring at Ma Rogers with hot eyes. But none of the real danger signs were there, the thrust-out lower lip, the clenched fists.

Re-read the story and answer the following questions.

1 Where was everyone going? _____

_____

2 Who had arranged the outing? _____

_____

3 How many times each year did they go on an outing? _____

_____

4 How else could children from Kirby House get to Alton Towers? _____

_____

5 Why did Mrs Rogers give the children instructions? _____

_____

_____

6 How did they get into Alton Towers from the coach park? _____

_____

7 For what sort of ride would the smaller children need a grown-up with them?

_____

_____

8 For what other activity did children need an adult with them?

_____

_____

9 Why didn't Mrs Rogers want to go on the rides that needed an adult?

_____

_____

10 What had put Katy off some of the rides? _____

_____

11 Why did she want Josh to go round with her? _____

_____

12 What was Josh's nickname? _____

_____

13 Do you think Josh often had a tantrum? _____

_____

14 What sort of place do you think Kirby House is? _____

_____

_____

15 Do you think the children liked living at Kirby House? _____

_____

_____

Tricks

Nearly every morning
my brother would lie in bed,
lift his hands up in the air
full stretch
then close his hands around an invisible bar.
'Ah, my magic bar,' he'd say.
Then he'd heave on the bar,
pull himself up,
until he was sitting up in bed.

Then he'd get up.
I said,
'You haven't got a magic bar above your bed.'
'I have,' he said.
'You haven't,' I said.
'Don't believe me then,' he said.
'I won't – don't worry,' I said.
'It doesn't make any difference to me
if you do or you don't,' he said,
and went out of the room.

'Magic bar!' I said.
'Mad. He hasn't got a magic bar.'
I made sure he'd gone downstairs,
then I walked over to his bed
and waved my hand about in the air
above his pillow.
'I knew it,' I said to myself.
'Didn't fool me for a moment.'

Michael Rosen

Re-read the poem and answer the following questions.

1 Who does the writer share a room with? _____

_____

2 Where are the two boys? _____

_____

3 Does the writer's brother do his trick every morning? _____

_____

4 What is the invisible bar? _____

_____

5 Do you believe he had an invisible bar? _____

_____

6 What skills would he need to be able to sit straight up if he didn't have a bar?

_____

_____

7 Why did the brother do the trick? _____

_____

_____

8 Why did the writer wave his hand round above his brother's pillow?

_____

_____

_____

9 Why did the writer wait until his brother had gone downstairs?

_____

_____

_____

10 Does the brother want the writer to believe him? _____

_____

_____

_____

Tom Sawyer

Monday morning found Tom Sawyer miserable. Monday morning always found him so, because it began another week's slow suffering in school. He generally began that day with wishing he had had no intervening holiday, it made the going into captivity and fetters again so much more odious.

Tom lay thinking. Presently it occurred to him that he wished he was sick; then he could stay home from school. Here was a vague possibility. He canvassed his system. No ailment was found, and he investigated again. This time he thought he could detect colicky symptoms, and he began to encourage them with considerable hope. But they soon grew feeble and presently died wholly away. He reflected further. Suddenly he discovered something. One of his upper teeth was loose. This was lucky; he was about to begin to groan, as a 'starter', as he called it, when it occurred to him that if he came into court with that argument his aunt would pull it out, and that would hurt. So he thought he would hold the tooth in reserve for the present, and seek further. Nothing offered for some little time, and then he remembered hearing the doctor tell about a certain thing that had laid up a patient for two or three weeks and threatened to make him lose a finger. So the boy eagerly drew his sore toe from under the sheet and held it up for inspection. But now he did not know the necessary symptoms. However, it seemed well worth while to chance it, so he fell to groaning with considerable spirit.

But Sid slept on, unconscious.

Tom groaned louder, and fancied that he began to feel pain in the toe.

No result from Sid.

Tom was panting with his exertions by this time. He took a rest and then swelled himself up and fetched a succession of admirable groans.

Sid snored on.

Tom was aggravated. He said, 'Sid, Sid!' and shook him. This course worked well, and Tom began to groan again. Sid yawned, stretched, then brought himself up on his elbow with a snort, and began to stare at Tom. Tom went on groaning. Sid said:

'Tom! say, Tom!'

No response.

'Here, Tom! Tom! What is the matter, Tom?' And he shook him, and looked in his face anxiously.

Tom moaned out:

'Oh, don't, Sid. Don't joggle me.'

'Why, what's the matter, Tom? I must call Auntie.'

Re-read the story and answer the following questions.

1 What day was it? _____

2 Why was Tom miserable? _____

_____

3 Where was Tom? _____

_____

4 What did Tom think would stop him going to school? _____

_____

5 What were his first symptoms? _____

_____

6 What do you think is wrong if you are 'colicky'? _____

_____

7 What was the second thing he found that was wrong with himself? _____

_____

8 Why didn't Tom use his second idea? _____

_____

_____

9 What did Tom finally use as an excuse? _____

_____

10 Who slept in the same room as Tom? _____

_____

11 Was it easy to wake Sid up? _____

_____

12 Was Sid very worried about Tom? _____

_____

13 Did Tom have a good imagination? _____

_____

14 What do you think Aunt Polly will do? _____

_____

_____

_____

15 Why do you think Tom didn't want to go to school? _____

_____

_____

_____

_____

_____

El Niño

El Niño is the name given to the mysterious and often unpredictable lurch in the climate of the world. This strange phenomenon happens every five to eight years. It is called El Niño because it usually happens around the end of December, and El Niño is the Spanish for 'baby Jesus' or 'Christ child'. Christmas is supposed to bring good tidings and hope, but El Niño spreads fear and destruction.

This strange weather pattern starts in the Pacific Ocean. It is thought to be triggered by a failure in the trade winds, which affects the ocean currents driven by these winds. As the trade winds dwindle in strength, or even reverse direction, the ocean temperatures rise, causing the Peru current flowing in from the east to warm up by as much as 5°C. This bulge of warm water can be larger than the area of the United States.

The warming of the ocean has far-reaching effects. The hot, humid air over the ocean causes severe tropical thunderstorms. The rainfall is increased across South America, bringing floods to Peru. In the West Pacific, there are droughts affecting Australia and Indonesia. So while some parts of the world prepare for heavy rains and floods, other parts face drought, poor crops and starvation.

The warm water also has an effect on the sea life. Fish that usually live in that area of the Pacific Ocean are forced to move further south or north to find food as the warmer water temperature destroys their supplies. This particularly affects the fish industry in Peru, which depends on the usually abundant supplies of anchovies for use in animal feed and fertilisers.

El Niño usually lasts for about 18 months. The 1982–1983 El Niño brought the most destructive weather in modern history. Its effect was worldwide and it left more than 2000 people dead and caused over eight billion pounds worth of damage. The 1990 El Niño lasted until June 1995. Scientists estimate this to be the longest El Niño for 2000 years. The last long El Niño was 1939–1941 during World War II. This El Niño caused severe drought and famine in Bengal.

The effect of El Niño is felt in other ways. As a result of the strange weather, ski-resort managers worry about whether there will be enough snow. The prices of tropical foods such as sugar, coffee, tea and chocolate rise as droughts take a hold and crops fail. Even the price of soap and detergents is affected when the coconut oil harvest in the Philippines is ruined by drought.

Although weather experts are better at forecasting when an El Niño will strike, they are still not completely sure what triggers it or what affects how strong it will be. There is more than a suspicion, though, that El Niño may be linked to global warming.

Re-read the explanation and answer the following questions.

1   What is the name given to the strange weather phenomenon that happens every five to eight years? _____

_____

2   What does El Niño mean? _____

_____

3   At what time of the year does El Niño happen? _____

_____

4   Where does the strange weather start? _____

_____

5   What happens to the trade winds when they 'dwindle in strength'?

_____

_____

6   What happens to fish when the water gets warmer? _____

_____

7   What would happen to Peru's fish industry if they couldn't catch any anchovies?

_____

8   What are the two extremes of climate caused by an El Niño? _____

_____

9   What would have caused people to die during the 1982–1983 El Niño?

_____

_____

10   How could El Niño affect you in your everyday life? _____

_____

11   Why would ski resort managers be worried about there being enough snow ?

_____

_____

12   How do you think scientists know that the 1990 El Niño was the longest for 2000 years? _____

_____

13   How would you feel if you lived in Peru and knew an El Niño was coming?

_____

14   How do you think global warming could affect the El Niño phenomenon?

_____

_____

15   How do floods affect ordinary people? _____

_____

_____

The cure

SCENE 1

The Brown family are having breakfast. Mr Brown is reading the paper, Mrs Brown is reading a letter, Robert, Ethel and William are eating toast.

MRS BROWN: Great-Aunt Jane is very ill. *(Mr Brown lowers his paper, the children stop eating.)*

MR BROWN: What, my dear?

MRS BROWN: Great-Aunt Jane's very ill. They say there's not much chance of her getting better. They say... they say, she wants to see William! She's never seen him, you know. *(There is a gasp of surprise from Mr Brown, Robert and Ethel.)*

ROBERT: Goodness gracious! Fancy anyone wanting to see *William*!

ETHEL: When they are dying, too! You'd think they would like to die in peace! *(William glares at Robert and Ethel.)*

MR BROWN: How will you get William over to Ireland?

MRS BROWN: I suppose someone will have to take him.

MR BROWN: Good heavens! Who? I can't possibly leave the office for weeks!

ETHEL: I couldn't face the crossing – especially with William.

ROBERT: And I've got exams next year!

WILLIAM *(with dignity):* I can go alone, *thank* you!

SCENE 2

In Great-Aunt Jane's drawing-room. Present are Uncle John, Aunt Lucy, Cousin Francis who has blond curls and is rather fat, Mrs Brown looking pale and William.

AUNT LUCY: William, this is your cousin, Francis.

FRANCIS: How do you do, William? *(William and Francis shake hands.)*

WILLIAM: How do you do? *(William adds 'Fatty!' in a hoarse whisper. The boys glare at each other.)*

MRS BROWN: How is Great-Aunt Jane?

UNCLE JOHN *(gloomily):* Sinking fast.

WILLIAM *(looking interested):* I say, where is she? Is she out in the sea?

(Enter Nurse)

NURSE: She can see the little boy now.

SCENE 3

In Great-Aunt Jane's bedroom. She is propped up in bed. Francis and William stand with the nurse.

GREAT-AUNT JANE *(to William):* So, you are Margaret's youngest. I've seen all the others and I didn't want to die without seeing all my family. I'm going to rest. You boys can stay and get me what I need whilst Nurse has her tea.

(Exit Nurse. Great-Aunt Jane falls asleep. The boys sit down, one on each side of the bed.)

WILLIAM *(in a hoarse whisper):* Hello, Fatty!

FRANCIS: If you call me that again, I'll tell my mother!

WILLIAM: If you tell tales, I'll pull your hair off!

FRANCIS *(breathing hard):* Freckles!

WILLIAM: Softy!

FRANCIS: If I got hold of you, I could throw you out of the window!

WILLIAM: You couldn't throw anything, you're too fat!

FRANCIS: I could bash your old freckled face in!

WILLIAM: Come on then! Just you try!

(The boys go to the end of the bed and start to fight. Great-Aunt Jane wakes and looks on, excited.)

GREAT-AUNT JANE: Go it, William, bash his nose! Well done, Fatty, give him one back! Go on William, another, another! No biting, Fatty!

(Footsteps can be heard outside.)

GREAT-AUNT JANE: Oh dear! Quick, boys!

(The boys dart to their seats, smoothing their hair. Nurse enters.)

NURSE: I heard a row – it must have been in the street.

GREAT-AUNT JANE: I feel much better! *Ever* so much better!

NURSE *(peering at Great-Aunt Jane):* You certainly *look* better!

WILLIAM *(exchanging a wink with Great-Aunt Jane):* I think she's rising a bit!

Re-read the play and answer the following questions.
(Use the back of the sheet for questions 6 to 15.)

1 What are William's brother and sister called? _____

_____

2 What is wrong with Great-Aunt Jane? _____

_____

3 Where does Great-Aunt Jane live? _____

_____

4 Who has Great-Aunt Jane asked to see? _____

_____

5 What do Robert and Ethel think of William? _____

_____

6 Who took William to see Great-Aunt Jane?

7 How would William and his mother get to Ireland?

8 What did Uncle John mean when he said Great-Aunt Jane was 'sinking fast'?

9 Do you think Francis and William could be best friends?

10 What did Great-Aunt Jane think of the boys fighting?

11 What brought the nurse back to the bedroom?

12 How did the fight affect Great-Aunt Jane?

13 How did the fight start?

14 Who is Margaret?

15 What does William have on the skin of his face?

A country child

My name is Albert. Albert is a popular name for boys these days because of Prince Albert. I was born on the 21st of June in 1857, so I am ten years old now. I left our school in the village this summer. I liked it at school. We had a good teacher. I learned to read and I like doing that, and to write. We learned our tables and I can do sums well enough.

As soon as I left school, I went to work for Farmer Carter. One of my brothers, Harry, started work with him last year and one of my sisters, Daisy, has gone into service at the big house. She's a kitchen maid there.

It's hard work on the farm – I'd rather be at school! Farmer Carter pays me three shillings a week and I give most of that to my mother. I start work for the day at 5.30am. My first job is to clean out the stable and get the horses ready. When I have done that, I can have my breakfast. I bring bread and cheese from home and the Master lets us have half a pint of cider.

When breakfast is finished, I take the horses up to the field to begin the ploughing. I walk up and down guiding the horses until noon. I am given a quarter of an hour for my dinner and I have the same as my breakfast! After dinner, I keep on with the ploughing until three o'clock, then it's time to take the horses home. We get back by half past three. I look after the horses whilst the ploughman goes into the house to get his dinner. I feed the horses and help cut the chaff for them.

By the time I get home at seven o'clock, I am really tired. I have my supper with my brothers and sisters – we usually have potatoes and bacon, but nothing to drink. I am glad to get to bed by eight o'clock. It doesn't seem long before I have to get up again for another day at the farm.

A lot of the boys work on the farms around here, especially in the summer to help with the harvest. There are a lot of jobs for us to do depending on the season. In the winter, we go stone picking, collecting wood and acorning for the pigs as well as weeding and bird scaring. The summer is the best when we go haymaking and help with the harvest! I like the farm, but when I get older I want to see if I can be a blacksmith.

Re-read the recount and answer the following questions.

1 Who has the writer been named after? _____

_____

2 How old was the writer when he left school? _____

_____

3 What food and drink did he have all day? _____

_____

4 In which year was the story written? _____

_____

5 Does the writer have more brothers and sisters than Harry and Daisy? _____

_____

6 How long was the writer's working day? _____

_____

7 Why would the writer rather be at school? _____

_____

8 Would you like to live when the writer did? _____

_____

_____

9 Why did the farms have so many boys working on them? _____

_____

_____

10 How much rest does the writer have during the day? _____

_____

11 How important do you think the ploughman is on the farm? _____

_____

12 Why do you think stone picking is a job that needs to be done? _____

_____

13 What would the boys be bird scaring for? _____

_____

14 Would you like to leave school at ten years old and go to work? _____

_____

_____

15 Which of the jobs would you like to do most? _____

_____

_____

_____

_____

To the lady behind me

Dear Madam, you have seen this play;
I never saw it till today.
You know the details of the plot,
But, let me tell you, I do not.
The author seeks to keep from me
The murderer's identity,
And you are not a friend of his
If you keep shouting who it is.
The actors in their funny way
Have several funny things to say,
But they do not amuse me more
If you have said them just before;
The merit of the drama lies,
I understand, in some surprise,
But the surprise must now be small
Since you have just foretold it all.
The lady you have brought with you
Is, I infer, a half-wit too,
But I can understand the piece
Without assistance from your niece.
In short, foul woman, it would suit
Me just as well if you were mute;
In fact, to make my meaning plain,
I trust you will not speak again.
And – may I add one human touch? –
Don't breathe upon my neck so much.

A P Herbert

Re-read the poem and answer the following questions.

1 Who is the writer talking to? _____

_____

2 Where is the writer? _____

_____

3 What are they watching? _____

_____

_____

4 What is the lady doing? _____

_____

_____

_____

5 Who is with the lady? _____

_____

_____

6 What does the writer think of the lady? _____

_____

_____

_____

7 How is the play being spoiled for the writer? _____

_____

_____

_____

_____

8 Is this the first time the lady has seen the play? _____

_____

_____

9 What does the writer want the lady to do? _____

_____

_____

_____

10 Has the writer had a pleasant evening? _____

_____

_____

_____

_____

_____

_____

Mary's climb

Mary stood at the gate and looked up. High clouds moving made the steeple topple towards her.

'Father!'

She could hear his hammer, tac, tac, as he combed the stone.

The golden spark was a weathercock. It had been put up that week, and under its spike was the top platform. Father's head showed over the edge of the platform.

'Below!' His voice sounded nearer than he looked.

'I've brought your baggin!' Mary shouted.

'Fetch it, then!'

'All the way?'

'Must I come down when I'm working?'

'But what about the Governor?' said Mary.

'He's gone! I'm the Governor of this gang! There's only me stayed to finish! Have you the tea?'

'Yes!'

'Plenty of sugar?'

'Yes!'

'I can't spit for shouting! Come up!'

Mary hitched her frock and put the knot of the baggin cloth between her teeth and climbed the first ladder.

The ladders were spiked and roped, but the beginning of the steeple was square, a straight drop, and the ladders clattered on the side. She didn't like that.

'Keep fast hold of that tea!' she heard Father call, but she didn't lift her head, and she didn't look down.

Up she went. It felt worse than a rock because it was so straight and it had been made. Father made parts of it. She knew the pattern of his combing hammer on the sandstone.

Up she went.

'Watch when you change to the spire!' Father's voice sounded no nearer.

At the spire, the pitch of the ladders was against the stone, and Mary had to step sideways to change. The ladders were firmer, but she began to feel a breeze. She heard an engine get up steam on the railway. The baggin cloth kept her mouth wet, but it felt dry.

The spire narrowed. There were sides to it. She saw the shallow corners begin. Up and up. Tac, tac, tac, tac, above her head. The spire narrowed. Now she couldn't stop the blue sky from showing at the sides. Then land. Far away.

Mary felt her hands close on the rungs, and her wrists go stiff.

Tac, tac, tac, tac. She climbed to the hammer. The spire was thin. Father was not working, but giving her a rhythm. The sky was now inside the ladder. The ladder was broader than the spire.

Father's hand took the baggin cloth out of Mary's mouth, and his other hand steadied her as she came up through the platform.

The platform was made of good planks, and Father had lashed them, but it moved. Mary didn't like the gaps between. She put her arms around the spire.

'That was a bonny climb,' said Father.

'I do hope the next baby's a lad,' said Mary.

Re-read the story and answer the following questions.

1 Who has Mary gone to see? _____

2 What is Mary's father doing? _____

3 Where is Mary's father working? _____

4 What was the golden spark? _____

5 What is in the baggin cloth? _____

6 Did Mary like going up the ladder? _____

7 Why does Mary's father want the tea? _____

8 What were the sides of the steeple like? _____

9 Why did Mary have to take up her father's baggin? _____

10 Why did Mary's mouth feel dry? _____

11 What gave Mary a rhythm for climbing? _____

12 Where had Mary climbed to? _____

13 Did Mary like it where she was? _____

14 What did Mary's father think of her climb? _____

15 Why did Mary hope the next baby would be a boy? _____

Recount, page 64

A letter from Ella

Question types: 2 literal, 2 inferential, 1 evaluative, 1 deductive
1. Ella is staying at Little Drayton with her Granny and Grandpa.
2. Ella's mother has just had a new baby.
3. Your own answer.
4. The snow had made everywhere white.
5. The rabbit had left footprints in the snow.
6. Answers may vary – perhaps a new baby card or a postcard.

Instruction, page 65

Caring for your dog

Question types: 2 literal, 2 inferential, 1 evaluative, 1 deductive
1. I will need two dishes.
2. A dog needs meat because it is a meat-eater.
3. I could get a marrow bone from a butcher.
4. The dog would get very hungry and unhappy.
5. The dog could make the water dirty when it drinks.
6. Your own answer.

Drama, page 66

Mr Lion's soup

Question types: 2 literal, 2 inferential, 1 evaluative, 1 deductive
1. Mr Lion is in Brer Possum's Hotel.
2. Mr Lion might get cross and bite them.
3. Mr Lion wanted oxtail soup.
4. There was nothing wrong with the soup.
5. No, the table hadn't been set with a soup spoon.
6. Your own answer.

Narrative, page 67

Otto, the penguin chick

Question types: 3 literal, 2 inferential, 1 evaluative
1. Otto was a penguin chick.
2. Leo was another penguin chick.
3. They thought they lived at the bottom of the world.
4. Their fathers, Claudius and Nero, were looking after the chicks.
5. Claudius said they lived at the bottom of the world.
6. Answers may vary – Antarctica.

Report, page 68

The Cosy Café

Question types: 1 literal, 3 inferential, 1 evaluative, 1 deductive
1. The name of the café is the Cosy Café.
2. Mr and Mrs Parsons wanted everyone to know their café was good.
3. You could choose from three dishes for each course.
4. Answers may vary – the food guide's inspector had three courses.
5. Your own answer.
6. Answers may vary – the café was busy so people must like it.

Narrative, page 69

Pete's mouse
Question types: 2 literal, 2 inferential, 1 evaluative, 1 deductive
1. They wouldn't let Pete have a mouse.
2. He was in his tree house.
3. He was going to keep a mouse in his tree house.
4. He had read a book on how to keep mice many times.
5. He would need a cage and some food.
6. Your own answer.

Explanation, page 70

Your name, sir?
Question types: 1 literal, 2 inferential, 1 evaluative, 2 deductive
1. They had one name.
2. They used a second name so that people didn't get muddled up.
3. William Hill probably lived near a hill.
4. He would be called Robertson.
5. Yes, it is likely that the same name would be used in other villages, especially for occupations.
6. Your own answer.

Argument, page 71

Collections
Question types: 1 literal, 2 inferential, 2 evaluative, 1 deductive
1. Sir Hans Sloane's collections were put in the British Museum.
2. Answers may vary – a good thing is that anyone can go and look at the collections and learn from them.
3. Your own answer.
4. The people in those countries may want to keep the treasures for themselves.
5. Most people haven't the time or money to explore and collect for themselves.
6. Your own answer.

Instruction, page 72

A toy telephone
Question types: 2 literal, 1 inferential, 2 evaluative, 1 deductive
1. You need two long, narrow tins and a long piece of string.
2. The holes are made by hammering a nail through the ends of the tins.
3. If the edges were sharp, they could cut you.
4. Your own answer.
5. Your own answer.
6. The string needs to be tight for the sound to travel along it.

Poetry, page 73

Mice
Question types: 2 literal, 2 inferential, 1 evaluative, 1 deductive
1. The writer thinks mice are rather nice.
2. Mice run about and nibble things.
3. Mice sleep and keep out of sight during the day.
4. a) all b) white c) much.
5. No, the writer says that no one likes mice much.
6. Your own answer.

Narrative, page 74

The first house
Question types: 2 literal, 2 inferential, 1 evaluative, 1 deductive
1. He wanted to live in the field.
2. There were three animals in the field.
3. He got cold and wet when the wind blew and it rained.
4. He had lived in a cave.
5. He wanted to find a way to keep warm and dry.
6. Your own answer.

Report, page 75

The pet survey
Question types: 2 literal, 2 inferential, 1 evaluative, 1 deductive
1. There are eight pets listed in the survey.
2. The children go to Dunston Primary School.
3. Answers may vary – tortoises are not sold in the shops now.
4. Answers may vary – goldfish are easy for a child to look after, and they're cheap to buy, feed and house.
5. Your own answer.
6. Answers may vary – a goldfish or a budgie might be suitable if a person lived in a flat.

Narrative, page 76

The princess and the pea
Question types: 2 literal, 2 inferential, 1 evaluative, 1 deductive
1. The king, the queen and the prince lived in the family palace.
2. The prince would only marry a real princess.
3. The girl was soaking wet because of the storm.
4. The queen saw the girl's silk dress and pearl necklace.
5. The girl's skin had been bruised by the hard pea.
6. Your own answer.

Explanation, page 77

Guinea pigs
Question types: 1 literal, 2 inferential, 2 evaluative, 1 deductive
1. Another name for guinea pigs is cavies.
2. Baby guinea pigs are born in the open and not hidden in a hole or burrow.
3. Some plants in the garden are poisonous to guinea pigs.
4. If guinea pigs didn't chew, their teeth would grow too long.
5. The main reason is that they are friendly and don't mind being picked up.
6. Your own answer.

Argument, page 78

Children should earn their pocket money
Question types: 1 literal, 1 inferential, 2 evaluative, 2 deductive
1. Parents give their children pocket money.
2. Parents work to get money for food and the home. (Some parents may be unemployed, sick or disabled and receive money from the government instead.)
3. Answers may vary – children could wash up, vacuum and dust, keep their room tidy and set the table.
4. Your own answer.
5. Your own answer.
6. It means that money is not easily come by.

Poetry, page 79

Growing
Question types: 2 literal, 2 inferential, 1 evaluative, 1 deductive
1. The writer will be kind.
2. Answers may vary – the writer's parents are different from how he wants to be when he grows up. They get cross easily and keep telling him what to do.
3. Answers may vary – the writer is easy-going and he may be rather naughty.
4. The writer will let people do what they like and have an extra hour's play.
5. He likes to eat when he feels like it and wherever he wants.
6. Your own answer.

Narrative, page 80

The little girl who got out of bed the wrong side
Question types: 2 literal, 1 inferential, 1 evaluative, 2 deductive
1. The little girl was very cross.
2. Her jersey was tickly.
3. It was near Christmas time.
4. It means you get up in a bad mood.
5. The fruit in the mixture would make it smell delicious.
6. Your own answer.

Poetry, page 81

Coming home
Question types: 1 literal, 3 inferential, 1 evaluative, 1 deductive
1. She has been in hospital.
2. Yes, they probably have managed – they have cleaned the house and tidied the garden.
3. They tidied up so that mum would be pleased.
4. No, the time has gone very slowly.
5. They are giving her a present because they are so pleased to have her back.
6. Your own answer.

Argument, page 82

Holidays
Question types: 2 literal, 3 inferential, 2 evaluative, 3 deductive
1. The word holiday means 'holy day'.
2. The weather can be wet and cold in the summer in this country.
3. No, people didn't expect to have long holidays.
4. If you didn't like unusual food you could have a holiday in this country.
5. You wouldn't go to Spain in the summer if you didn't like hot weather.
6. We have to cross the English Channel to go abroad.
7. Having a holiday in this country helps the holiday places earn money.
8. If you couldn't understand the language it would be difficult if you were in trouble.
9. Your own answer.
10. Your own answer.

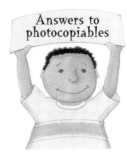

Answers to
photocopiables

Book 1

Narrative, page 84

Chalk and cheese

Question types: 3 literal, 2 inferential, 2 evaluative, 3 deductive

1. The names of the sisters are Lily and Jo.
2. Jo is short for Joanne.
3. Lily didn't like having the same name as a flower and she thought her name was too girlish.
4. The sisters always argued.
5. The sisters could have worn each other's clothes.
6. Answers may vary – they are different from each other in age, appearance, clothes and shoes they like and their favourite games.
7. No, older sisters do not always have their own way because giving in to the younger child can prevent arguments and save time.
8. Your own answer.
9. Jo gave in to Lily so they could have a game.
10. The sisters argue because they don't like doing the same things.

Narrative, page 86

Jim and the beanstalk

Question types: 2 literal, 4 inferential, 2 evaluative, 2 deductive

1. He saw an enormous plant.
2. He climbed a beanstalk.
3. Jack was the boy in the story Jack and the Beanstalk.
4. The giant couldn't eat him without any teeth.
5. The giant didn't know there were such things as reading glasses.
6. Your own answer.
7. No, Jim had beef and beer for breakfast and he had wanted cornflakes.
8. Your own answer.
9. The plant must have grown from a seed from the first beanstalk.
10. He wants to be able to read his books again.

Narrative, page 88

The glass eye

Question types: 3 literal, 4 inferential, 2 evaluative, 1 deductive

1. One of Mrs Twit's eyes was made of glass.
2. Mr Twit was drinking beer.
3. He found Mrs Twit's glass eye.
4. Answers may vary – probably not very good, as one of her eyes was glass.
5. Mr Twit had gone all quiet.
6. Mr Twit had a beard and moustache.
7. She wanted to be ready for his next nasty trick.
8. She was able to take out her glass eye and put it in different places.
9. They liked playing nasty tricks on each other.
10. Your own answer.

Explanation, page 90

The first oven

Question types: 2 literal, 2 inferential, 2 evaluative, 4 deductive

1. The people used fire to keep warm, light their homes and scare away wild animals.
2. They cooked their food by putting it in the fire.
3. Animals are scared of getting burnt.
4. The meat was covered in ashes and sometimes got burnt.
5. The food cooked in the oven was clean and it would be less likely to get burnt.

6. The pit was lined with leaves to help keep the heat in and the food clean.
7. They would cook animals they caught for food in the oven.
8. Your own answer.
9. The heat of the stones would depend on how long they had been in the fire and how hot the fire was.
10. Your own answer.

Poetry, page 92

These are the clothes that my big brother wore
Question types: 2 literal, 3 inferential, 2 evaluative, 3 deductive
1. The writer is a boy.
2. He has three brothers.
3. The clothes are too big and worn out.
4. The holes are so large that a seagull could fly through them.
5. Your own answer.
6. Your own answer.
7. The matching socks have been lost.
8. The writer is much smaller than his brother was at the same age.
9. The mother is proud of the writer's brothers.
10. The writer has been told to wear short pants, a hat, socks, jumpers and shoes.

Poetry, page 94

A centipede
Question types: 1 literal, 2 inferential, 1 evaluative, 2 deductive
1. A centipede has one hundred legs.
2. It costs a fortune in pegs because the centipede needs so many.
3. A centipede would need 50 pairs of wellingtons.
4. a) pegs b) rain.
5. The front gets where it is going before the back has left because the centipede is very long.
6. Your own answer.

Answers to
photocopiables

Recount, page 95

My new school

Question types: 2 literal, 2 inferential, 2 deductive, 2 evaluative
1. The writer's dad is a policeman.
2. His new job is in Dorset.
3. I think the writer is a girl.
4. It means, 'Where do you live?'
5. Your own answer.
6. Your own answer.
7. If Selina comes round for tea it will show the writer wants to be friends.
8. The writer can join the recorder group and make more friends.

Drama, page 96

Treasure trove

Question types: 2 literal, 2 inferential, 2 evaluative, 2 deductive
1. The boys were playing football.
2. Will had kicked the ball over the hedge.
3. The dagger punctured the ball.
4. They took their find to the Police Station because it was valuable.
5. If their find had been put there on purpose and if it were solid silver, it would be treasure trove.
6. Your own answer.
7. Your own answer.
8. Solid silver means that the things were made of pure silver.

Narrative, page 97

The first chick

Question types: 2 literal, 2 deductive, 2 inferential, 2 evaluative
1. Otto was bouncing on Claudius's feet and waving his flippers.
2. Otto wanted to fly.
3. Penguins use their flippers to swim.
4. The skua was looking for food.
5. Answers may vary – Antarctica.
6. Otto was puzzled that Claudius liked chicks and so did the skua.
7. Your own answer.
8. Your own answer.

Narrative, page 98

A birthday for Frances

Question types: 2 literal, 2 inferential, 2 evaluative, 2 deductive
1. Mother and Gloria were sitting at the table.
2. Frances was in the broom cupboard.
3. Frances is older than Gloria.
4. Alice is not a real person.
5. No one can see Alice because she is not real.
6. Frances uses the letters to spell cake and candy because she cannot spell yet.
7. Answers may vary – 'candy' suggests that it is American.
8. Your own answer.

Instruction, page 99

Fruit and cheese kebabs

Question types: 2 literal, 2 inferential, 2 evaluative, 2 deductive
1. The shopping list would be cheese of different types, green and black grapes, mandarin oranges, pineapple chunks and cocktail sticks or kebab skewers.
2. Your own answer.
3. The cheese needs to be firm to thread it on to the skewer.

4. You must always wash you hands.
5. Your own answer.
6. You could use apple, celery or cucumber.
7. The grapes may be dusty or may have been sprayed.
8. If the grapes and fruit were wet they would spoil the cheese.

Poetry, page 100

Crayoning
Question types: 2 literal, 2 inferential, 2 evaluative, 2 deductive
1. The poem describes the paper as white, quiet and like a drift of snow,
2. Answers may vary – the words 'smooth', 'clean', 'fresh', 'blank', 'new' and 'plain' would describe paper.
3. You might see adults' clothes and children's clothes hanging on the line.
4. The words that rhyme are 'goes' and 'shows', 'shine' and 'line', 'grow' and 'snow'.
5. The words 'goes' and 'shows' sound the same but look different.
6. The sheet of paper has not been used.
7. Your own answer.
8. Your own answer.

Narrative, page 101

The owl who was afraid of the dark
Question types: 2 literal, 2 inferential, 2 evaluative, 2 deductive
1. Plop was a Barn Owl.
2. Plop didn't like the dark.
3. Owls are night birds because they hunt at night.
4. Mrs Barn Owl will need patience to get Plop used to the dark.
5. Plop wants to be a day bird because he doesn't like the dark.
6. Your own answer.
7. Plop is only a baby and hasn't been out of the nest yet.
8. Your own answer.

Report, page 102

Dunston Primary School PTA
Question types: 2 literal, 2 inferential, 2 evaluative, 2 deductive
1. PTA stands for Parent-Teacher Association.
2. The PTA organised six events.
3. Your own answer.
4. The barn dance made £646 altogether.
5. The barn dance made the most money.
6. A lifeguard is needed for safety.
7. A parent who is interested in the school would belong to the PTA.
8. Your own answer.

Narrative, page 103

Ursula Bear
Question types: 2 literal, 2 inferential, 2 evaluative, 2 deductive
1. Ursula was very fond of bears.
2. Ursula had been to a dancing lesson.
3. Your own answer.
4. The poster could be advertising a circus.
5. Your own answer.
6. She got flour on her nose when she was making gingerbread.
7. Being a bear had got her into trouble.
8. It was easy to turn into a bear.

Explanation, page 104

Toothpaste

Question types: 2 literal, 2 inferential, 2 evaluative, 2 deductive

1. Toothpaste was made of ground-up burnt eggshells, cuttlefish bone or coral.
2. Bacteria in the plaque can decay teeth.
3. The grit scrapes away the layer on our teeth left by food and drink.
4. Answers may vary – probably no, because flouride in toothpaste helps to prevent our teeth decaying.
5. Foam gets in between the teeth.
6. Your own answer.
7. Sticky sweets will leave a sticky layer on our teeth.
8. The outside layer of a tooth is made of enamel.

Argument, page 105

Early to bed

Question types: 2 literal, 2 inferential, 2 evaluative, 2 deductive

1. They make a fuss when they are told to go to bed.
2. Young children need twelve hours sleep.
3. Answers may vary – children may want to keep on playing or watching TV.
4. The brain gets tired from working all day.
5. Answers may vary – people who are tired could drop things and make mistakes.
6. No, an adult's skeleton is hard.
7. Your own answer.
8. Your own answer.

Poetry, page 106

John and Jim

Question types: 2 literal, 2 inferential, 2 evaluative, 2 deductive

1. John's secret friend is called Jim.
2. Your own answer.
3. John could box his own shadow, which could be Jim.
4. Jim can't be seen because he isn't real.
5. John's secret friend lives at home with him.
6. They talk, walk and fight together.
7. 'Walking' rhymes with 'talking' and 'fighting' rhymes with 'writing'.
8. Your own answer.

Narrative, page 107

The Twits

Question types: 2 literal, 2 inferential, 2 evaluative, 2 deductive

1. The Twits had Bird Pie for supper on Wednesdays.
2. Mr Twit climbed into The Big Dead Tree.
3. Mr Twit put glue on the branches on Tuesday, the day before Bird Pie day.
4. The birds wanted to rest for the night.
5. Your own answer.
6. He saw the birds roosting and thought glue would be a good way to catch them.
7. Mrs Twit would have to pluck the feathers off.
8. Your own answer.

Report, page 108

The playground

Question types: 2 literal, 2 inferential, 2 evaluative, 2 deductive

1. A reporter for a local paper writes about things that have happened in the area.

2. A new slide and playhouse are next to the sandpit.

3. Children over 14 years could break the equipment.

4. The rubber tiles are to stop children hurting themselves.

5. Your own answer.

6. Your own answer.

7. Dunston County Council looks after the playground.

8. The money came from the National Lottery Small Claims Board.

Explanation, page 109

The library
Question types: 2 literal, 2 inferential, 2 evaluative, 2 deductive

1. Local people in the area would use the public library.

2. A collection of books is called a library.

3. Melvil Dewey put non-fiction books into subject groups.

4. A book about computers would be non-fiction.

5. A Dewey number tells you what subject group the book is in.

6. Non-fiction books have been grouped by subject for 122 years. (*Note:* answer will alter depending on the present year.)

7. Your own answer.

8. Your own answer.

Argument, page 110

Saving wild flowers
Question types: 2 literal, 3 inferential, 1 evaluative, 2 deductive

1. Dandelions, daisies, sowthistles and buttercups are unlikely to become extinct.

2. The farmers think of the wild flowers as weeds.

3. Your own answer.

4. They can have part of their garden as a wild garden.

5. The rarer flowers do not like all soils.

6. A gardener might find the rarer wild flowers will not grow.

7. People who pick the wild flowers could cause them to disappear.

8. You could look to see which wild flowers can be found growing in your area.

Instruction, page 111

First aid for a grazed knee
Question types: 3 literal, 2 inferential, 2 evaluative, 3 deductive

1. You could fall and slide along the ground.

2. The graze would be sore.

3. You need warm water, cotton wool balls, sterile gauze and adhesive tape or dressings.

4. Answers may vary – you could be running outside.

5. Your own answer.

6. Your own answer.

7. 'Germ free' means the same as sterile.

8. The graze could get infected.

9. Your own answer.

10. You should dial 999 for an ambulance.

Poetry, page 112

The witches' ride
Question types: 3 literal, 2 inferential, 2 evaluative, 3 deductive

1. The poem is about witches.

2. They are riding through the skies.

3. It is night-time.

4. Your own answer.

5. The witches are going to the moon.

6. Answers may vary – they are probably riding on a broom.

7. The word 'ebony' is used because the night is black.

8. The pairs of words that rhyme are 'light' and 'night', 'eyes' and 'skies', 'sleep' and 'deep', 'bare' and 'air', 'tune' and 'moon'.

9. Answers may vary – the 'slippery deep' refers to the depth of the sea or the sea-bed.

10. Your own answer.

Poetry, page 113

Water

Question types: 2 literal, 1 inferential, 2 evaluative, 5 deductive

1. Water is found in the waterfall, the pump, the tap, the well, in rain, the bath, the pond, at sea and in tears.

2. Answers may vary – water can be found in lakes and rivers.

3. Your own answer.

4. It says water has no taste or smell.

5. Answers may vary – water is clear and liquid.

6. Four more pairs of words that rhyme are 'all' and 'waterfall', 'about' and 'out', 'rain' and 'again', 'tears' and 'ears'.

7. Your own answer.

8. He has dirt behind his ears.

9. Answers may vary – it is used in car washes and by the fire service.

10. Answers may vary – frogs, newts, fish, water insects, crocodiles and alligators live in water.

Narrative, page 114

No roses for Harry

Question types: 2 literal, 3 inferential, 3 evaluative, 2 deductive

1. Harry was a white dog with black spots.

2. Grandma gave Harry the sweater.

3. Your own answer

4. It was nice and warm.

5. People kept finding the sweater and giving it back to Harry.

6. They didn't want Harry to lose the sweater.

7. Answers may vary – perhaps Harry didn't feel like playing with his friends because he was wearing the sweater that he didn't like, and he must have been feeling tired after trying so hard to lose it on the shopping trip.

8. Your own answer.

9. No, Harry didn't mean the bird to take the wool.

10. Your own answer.

Explanation, page 116

Water

Question types: 2 literal, 2 inferential, 2 evaluative, 4 deductive

1. We use water for washing machines, dishwashers, showers, baths and lavatories.

2. The water comes from the rain.

3. We use water to drink, cook, clean our teeth and water indoor plants.

4. There would be no water.

5. There might be fish, chemicals and rubbish in the river.

6. We might get ill.

7. Your own answer.

8. We would need to take out the salt.

9. Your own answer.

10. A reservoir is used to store water.

Argument, page 118

Dental hygiene

Question types: 2 literal, 2 inferential, 3 evaluative, 3 deductive

1. A baby's first teeth are called milk teeth.
2. The teeth will decay.
3. Our teeth grind up our food to make it easier to swallow and digest.
4. Rinsing your teeth will wash out the food and drink left in your mouth.
5. Your own answer.
6. Your own answer.
7. If a tooth decayed it would hurt and you would have to have a filling or even have the tooth taken out.
8. Your own answer.
9. They are called milk teeth because they come when babies are still fed on milk.
10. If the teeth are brushed from side to side the bristles of the toothbrush cannot clean between the teeth.

Narrative, page 120

Charlie and the Chocolate Factory

Question types: 2 literal, 3 inferential, 2 evaluative, 3 deductive

1. The room was like a gigantic witch's kitchen.
2. He was excited because it was his favourite room.
3. The delicious rich smells were being made by the mixtures cooking.
4. He couldn't decide which to look at first.
5. She thought an Everlasting Gobstopper was like chewing gum because it lasted a long time.
6. The Everlasting Gobstoppers lasted for ever so they wouldn't need to buy another.
7. Your own answer.
8. Your own answer.
9. Charlie was surprised at the gigantic room.
10. It was a hard, round, green ball, the same size and shape as a marble.

Poetry, page 122

Bones

Question types: 2 literal, 3 inferential, 2 evaluative, 3 deductive

1. Bones is a dog.
2. Bones is good with children.
3. He stopped the dodgems.
4. He lives in the country.
5. Your own answer.
6. He goes to school to look for the children.
7. He gets into trouble.
8. Answers may vary – perhaps the children's mother says 'Bad' to Bones.
9. Your own answer.
10. Answers may vary – he may have got his name because he likes bones.

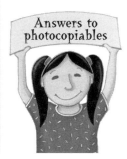
Instruction, page 123

Battleships

Question types: 2 literal, 2 inferential, 3 evaluative, 3 deductive

1. The game needs two players.
2. You need squared paper.
3. Answers may vary – you could put in an aircraft carrier, a minesweeper or a corvette.
4. The letters and numbers give the grid reference.
5. Your own answer.
6. You could measure out and draw the squares yourself.
7. Your own answer.
8. Your own answer.
9. You could fire more than one shot at each turn.
10. You need to be able to read a grid reference.

Explanation, page 124

The water cycle

Question types: 2 literal, 4 inferential, 3 evaluative, 1 deductive

1. The water in the puddles evaporates.
2. The clouds are made of little droplets of water.
3. The water in the clothes evaporates.
4. The clouds turn grey when the water droplets join and get bigger and bigger.
5. Your own answer.
6. You would need to wear rainproof clothes.
7. Snow is formed by water drops in the clouds freezing into ice crystals.
8. Your own answer.
9. Your own answer.
10.

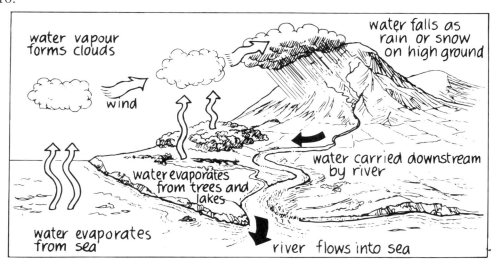

Recount, page 125

Swimming lessons

Question types: 2 literal, 5 inferential, 2 evaluative, 1 deductive

1. The writer lived by the canal.
2. The writer's mum was worried about him drowning.
3. Your own answer.
4. He liked to try to catch fish and throw stones at pieces of wood in the water.
5. It was difficult to make your arms and legs work together.
6. The boy found it easy to learn to swim.
7. The pool is 25 metres long.
8. Your own answer.
9. The writer is a boy.
10. None of the children could swim when they started.

Narrative, page 126

Cam Jansen and the mystery of the UFO

Question types: 2 literal, 2 inferential, 2 evaluative, 4 deductive

1. It was late afternoon.
2. Eric wanted to take photographs.
3. They saw a grey and white kitten.
4. Cam put some tuna fish on the branch.
5. No, it is a shortened name.
6. Cam knew that cats like fish.
7. Your own answer.
8. Cats are good at balancing.
9. Answers might vary – he might give it to a local newspaper.
10. They are not related, and their hair colour is very different. Cam has bright red hair and Eric's is dark brown.

Narrative, page 128

The story of Giant Kippernose

Question types: 2 literal, 3 inferential, 2 evaluative, 3 deductive

1. The giant was called Kippernose.
2. His favourite foods were ice-cream, cakes, lollipops and sausages.
3. He was lonely.
4. Your own answer.
5. He thought the people would like his stories.
6. A person would get very dirty and smelly.
7. He was too dirty to go near.
8. 'In a trice' means very quickly.
9. Kippernose thought the people were afraid of him.
10. Your own answer.

Instruction, page 129

Making an aquarium

Question types: 2 literal, 2 inferential, 1 evaluative, 5 deductive

1. You will need a straight-sided glass tank.
2. You should use rainwater or pond water.
3. Tap water has been purified with chlorine.
4. You could get water snails from a pond or a shop.
5. Water snails keep the tank clean.
6. The water might get too hot in a sunny place.
7. Oxygen from the pond weed goes into the water.
8. Your own answer.
9. The water needs to be the same so that the fish don't have a sudden change of temperature.
10. You will need to change the water regularly – if the water becomes cloudy it is a sign that it should be changed.

Poetry, page 130

Thirty-two lengths

Question types: 2 literal, 2 inferential, 3 evaluative, 3 deductive

1. The boy was about ten years old.
2. He swam a mile on a Tuesday.
3. Half a mile would be sixteen lengths.
4. He told the man because he was so pleased to have swum a mile.
5. The boy was very tired.
6. The man was huge and had enormous muscles.
7. Your own answer.
8. Your own answer.
9. Your own answer.

10. Answers may vary – only a strong swimmer would be able to swim thirty-two lengths, even though the boy whom the man knew could swim ninety.

Explanation, page 131

Ice-caps

Question types: 2 literal, 2 inferential, 2 evaluative, 4 deductive

1. The polar regions are at the North and South Poles.
2. The sea has frozen.
3. The sun at the polar regions is not very warm.
4. The warmth of the sun melts the edge of the ice-cap.
5. Your own answer.
6. The land would get much smaller and change its shape.
7. The ships might run into the icebergs and be badly damaged by them.
8. Your own answer.
9. You would freeze to death.
10. An explorer could use melted ice for water.

Drama, page 132

The strange creature

Question types: 2 literal, 2 inferential, 3 evaluative, 3 deductive

1. The lady is talking to a reporter.
2. She had been walking by Poddle Wood.
3. She was upset because a strange creature had frightened her.
4. Answers may vary – it is probably not very far from the Daily Bugle office, certainly within walking distance.
5. Your own answer.
6. The hissing noise was the gas coming out of the balloon.
7. Your own answer.
8. The lady thought that the man needed a cup of tea because he had had an accident.
9. She went to the Daily Bugle because she wanted her story to be put in the paper.
10. Your own answer.

Report, page 133

The Garden Produce Show

Question types: 2 literal, 4 inferential, 3 evaluative, 1 deductive

1. The Garden Produce Show was held in the Community Hall.
2. The Dibble twins won first prize.
3. Tomato growing and cake making classes had been held for the first time the year before.
4. Perhaps she thought he had taken the runner bean from her garden.
5. Your own answer.
6. The show has not been held in the Community Hall before as it is new.
7. Your own answer.
8. Your own answer.
9. The flowers in the show would make a blaze of colour.
10. People expected Mrs Green to win.

Narrative, page 134

Harry's Mad

Question types: 2 literal, 4 inferential, 2 evaluative, 2 deductive

1. The name of the parrot is Madison.
2. Harry couldn't do his homework.
3. Harry had English for homework.
4. He didn't understand what to do.
5. Answers may vary – Harry was doing his homework upstairs in his bedroom.

6. Madison can do the homework easily.

7. Eventually, the parrot did help Harry to understand.

8. Harry didn't usually get his homework right.

9. Your own answer.

10. Your own answer.

Argument, page 135

Homework

Question types: 3 literal, 2 inferential, 3 evaluative, 2 deductive

1. Children need to do homework to be able to learn enough to pass exams.

2. No, not all parents and teachers think homework is a good thing.

3. It helps parents to understand what their children are doing at school.

4. There may be a lot of people in the family and no quiet rooms.

5. The children would make a fuss if they wanted to play or watch TV, or if they felt too tired to concentrate.

6. Your own answer.

7. Your own answer.

8. They need to get into the habit for when they are older and have to work for exams.

9. It will be easier to study.

10. Your own answer.

Instruction, page 136

How to find information in a book

Question types: 2 literal, 4 inferential, 3 evaluative, 2 deductive

1. Information books have a subject number on their spines.

2. The number will be in the subject catalogue.

3. The words used in a title could give a hint.

4. 'Key words' are words that can be thought of as important within a particular subject.

5. Your own answer.

6. The index gives the page numbers where information can be found.

7. Your own answer.

8. Your own answer.

9. Made-up stories are fiction, so they will not be in the non-fiction section.

10. The chapter headings will be in the contents list.

Poetry, page 137

Grammar

Question types: 3 literal, 2 inferential, 3 evaluative, 2 deductive

1. The teacher is talking to George.

2. A noun is a naming word.

3. A verb is a doing word.

4. The word 'enormous' would be an adjective.

5. Your own answer.

6. George doesn't understand the lesson.

7. Your own answer.

8. A noun gives objects a name.

9. Your own answer.

10. Your own answer.

Explanation, page 138

Canal locks

Question types: 3 literal, 3 inferential, 3 evaluative, 3 deductive

1. Locks were invented in the 1500s.

2. They were able to sail over hills.

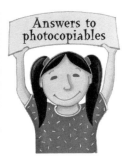

3. A river is a natural waterway and a canal is man-made.
4. Bricks and concrete are used to make the sides and the bottom of the lock.
5. Sluices control the flow of water by opening or shutting.
6. A boat has to wait for the water to get to the right level in a lock.
7. Your own answer.
8. Your own answer.
9. Your own answer.
10. The gates open and the boat goes into the lock. The lock gates are shut and the sluice opened. The water rises in the lock. The lock gates are opened and the boat leaves the lock.
11. No, the water in a canal does not flow like a river.
12. No, travelling on a canal is a slow way to travel.

Drama, page 140

The rescue
Question types: 2 literal, 3 inferential, 2 evaluative, 5 deductive
1. Jack and Tina are fishing.
2. Tina has caught a stickleback.
3. The lady was trying to attract the children's attention.
4. He lost his balance when the boat bumped into the lock gate.
5. She wanted to let their mum know where they were.
6. She was afraid they might fall in the canal and drown.
7. No, the children haven't always lived there.
8. Your own answer.
9. She didn't want the boat to bump into the lock gate.
10. They didn't have to wait for the lock to fill.
11. Fred had to open the sluices to let the water out of the lock.
12. Your own answer.

Report, page 142

The Ashton Cricket Club
Question types: 3 literal, 2 inferential, 3 evaluative, 4 deductive
1. The club was called the Ashton Cricket Club.
2. The president of the club was Mr Legg.
3. The club had three teams.
4. An away match is played at an opponent's pitch.
5. Tom Kipper scored 100 runs.
6. A coaching course will improve their play.
7. He was unable to see properly what was happening in the game.
8. The matches were played on Sundays.
9. There are 100 runs in a century.
10. Your own answer.
11. Your own answer.
12. Your own answer.

Narrative, page 144

Dreams
Question types: 3 literal, 3 inferential, 3 evaluative, 3 deductive
1. The Big Friendly Giant was doing his homework.
2. Sophie was watching the Giant.
3. There was a dream in the glass jar.
4. The BFG collects dreams.
5. Sophie and the Giant are friends so she is not afraid.
6. Human beans are really human beings.
7. The Giant's ears can understand the music the dreams make.
8. Your own answer.
9. Your own answer.

10. A 'spindel' is a spine in this story.
11. The Giant is good at keeping things in order because he labels the jars.
12. Your own answer.

Poetry, page 146

Cinderella
Question types: 3 literal, 3 inferential, 3 evaluative, 3 deductive
1. Cinderella was in a cellar.
2. The Ugly Sisters had gone to the Palace Ball.
3. The rats were nibbling Cinderella's feet.
4. The Magic Fairy was the Fairy Godmother.
5. The word 'jalous' is used to rhyme with 'palace'. The word should be 'jealous'.
6. No, Cindy went to the Palace by magic.
7. They wanted to dance with the Prince themselves.
8. She wanted the Prince to notice her.
9. Cindy was holding the Prince very tightly.
10. Your own answer.
11. Your own answer.
12. Your own answer.

Recount, page 148

The Beatles
Question types: 3 literal, 3 inferential, 3 evaluative, 3 deductive
1. There were four young men in the Beatles.
2. Ringo Starr's real name was Richard Starkey.
3. Their fame swept the world in the 1960s.
4. Answers may vary – they were excited because they were seeing the group that they liked so much.
5. Answers may vary – they were not wealthy and times were hard.
6. They went to school in different parts of Liverpool.
7. The Beatles became rich because they sold thousands of records.
8. Your own answer.
9. The boys had always liked music.
10. A posh hotel is one that is usually modern, comfortable and expensive.
11. The boys had to work very hard when they gave a concert.
12. They wanted to touch them because they were seeing them in real life. They wanted to have something belonging to the Beatles.

Narrative, page 150

The cave
Question types: 3 literal, 3 inferential, 3 evaluative, 3 deductive
1. Barney was looking round the den.
2. The den belonged to Stig.
3. The bed was made of bracken and newspapers.
4. Barney liked the den being untidy and full of interesting things.
5. Stig was pleased that Barney liked his home.
6. Yes, the rain would be helpful, as Stig's water came through the roof of the cave.
7. Stig cooked his food on a fire.
8. He uses the pages to light his lamp.
9. The fire was at the front so the smoke could go out.
10. Your own answer.
11. Answers may vary – he felt proud of his den.
12. Your own answer.

Instruction, page 151

Easy pizza

Question types: 2 literal, 3 inferential, 2 evaluative, 3 deductive

1. A loaf of thick-sliced white or brown bread, Cheddar cheese, butter or margarine, four tomatoes, tomato ketchup or tomato purée, one tin of anchovies, eight black olives, dried oregano or thyme, pepper.

2. The butter is melted so that the bread soaks it up.

3. You could use olives on their own if you didn't like anchovies, or you could do without both ingredients – they are optional.

4. Your own answer.

5. Your own answer.

6. Easy Pizza is made with ordinary bread. A real pizza is made with special pizza dough.

7. The garnish is to make the pizza look appetising.

8. You need oven gloves because the baking sheet will be very hot.

9. The recipe needs Cheddar cheese.

10. The bread is covered with melted butter to prevent it drying out when it is cooking.

Argument, page 152

Zoos

Question types: 3 literal, 3 inferential, 2 evaluative, 2 deductive

1. A zoo is a place where a collection of animals is displayed.

2. They go to see animals they would not be able to see otherwise.

3. They think it is cruel to keep wild animals in a cage. In captivity, even if the animals are not in a cage, they are contained within a much smaller space than if they were in the wild.

4. One of the greatest advantages of a zoo is that it saves animals from becoming extinct.

5. Baby animals in the wild are hunted for food by other animals.

6. You could learn what the animal looks like, how it moves, its habits and what it sounds like.

7. Your own answer.

8. Some animals may find our climate too hot, others may find it too cold and wet.

9. Your own answer.

10. If an animal becomes extinct it means it no longer exists in the world.

Narrative, page 153

Arthur, King of Britain

Question types: 3 literal, 3 inferential, 2 evaluative, 2 deductive

1. Kay had forgotten his sword.

2. Arthur went to fetch Kay's sword.

3. A tourneying is a jousting competition.

4. Arthur found the sword in the anvil before the great church.

5. Kay is the older brother because he is taking part in the tourneying.

6. Your own answer.

7. Yes, he needed to be seen, as it would be proof that he could pull out the sword.

8. Only the king of Britain could pull out the sword.

9. Kay thought he was king because Arthur had given him the sword from the anvil.

10. Your own answer.

Recount, page 154

Douglas Bader

Question types: 3 literal, 3 inferential, 2 evaluative, 2 deductive

1. Douglas Bader was a pilot.

2. His plane crashed on take-off.

3. His legs had to be amputated after the crash.

4. They thought it would be too difficult to fly with artificial legs.
5. Answers may vary – a special feature of his personality was his determined nature.
6. Douglas Bader was born in 1911.
7. Your own answer.
8. They thought he was a difficult person.
9. He would fly on bombing missions again.
10. It was difficult for Bader to learn to walk again.

Poetry, page 155

The silent spinney
Question types: 2 literal, 3 inferential, 2 evaluative, 3 deductive
1. The writer heard a cat.
2. The writer is afraid of the darkness.
3. Your own answer.
4. No, it is the first time the writer has been that way.
5. Your own answer.
6. The writer thinks it could be a person.
7. The trees are tall and dark and do not make a sound. Also, their shadows would be frightening.
8. Answers may vary – the writer's sisters are afraid of spiders rather than the dark.
9. A spinney is a small wood.
10. No, the writer is not afraid of spiders and mice.

Instruction, page 156

How to make a scarecrow
Question types: 2 literal, 2 inferential, 3 evaluative, 3 deductive
1. You need two straight pieces of wood.
2. You need a piece of material, 1 metre square.
3. Answers may vary – a gardener who grows fruit and vegetables or someone who was a very keen gardener would want a scarecrow.
4. The long stick will need to be pushed down into the ground.
5. Rainwater would drain easily through the straw. Rags would hold the water.
6. Your own answer.
7. You would expect to see a scarecrow in a kitchen garden or on an allotment.
8. Answers may vary – a farmer would be an appropriate person.
9. Gardeners would want to stop birds eating the fruit in their gardens.
10.

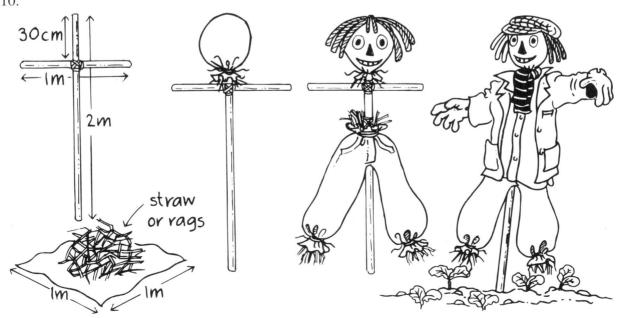

Report, page 157

Hazard Hill

Question types: 3 literal, 3 inferential, 3 evaluative, 1 deductive

1. Mrs Spinks is the spokesperson for the action group.
2. The action group is trying to get Church Hill made safer.
3. The experts say the road is in good condition.
4. The danger spot is the bend at the bottom of the hill.
5. Straightening the road would not make it completely safe.
6. No, Church Hill is an area of Splatborn, probably on the outskirts of the town.
7. The notice would warn motorists about the dangerous bend.
8. The overhanging trees would cause the most problems in the summer when the trees are in full leaf.
9. Your own answer.
10. Your own answer.

Explanation, page 158

Washday blues

Question types: 3 literal, 2 inferential, 2 evaluative, 3 deductive

1. The laundry washed people's clothes.
2. Most people did their own washing and it was done by hand.
3. There was more washing because the families were bigger.
4. Answers may vary – their hands would be dry, red and wrinkled.
5. Soap powder had not been invented.
6. Answers may vary – they probably felt very tired.
7. They were sorted into piles because the materials in each pile needed to be washed differently.
8. The house would be filled with steam caused by the clothes drying indoors.
9. The copper boiler would be heated by a fire beneath it.
10. Your own answer.

Narrative, page 159

The Chief Rabbit

Question types: 2 literal, 4 inferential, 2 evaluative, 2 deductive

1. Hazel and Fiver are rabbits.
2. Fiver had woken Hazel.
3. Fiver was having a nightmare.
4. They are in a burrow.
5. The black lines were writing on a noticeboard.
6. Hazel is the Chief Rabbit.
7. Your own answer.
8. They had to swim.
9. Hazel went down a dark tunnel of water.
10. Your own answer.

Poetry, page 160

Shoot the messenger!

Question types: 2 literal, 4 inferential, 3 evaluative, 1 deductive

1. She was on playground duty.
2. The messenger would get shot for bringing bad news.
3. They shot the messenger because they didn't want the news to be true.
4. They believed Miss Martin because she was smart.
5. Yes, the children were surprised.
6. Your own answer.
7. Your own answer.
8. Your own answer.
9. The messenger had come from the battle front.
10. Your own answer.

Narrative, page 162

The Bakerloo flea

Question types: 3 literal, 2 inferential, 2 evaluative, 3 deductive

1. The writer was in a pub.
2. The woman used to be a cleaner for the Underground.
3. She told him about the Bakerloo flea.
4. The rats had grown enormous.
5. The fleas grew bigger because the rats grew bigger.
6. The Underground is a network of tube trains.
7. Garbage is rubbish.
8. The story is set in London.
9. Your own answer.
10. Your own answer.

Instruction, page 163

How to make a papier mâché toby jug

Question types: 3 literal, 2 inferential, 2 evaluative, 3 deductive

1. Papier mâché is made of newspaper, water and wallpaper paste.
2. The paper will be easier to use in narrow strips.
3. The wallpaper paste and water makes the paper a sticky pulp.
4. You need to soak the strips in water.
5. You need to feel if the paper is sticky enough.
6. The papier mâché layer needs to be thick enough to cover the surface of the jar, including the handle.
7. If the papier mâché is not dry when you paint it, the paint will run.
8. The varnish helps to make the jug waterproof.
9. Your own answer.
10. Your own answer.

Report, page 164

A Devon disaster

Question types: 4 literal, 4 inferential, 3 evaluative, 4 deductive

1. The Lynmouth flood happened on 15 August 1952.
2. The name of the moor is Exmoor.
3. The East Lyn and West Lyn meet at Lynmouth.
4. The ground was saturated with water and could hold no more.
5. The lights would fail when the power lines were washed away.
6. Your own answer.
7. Young children would have been in bed.
8. Your own answer.
9. The boats would be smashed by waves and debris falling into the sea.
10. The rest of the country could help by collecting money, clothes and household furniture.
11. More people were in Lynmouth because it was holiday time.
12. Your own answer
13. The blocked roads would make it difficult for rescue workers.
14. The safest place would be on higher ground above Lynmouth.
15. Ninety-three families lost their homes.

Argument, page 166

Waging a war on waste

Question types: 4 literal, 4 inferential, 4 evaluative, 3 deductive

1. Recycling our waste has become an important issue.
2. The population is growing.
3. The rubbish is buried in landfills.
4. The county councils are worried because landfills are getting used up.
5. People in flats do not usually have gardens so they don't need compost.

6. Your own answer.

7. Your own answer.

8. Your own answer.

9. Your own answer.

10. Answers may vary – the list could include batteries, cakes, sandwiches, pizzas and so on.

11. People will not have these things to use.

12. A growing population uses more resources and makes more rubbish.

13. Recycled paper is made from used paper, magazines and newspapers.

14. About 50 per cent of our rubbish could be recycled.

15. There would be too much rubbish to put in the landfills.

Narrative, page 168

The Watchers

Question types: 3 literal, 5 inferential, 3 evaluative, 4 deductive

1. They were all going on a trip to Alton Towers.

2. The Round Table had arranged the outing.

3. They went once a year.

4. They could catch a bus.

5. Your own answer.

6. They went in on the Monorail.

7. They would need a grown-up on the rides that went up high.

8. They needed an adult with them if they went on the lake.

9. Mrs Rogers didn't like heights.

10. Katy had been very frightened on a ride she had been on before.

11. It would give her an excuse not to go on the high rides.

12. Josh's nickname was Chips.

13. Your own answer.

14. Answers may vary – Kirby House could be a children's home.

15. Your own answer.

Poetry, page 170

Tricks

Question types: 3 literal, 3 inferential, 2 evaluative, 2 deductive

1. The writer shares a room with his brother.

2. The two boys are in their bedroom.

3. No, the brother doesn't do his trick every morning.

4. It is the brother's magic bar that cannot be seen.

5. Your own answer.

6. Answers may vary – he would need to be good at sit-ups.

7. Your own answer.

8. He wasn't really sure there wasn't a magic bar.

9. He didn't want his brother to think he believed his trick.

10. The brother isn't bothered whether the writer believes him or not.

Narrative, page 172

Tom Sawyer

Question types: 4 literal, 5 inferential, 3 evaluative, 3 deductive

1. It was Monday.

2. Tom was miserable because he had to go to school.

3. Tom was in bed.

4. He could stay away from school if he was sick.

5. His first symptoms were symptoms of colic.

6. If you are 'colicky' you have tummy ache.

7. The second thing was his loose tooth.

8. He didn't use his tooth as a second idea because he knew his aunt would pull it out and it would hurt.

9. Tom finally used his sore toe as an excuse.
10. Sid slept in the same room as Tom.
11. No, it was difficult to wake Sid up.
12. Sid seemed very worried about Tom.
13. Your own answer.
14. Your own answer.
15. Your own answer.

Explanation, page 174

El Niño

Question types: 4 literal, 5 inferential, 3 evaluative, 3 deductive
1. The name given to the phenomenon is El Niño.
2. El Niño means 'baby Jesus' or 'Christ child'.
3. El Niño usually happens at the end of December.
4. The strange weather starts in the Pacific Ocean.
5. The trade winds die down and they lose their strength.
6. The fish have to move to cooler water.
7. The fish industry would have to close down.
8. The two extremes are floods and droughts.
9. People would have died from starvation and drowning.
10. It could make the things we buy in the shops more expensive.
11. If there weren't enough snow at the ski resorts, no one would come to ski.
12. Your own answer.
13. Your own answer.
14. Your own answer.
15. Answers may vary – floods affect ordinary people by spoiling their homes and preventing them from getting to the shops and work.

Drama, page 176

The cure

Question types: 3 literal, 5 inferential, 3 evaluative, 4 deductive
1. They are called Robert and Ethel.
2. Great Aunt Jane is very ill and is near death.
3. Great Aunt Jane lives in Ireland.
4. Great Aunt Jane has asked to see William.
5. Answers may vary – he is their annoying brother whom they can't imagine anyone wanting to see.
6. William's mother took him to see Great Aunt Jane.
7. They would get to Ireland by boat or plane.
8. He meant that Great Aunt Jane was getting weaker and nearer to death.
9. Your own answer.
10. Your own answer.
11. The noise of the fight brought the nurse back to the bedroom.
12. The fight brought Great Aunt Jane round. She became very excited and enjoyed it. Overall, it made her feel better!
13. The fight started by William calling Francis 'Fatty'.
14. Margaret is William's mother.
15. William has freckles on his face.

Recount, page 178

A country child

Question types: 3 literal, 4 inferential, 4 evaluative, 4 deductive
1. He has been named after Prince Albert.
2. He was ten years old when he left school.
3. He had bread, cheese, bacon and potatoes and a pint of cider.
4. The story was written in 1867.
5. The writer has more than one brother and sister.

6. His working day was from 5.30am to 7.00pm: thirteen and a half hours.

7. He would rather be at school because it is not such hard work.

8. Your own answer.

9. There was no machinery to do the jobs, and employing boys was cheap for the farmer.

10. He is only able to rest when he is eating, so he has about half an hour's rest during the day.

11. Your own answer.

12. Stones in the fields could damage the ploughs.

13. They would be keeping the birds off the crops.

14. Your own answer.

15. Your own answer.

Poetry, page 180

To the lady behind me

Question types: 2 literal, 3 inferential, 2 evaluative, 3 deductive

1. The writer is talking to the lady sitting behind him.

2. The writer is in a theatre.

3. They are watching a play.

4. The lady is talking all the time.

5. The lady has her niece with her.

6. Your own answer.

7. The lady is saying what is going to happen next.

8. Yes, and she knows the play well.

9. The writer wants the lady to be quiet.

10. Answers may vary – it is very likely that he has not had a pleasant evening.

Narrative, page 182

Mary's climb

Question types: 4 literal, 4 inferential, 3 evaluative, 4 deductive

1. Mary has gone to see her father.

2. Mary's father is combing the stone.

3. Mary's father is working on a church spire.

4. The golden spark was a weather cock.

5. Some tea and food is in the baggin cloth.

6. Your own answer.

7. He is thirsty.

8. The sides of the steeple were square.

9. He didn't want to stop work to come down.

10. She was frightened of climbing ladders.

11. Her father's hammer taps gave Mary a rhythm.

12. Mary had climbed to the top of the spire.

13. Your own answer.

14. Your own answer.

15. If the next baby were a boy, then he could take up her father's baggin.

COMBAT
LEGEND

SPITFIRE
Mks VI–F.24

Peter Caygill

Airlife

Text written by Peter Caygill
Profile illustrations drawn by Dave Windle
Cover painting by Jim Brown – The Art of Aviation Co. Ltd

First published in the UK in 2004
by Airlife Publishing, an imprint of The Crowood Press

British Library Cataloguing-in-Publication Data
    A catalogue record for this book
    is available from the British Library

ISBN 1 84037 400 4

Printed in Malaysia

*Contact us for a free catalogue that describes the complete range of Airlife
books for pilots and aviation enthusiasts.*

Airlife
An imprint of The Crowood Press
Ramsbury, Marlborough, Wiltshire SN8 2HR
E-mail: enquiries@crowood.com

www.crowood.com

Contents

Spitfire VI–F.24 Timeline

30 July 1942
First combat success for the Spitfire IX (Fw 190 of JG 26) recorded by F/L Don Kingaby of 64 Squadron in BR600.

12 September 1942
F/O Galitzine engages a Ju 86R in a Spitfire IX at 43,000ft over Southampton, the highest recorded combat of WWII.

20 November 1942
First production Spitfire VIII (JF274) flies at Eastleigh.

February 1943
The first Griffon-engined Spitfire XIIs are delivered to 41 Squadron at High Ercall.

17 May 1943
F/O F.D. Fray in a Spitfire PR.IX of 542 Squadron brings back photographs of the Moehne and Eder dams after the attack by 617 Squadron Lancasters.

27 April 1944
S/L A.F. Martindale dives Spitfire PR.XI EN409 to Mach 0.89 (606 mph) but loses his propeller in the process.

5 October 1944
Spitfire IXBs of 401 Squadron are the first Allied aircraft to shoot down a Messerschmitt Me 262 jet fighter.

29 December 1944
F/L R.J. Audet of 411 Squadron flying Spitfire LF.IX RR201 shoots down five German fighters in a single sortie, a feat unequalled by any other Spitfire pilot.

January 1945
91 Squadron at Manston is the first RAF unit to receive the Spitfire F.21.

2 April 1945
Jeffrey Quill takes the first production Spiteful (RB515) on its maiden flight.

The Griffon engine ensured that Spitfire performance kept pace with its rivals. The Spitfire XII seen here was particularly effective at low level due to its low-altitude rated, single-stage supercharged Griffon III. MB882 has a retractable tail wheel, indicating that it is a late production machine. (*Philip Jarrett*)

28 May 1945
The first Spitfire FR.XVIII (SM844) is delivered to the RAF for use by 28 Squadron in Hong Kong.

22 May 1948
Spitfire FR.XVIIIs of 208 Squadron shoot down four Egyptian Air Force Spitfire IXs after attacks on Ramat David airfield.

12 May 1949
The last Seafire FR.47 (VR971) is delivered to the Royal Navy.

1 June 1950
HMS *Triumph* sails for the Korean War with Seafire FR.47s of 800 Squadron aboard.

1 January 1951
FR.XVIIIs of 60 Squadron carry out the last RAF Spitfire strike on a target at Johore during Operation *Firedog* in Malaya.

16 January 1951
F/L E.C. Powles carries out the first of 107 photographic reconnaissance missions over China in a Spitfire PR.XIX.

1 April 1954
Last operational sortie by an RAF Spitfire is flown by PR.XIX PS888 of 81 Squadron in Malaya.

23 November 1954
The last Seafire XVIIs are retired from Royal Navy service with 764 Training Squadron at Yeovilton.

June 1957
The last three Spitfire PR.XIXs of the THUM (Temperature and HUMidity) flight at Woodvale are retired.

1. Late Mark Spitfires: Prototypes and Development

Although the Spitfire is rightly regarded as the supreme short-range fighter of World War Two, anyone attempting to predict its future early in 1941 could have been forgiven for considering that R.J. Mitchell's masterpiece was already past its prime. Intelligence assessments of the Focke-Wulf Fw 190A were that the new German fighter was capable of performance levels that were likely to eclipse all existing Spitfires. In response the RAF was looking towards its own second-generation fighters, the Hawker-designed Tornado and Typhoon. The ultimate demise of the Tornado due to the failure of its Rolls-Royce Vulture engine and the disappointing altitude performance of the Napier Sabre-powered Typhoon, however, meant that the Spitfire would continue far longer, and be developed to far higher levels than might otherwise have been the case.

High altitude performance

Following on from the Spitfire V (see Spitfire Marks I-V in the Combat Legend series) the next in line, numerically, was the Mark VI. It featured a high-altitude rated Rolls-Royce Merlin 47 of 1,415 hp, a pressurised cabin fed by a Marshall Mark IXA blower and extended wingtips that increased span to 40 ft 2 in. The cabin pressure differential was a modest 2 lb/sq in, but at an altitude of 37,500 ft the pressure experienced in the cockpit was equivalent to normal flight at 28,500 ft, greatly easing pilot comfort. The pressure cabin was formed by two additional bulkheads fore and aft of the cockpit, together with the sealing of all joints. Control runs passing through the cabin were routed through pressure-tight glands. The hood could not be moved when airborne, although it could be jettisoned in an emergency.

Spitfire VI BR289 was tested at the Air Fighting Development Unit (AFDU) at Duxford in May 1942 with generally favourable results during comparative trials with a Spitfire V. At heights above its rated altitude of 22,000 ft the Spitfire VI was faster (6 mph at 22,000 ft), had a better rate of climb (especially so above 30,000 ft) and could get on the tail of the Mark V in 1.5 turns at 32,000 ft. At the highest indicated altitude of 37,500 ft when Outside Air Temperature (OAT) was –42 degrees C, the temperature in the cockpit was a relatively cosy +8 degrees C. There were no problems with internal cockpit icing as the constant supply of warm air prevented misting up, even during rapid descents. Negative aspects included heavier aileron controls, a lack of agility caused by the control runs passing through air-tight seals in the cockpit and increased span, a slightly higher stall speed necessitating a faster approach and a worsening of the aircraft's characteristics when taxiing in crosswind conditions. Although the cockpit environment was ideal at altitude, it could become uncomfortably hot below 15,000 ft and on one occasion when OAT was +28 degrees C, cockpit temperature was measured at a sweltering +37 degrees C. Despite the increased altitude performance of the Spitfire VI, it was still

Spitfire VI AB200 was delivered to Boscombe Down on 29 January 1942 for diving trials. During one dive the aircraft pulled out violently, blacking out the pilot and buckling the wings in spite of full forward trim and a strong push force on the control column. With a new set of wings AB200 later flew with 124 Squadron. (*Philip Jarrett*)

incapable of intercepting high-flying Ju 86P reconnaissance/bomber aircraft which operated at heights up to 42,000 ft and the RAF would not have a true high altitude capability until the arrival of the Spitfire IX.

Just as the Spitfire V had been a temporary measure, the Mark IX was rushed into service ahead of the VII and VIII, which were the subject of a major structural re-design of the basic Spitfire airframe. Although all these variants were powered by the two-speed, two-stage supercharged Rolls-Royce Merlin 60/70 series, the Spitfire IX was basically a Mark VC with the minimum amount of strengthening of the fuselage longerons to accept the new engine. The undercarriage was also altered slightly to maintain Centre of Gravity (C.G.). Apart from the longer nose profile, the other main recognition feature of the Mark IX was a revised system of underwing radiators, the duct under the starboard wing housing coolant and intercooler radiators, with that under the port wing accommodating another coolant radiator and the oil cooler. This splitting of the coolant radiators under each wing eased the problem of gun heating which had plagued the earlier marks of Spitfire as hot air could now be ducted from the back of each radiator to the adjacent gun bay.

Although the Spitfire IX was intended merely as a stopgap until the Spitfire VIII was available, it was produced in large numbers and was steadily developed throughout its life. Built initially with the 'C' Type wing (two 20 mm Hispanos and four 0.303 in Brownings) many late-model Mark IXs featured the 'E' Type wing with two Hispano cannon mounted outboard of two 0.5 in Browning machine-guns, a pointed, broad-chord rudder and two additional fuel tanks situated behind the pilot holding 75 gallons.

Teardrop canopy

Some aircraft also had a teardrop canopy and cut-back rear fuselage, in which case the extra fuel capacity was reduced to 66 gallons. C.G. problems caused by the tanks led to the air and oxygen bottles being moved from the rear fuselage to spaces in the wing formerly taken up by the 0.303 in guns. The basic F.IX was powered by a Merlin 61, 63 or 63A, with specialised versions resulting in the low-altitude LF.IX (Merlin 66) and high-altitude HF.IX (Merlin 70). A reconnaissance version, the FR.IX, saw service in small numbers and carried an oblique camera mounted in the rear fuselage, facing port. The Spitfire XVI was basically an LF.IX fitted with a Packard-built Merlin 266.

The Spitfire IX proved to be an immediate success and was reported on in enthusiastic terms by AFDU in April 1942. Whereas the

The extended wing tips of the Spitfire VI are clearly visible in this view of X4942. Built as a Spitfire I and subsequently modified to Mark V standard, X4942 became the second prototype for the Mark VI with a Merlin 47 and pressure cabin. (*Philip Jarrett*)

Spitfire V had struggled much above 30,000 ft in operational trim, the Mark IX was climbed to 39,500 ft (indicated) at which point it still had a climb rate of 1,000 ft/min. Its manoeuvrability at height was excellent and it could pull relatively tight turns at 38,000 ft without losing height thanks to the power of its Merlin 61. A maximum speed of 409 mph was recorded at 28,000 ft and during comparative trials with a Typhoon, the Spitfire IX was marginally faster at all heights. Overall it was rated as being 'outstandingly better' than the Spitfire V.

In August 1942, two months after the Spitfire IX had entered service with 64 Squadron at Hornchurch, Supermarine produced the first high-altitude Spitfire VII. It featured a fully strengthened fuselage to cater for the increased weight and power of the Merlin 61, a retractable tail wheel and revised wing with a 14-gallon flexible self-sealing fuel tank in each

The second production Spitfire VII BS142 clearly shows the elongated blister for the blower intake situated under the exhaust stack. This aircraft went on to serve with 124 Squadron and was credited with shooting down an Fw 190 on 15 May 1943. (*Philip Jarrett*)

Spitfire VIII MD249 served in India. It failed to return from operations on 14 December 1944. (*Philip Jarrett*)

leading edge. By careful re-design the capacity of the main fuselage fuel tanks was increased to 96 gallons. The cockpit was pressurised and (unlike the Mark VI) the hood could be opened in flight for take off and landing. Most early production aircraft had long-span wings with the same planform as the Spitfire VI, later machines appearing with standard wings. A further change seen with the Mark VII and subsequent aircraft was a reduction in span of the ailerons outboard of the outer hinge to

reduce the risk of aileron flutter. With the Spitfire IX proving to be more than capable of dealing with the threat of high-altitude attack there was little requirement for a pressurised fighter and the Mark VII ceased production in early 1944 after 141 had been built.

The Spitfire VIII had all the modifications of the Mark VII but with the pressure cabin deleted and eventually 1,654 were produced, many seeing service in the Far East and Mediterranean. Sub-variants were the same as

Spitfire VIII JF299 was flown for the first time on 30 January 1943 and delivered to Boscombe Down in September 1943 for handling trials with the low-back fuselage and teardrop canopy. As this photo shows it was also fitted with a pointed, broad-chord rudder and whip aerial. (*Philip Jarrett*)

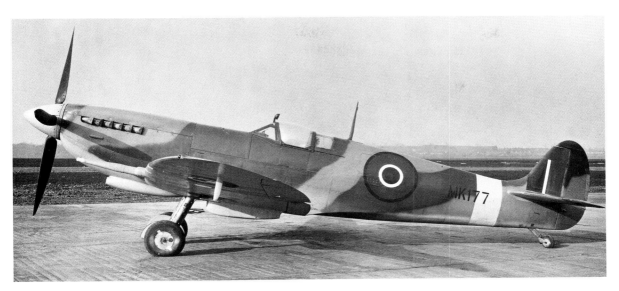

After service with 441 (RCAF) Squadron, Spitfire LF.IX MK177 was transferred to 302 Squadron. Flown by F/Sgt Hajduk, it was lost on 20 January 1945 in a dive-bombing attack on German ground positions. (*Philip Jarrett*)

for the Spitfire IX and later aircraft were fitted with the pointed, broad-chord rudder. Like the IX it employed a neat air filter contained within the bottom engine cowling, with a pilot-operated by-pass. The radiators and gun heating systems were also the same. Early aircraft had long-span wings like the Mark VII but as these tended to reduce rate of roll, most Spitfire VIIIs were delivered with standard wings.

With the Merlin 61 offering excellent performance at altitude it was not long before a dedicated reconnaissance version powered by this engine appeared, the first PR.XI rolling off the production lines in November 1942. However, such was the desperate need for photographic intelligence, fifteen Spitfire IXs had already been modified as photo-reconnaissance machines by the installation of two vertical cameras in the rear fuselage, an enlarged oil tank under the nose and the removal of armament. Unlike the interim PR.IX, the PR.XI carried 66.5 gallons of additional fuel in tanks in each wing leading edge (as did the PR.IV before it) and it also featured a retractable tail wheel, broad-chord rudder, but long-span ailerons. Thanks to the removal of the guns, the replacement of the bullet-proof windscreen with a plain, curved screen and a

clean leading edge, the top speed of the PR.XI proved to be 5 mph better than the Mark IX. Further PR variants included the PR.X, which was basically a pressure cabin F.VII with the wings and camera installation of the PR.XI. Only 16 examples were produced and these saw service with 541 and 542 Squadrons in the high-altitude photo-reconnaissance role. The PR.XIII was similar to the PR.VII, a derivative of the Spitfire I/V, formerly referred to as the PR.IG. The PR.XIII was powered by the low-altitude Merlin 32 and had the wing cannons deleted.

Griffon Spitfires

Although use of the Merlin 61 had allowed the Spitfire to compete on more or less equal terms with the latest versions of the Focke-Wulf Fw 190 and Messerschmitt Bf 109, by the end of 1942 the engine had reached the end of its development potential. At 27 litres, the Merlin was the smallest fighter engine of World War Two by some margin, much of its power being due to Rolls-Royce's expertise in the field of supercharging and the use of high octane fuels. It was clear that if the Spitfire were to benefit from even greater power it would have to use a larger engine of increased capacity. The fact that an engine already existed owed much to Rolls'

Spitfire PR.XI EN654 in its element above the clouds. This aircraft saw service with 16 Squadron before being used as a high-speed mail carrier. (*Philip Jarrett*)

participation in the Schneider Trophy as the 36.7-litre Griffon was developed from the 'R' engine of the Supermarine S.6B. The first Spitfire to fly with a Rolls-Royce Griffon was the Mark IV prototype DP845 which quickly became the Spitfire XX (to avoid confusion with the PR.IV) and later the Spitfire XII.

Early Griffons

The Griffon was initially rated at around 1,500 hp and thanks to its racing pedigree, frontal area was only marginally greater than the Merlin (7.9 sq.ft as opposed to 7.5 sq.ft). It was only 3 in longer but was 600 lb heavier, which necessitated a change from the tubular-type dural engine mounting used on Merlin variants to a girder-type steel longeron. The oil tank was moved from under the engine to a position near the fireproof bulkhead adjacent to the main fuel tanks, a move which reduced fuel capacity by around 10 gallons. A further change was that a shaft-driven accessory gearbox mounted on the bulkhead replaced individual, engine-driven accessories.

The Griffon was set slightly lower in the airframe than the Merlin and careful contouring of the top cowling, together with close fitting elongated blisters over the cylinder

blocks, resulted in the sighting view for gun aiming being improved to 4 degrees downward view. The other main feature from the pilot's point of view was that the Griffon rotated in the opposite direction to the Merlin (left-hand instead of right-hand when seen from the cockpit) so that the aircraft tended to swing in the opposite direction on take off (i.e., to the right) due to torque reaction.

Spitfire XIIs were essentially modified VC airframes with an enlarged rudder, retractable tail wheel and longer spinner. As the early 1,735 hp Griffon III had a single-stage supercharger it developed maximum power at low level so that the Mark XII was in its element below 10,000 ft. During trials at Boscombe Down in September 1942 DP845 achieved 372 mph at 5,700 ft, albeit with considerable attention to its surface finish, which included flush riveting and a highly polished skin. Production aircraft featured clipped wings and the speed attained by EN223, the third production machine, was almost identical with DP845 when tested at Duxford in December 1942. Comparative trials with a Spitfire LF.IX (Merlin 66) showed the Mark XII to be 14 mph faster at sea level, this advantage gradually decreasing until the IX became the faster at heights above 20,000 ft.

Although it performed well in the dive, the climb performance of the Spitfire XII was found to be inferior to the IX at all heights. Manoeuvrability was excellent and pilots also reported on an improvement in the aircraft's longitudinal stability over earlier marks.

It was clear that the benefits of two-stage supercharging would be the making of the Griffon just as it had been for the Merlin and so the Spitfire XII was only produced in small numbers (100) to fill a specialised low-level role. The first Griffon-powered Spitfires entered service with 41 Squadron at High Ercall in February 1943 and two months later the first Mark XIIs arrived for 91 Squadron at Honiley. The type proved to be extremely effective in countering hit-and-run raids by bomb-carrying Fw 190s and later had considerable success when used against V-1 flying bombs.

Spitfire XIV

The second quantum leap in performance came with the arrival of the Spitfire XIV powered by the two-speed two-stage supercharged Griffon 61/65 of 2,050 hp. To cater for the increase in power a five-blade constant-speed Rotol propeller was used, contra-rotating units still being in the development stage. Increased torque and blade area required additional fin area to restore directional stability and initially

a straight edged fin was experimented with before the familiar curved outline appeared on production machines. The airframe used for the XIV was essentially a strengthened and modified Mark VIII with length increased to 32 ft 8 in to allow for the two-stage Griffon with intercooler. Loaded weight was now 8,500 lbs, around 1,000 lbs more than a Spitfire IX.

The first Spitfire XIVs were modified VIIIs (JF316-320) and were often referred to by Supermarine test pilots as Mark VIIIG. Like the earlier Griffon-powered Spitfire, the oil tank was positioned directly behind the fireproof bulkhead. Although this again resulted in a reduction in the amount of fuel capable of being held in the upper tank, it greatly improved the situation regarding engine changes, as the powerplant was now fully inter-changeable. The fuel situation was eased slightly by the incorporation of two leading edge tanks, each of 12.75 gallons capacity. A new fuel selector cock was fitted on the port side of the cockpit so that the pilot could transfer the contents of the wing tanks (either left or right) to the top main tank, and there was also a warning light to inform him when fuel was down to 30 minutes flying time. As the throttle quadrant had remained unchanged since the very first Spitfire, which had only half the power of the XIV, a revised control was

DP845, the first Griffon-engined Spitfire, was first flown on 27 November 1941 as a Spitfire IV before subsequently becoming the prototype Mark XII. During testing at Boscombe Down in September 1942 it recorded a top speed of 397 mph at 17,800 ft. Flown initially with standard wings, it later had clipped wings as seen here. (*Philip Jarrett*)

installed with greater linear movement that greatly eased throttle control. The use of a more powerful engine also made it necessary to increase the depth of the radiator ducts.

Like the Mark IX before it, the Spitfire XIV was intended as a temporary measure pending the arrival of the Spitfire XXI (which became 21 after the war), but its performance was so far in advance of previous marks that eventually 957 were produced. Although it was not necessary to produce dedicated LF and HF variants for low and high-level operations, the Mark XIV did appear in a number of different guises. Whereas initial versions carried standard 'C' Wing armament, the later XIVE introduced the type 'E' wing with two 20 mm Hispano cannon and two 0.5 in Browning machine-guns and towards the end of the production run Spitfire XIVs appeared with teardrop canopies and cut-back rear fuselage.

The FR.XIV was used for low-level photo-reconnaissance and was fitted with an F.24 oblique camera (viewing left or right) in the rear fuselage together with an additional fuel tank of 33 gallons. As speed and agility were prime requirements it featured clipped wings. In 1944 a small number of Mark XIVs were modified to give even greater performance at low level for 'anti-*Diver*' (V-1) operations, the use of 150-octane fuel allowing the Griffon to be operated at +21 lbs boost pressure instead of the more normal +18 lbs boost.

Griffon versus Merlin

In February and March 1944 a Spitfire XIV (RM179) was tested at AFDU, Duxford against a Mark IX. Its speed was found to be 25-35 mph faster at all heights and with a climb rate of around 5,000 ft/min, the XIV had better climb performance than any aircraft previously tested. Due to its power and increased weight the Spitfire XIV also pulled away easily from the Mark IX during dives. Overall manoeuvrability was similar, although the XIV appeared to turn left more readily than it did to the right. The Mark XIV's greatest deficiency, however, was its short endurance. Even though internal fuel (110 gallons) was more than the Spitfire IX, its consumption was around 25% higher at similar engine settings so endurance was less. In terms of actual range however, the

two were fairly even as the XIV flew at a higher speed for any given engine setting. The AFDU report concluded that long-range tanks would be essential for operations; in particular the 90-gallon slipper tank would be required rather than the more normal 30 and 45-gallon tanks.

In number sequence (if not in chronology) the next Spitfire was the Mark XVIII which was the first variant to be specifically designed for the Griffon engine, rather than being a modification of an existing airframe. In appearance it was almost indistinguishable from the low-back XIVE. Most of the differences were internal, in particular its revised wing structure with solid instead of tubular spar booms. Internal fuel capacity was also raised to 175.5 gallons by the installation of two tanks mounted in the rear fuselage.

Fighter and reconnaissance

The fighter-reconnaissance FR.XVIII which was fitted with two vertical and one oblique F.24 cameras (or one vertical F.52) could carry only one rear-mounted fuel tank which reduced total capacity to 142.5 gallons. Both the normal fighter and FR versions featured type 'E' armament, teardrop hood with cut-back rear fuselage and a retractable tail wheel. The Spitfire XVIII entered service with 60 Squadron at Seletar, Singapore shortly after the end of the war and was also used by 11, 28, 32, and 208 Squadrons in the Middle and Far East.

A photo-reconnaissance version of the Griffon-engined Spitfire was quickly developed and resulted in the PR.XIX. It was essentially a Mark XIV, fitted with wings from the Mark XI, and the Griffon 65 powered the first 22 aircraft. Later machines had the Griffon 66 and were fitted with a pressure cabin controlled by a Marshall Mark XIV blower. As total internal fuel capacity had been increased to 256 gallons, allowing missions of 5-6 hours to be flown at heights of around 40,000 ft, a pressure cabin was something of an operational necessity and the improvement in the pilot's working environment was considered more important than a slight drop in performance due to the increase in all-up weight. No armament was carried and the camera installation consisted of two vertical F.52, two vertical F.8, or two vertical and one oblique F.24. Production of the

JF318 was one of six Spitfire VIIIs fitted with Griffon engines to act as prototypes for the Mark XIV. It was used for trials work at Boscombe Down but was damaged in a forced landing following an engine failure. A second engine failure at high altitude on 23 September 1944 resulted in the pilot baling out. The aircraft crashed and was burnt out at Amesbury cemetery. (*Philip Jarrett*)

PR.XIX ran to 224 and the variant remained in first-line service until April 1954.

The second major re-design of the Spitfire resulted in the Mark 21. DP851 (which began life as the second Spitfire XX prototype) was flown in December 1942 as an interim F.21, featuring stronger wings, curved windscreen, a broad-chord rudder on a standard fin and extended wingtips. Although the Spitfire had always been able to out-perform the Bf 109 and Fw 190 during sustained turns, it was not as good in terms of roll response, the Focke-Wulf (mainly due to its large ailerons) having the ability to initiate rolling manoeuvres that a Spitfire had difficulty following.

Improved roll response

Supermarine had been looking to improve this aspect of the Spitfire's performance for some time but it was clear that an increase in roll rate would only be possible if the wing could be stiffened to avoid the possibility of 'aileron-reversal'. This was caused by the wing twisting in the opposite direction to aileron deflection due to a lack of torsional rigidity. The main structural element of the Spitfire wing was the D-shaped torsion box formed by the single spar and heavy-duty leading edge skinning. On the Mark 21 this was augmented by a number of torque-boxes behind the spar that increased

stiffness by 47% and upped the theoretical aileron reversal speed from 580 mph to 825 mph.

Jeffrey Quill flew the first fully modified Spitfire 21 (PP139) on 24 July 1943. As well as having the final strengthened wing structure (DP851 had an interim version) it also featured increased span ailerons, which were attached by piano-type hinges. The ailerons were also fitted with inset balance tabs. The main undercarriage legs were revised, the oleos being extended by 4 in to allow sufficient ground clearance for a five-blade Rotol propeller of 11 ft diameter to be fitted. The legs were also placed further apart, increasing track from 5 ft 9 in to 6 ft 8 in. Fairing doors, operated hydraulically, covered the lower part of the wheel that had previously been exposed when the undercarriage was retracted. The underwing radiators of the F.21 reversed the layout as seen on the Mark XIV in that the oil cooler was positioned behind the main radiator under the starboard wing with the intercooler radiator ahead of the other main radiator under the port wing. Armament for the F.21 was standardised at four 20 mm Hispano cannon and the aircraft entered service with 91 Squadron at Manston in January 1945.

Flight testing of DP851 had shown that the Spitfire F.21 had major problems with regard to

RW396 of the Central Gunnery School shows standard Spitfire XVI features – clipped wings and a pointed, broad-chord rudder. It also has the whip aerial that was introduced on late mark Spitfires. RW396 joined the CGS on 2 April 1946 but following an engine failure it was damaged beyond repair during a forced landing at West Skipsea firing range on 6 January 1949. (*Philip Jarrett*)

directional and longitudinal stability. In his book *Spitfire, A Test Pilot's Story* (Crecy, 1998), Jeffrey Quill described the aircraft's handling in pitch and yaw as 'appalling' and pilots at the Central Fighter Establishment (CFE) recommended that the Spitfire F.21 be withdrawn from operations until instability in the yawing plane had been corrected. The handling problems were largely overcome by adjustments to the rudder and elevators – the removal of the balance function of the rudder trim tab and a reduction in the gearing to the elevator trim tab, together with slightly smaller horn balances. This was something of a temporary bodge, the only really effective solution being an increase in tailplane area, which was introduced on the Spitfire 22 and 24.

As the Mark 22/24 machines were so similar to the F.21 no prototype was built and the first Spitfire 22 off the line was PK312. It featured a teardrop canopy and cut-back rear fuselage but initially retained the original tail surfaces, the enlarged tail being fitted towards the end of 1945. The Spitfire 24 was virtually identical except that it had two 33-gallon fuel tanks in the rear fuselage and later aircraft were fitted with four short-barrel Hispano Mark V cannon. The Spitfire 23 was to have had an altered wing of revised section incorporating features of the laminar flow wing developed for the Spiteful. A Spitfire VIII (JG204) was fitted with the new wing but adverse handling characteristics at the stall led to this variant being abandoned.

Griffon Seafires

Following the success of the Merlin-engined Seafire Marks I/II/III in Fleet Air Arm service, the Air Ministry issued specification N.4/43 in 1943 to cover the first of the Griffon-powered Seafires, the Mark XV. The engine selected was the Griffon VI of 1,750 hp driving a 10 ft 5 in four-blade Rotol propeller. The fuselage was similar to the Seafire III, but with the engine installation of the Spitfire XII and a Mark VIII empennage with broad-chord rudder. Total internal fuel amounted to 100 gallons (including wing tanks) plus a further 60 gallons in external drop tanks. The wing folding mechanism was as used on previous Seafires. The first 50 (out of 450) featured the old A-frame arrester hook, subsequent aircraft being fitted with a sting-type hook attached to the rear fuselage stern post. To facilitate this the base of the rudder was cut away, the rudder area being slightly enlarged to compensate. From the 75th aircraft provision was made for use of RATOG (rocket-assisted take-off gear). Following trials with NS493, the last few Seafire XVs were produced with cut-back rear fuselages and teardrop canopies that were to be a standard feature of the later Seafire XVII. The Seafire XV entered service with 802 Squadron in May 1945 and was also flown by 803, 805 and 806 Squadrons.

NS493 became the prototype for the Seafire XVII and as well as having the cut-back rear

NH872 was the first Spitfire XVIII and was flown for the first time in June 1945. It was used exclusively for development work including trials with a 99-gallon drop tank. (*Philip Jarrett*)

Spitfire PR.XIX PS858 was used to test various sizes of slipper tanks including the 170-gallon tank as seen here. It subsequently flew with 541 Squadron from Benson. (*Philip Jarrett*)

fuselage and teardrop canopy, it featured a curved windscreen in front of the bullet-proof glazing, a 24-volt electrical system, rear-mounted fuel tank of 33 gallons capacity and long-stroke oleo legs. Like its predecessor, the Seafire XVII mounted two 20 mm Hispano cannon and four 0.303 in Browning machine-guns but could also accommodate eight 60-lb rocket projectiles. A fighter-reconnaissance version, the FR.XVII, was produced with two F.24 cameras (one vertical and one oblique) in

the rear fuselage in place of the aft fuel tank. The Seafire XVII entered service with 883 Squadron in September 1945 and was used by RNVR and training squadrons until November 1954.

The promise shown by the Spitfire F.21 naturally prompted the Admiralty to enquire about a navalised version and specification N.7/44 was issued resulting in the Seafire F.45. The prototype (TM379) was a converted Spitfire F.21 with a sting-type hook, modified

This view of Spitfire F.24 PK713 emphasizes the principle features of the later Griffon-Spitfires – five-blade propeller, four Hispano cannon, deep section radiators and higher 'sit' due to extended oleos. PK713 had an undistinguished career, the only highlight being an emergency landing on its delivery flight to 33 MU when the port undercarriage leg refused to retract. (*Philip Jarrett*)

undercarriage and a tail wheel guard to prevent fouling by arrester wires on landing. The F.45 was the first Seafire to feature a Griffon 61 with a five-blade propeller. As torque reaction on take off was strong, TM379 (together with LA442 and LA444) was tested with a Griffon 85 driving a six-blade contra-rotating propeller leading to the Seafire F.46/47. Armament comprised four 20 mm cannon, but no wing folding was provided. Only 50 F.45s were built and all served at shore-based establishments.

The ultimate Seafires were the F.46 and F.47. The F.46 was based on the Spitfire F.22, having the teardrop hood and cut-back rear fuselage. Although early aircraft featured the original tail and five-blade prop, later machines had the enlarged tail surfaces of the Spitfire F.24 and contra-rotating propellers. Very much an interim version pending the arrival of the F.47, the F.46 did not feature wing folding and was used by just two squadrons, 781 at Lee-on-Solent and 1832 (RNVR) at Culham. A few aircraft had an F.24 oblique camera installed, these being designated FR.46.

The Seafire F.47 entered service with 804 Squadron in February 1948, the principal difference from the F.46 being the inclusion of

wing folding. Whereas the system used on previous Seafires had employed a double hinge, the F.47 employed a single hinge just outboard of the wheel wells. At first wing folding was conducted manually, together with the use of a jury strut to secure the wings when folded, but later aircraft had a hydraulic wing-folding mechanism. Externally the F.47 could be recognised by the extended air intake duct under the nose. With a top speed of 452 mph, the F.47 was the fastest Seafire and it also had the longest range (around 1,000 miles) due to its ability to carry a 90-gallon drop tank under the fuselage and two 23-gallon blister tanks under the wings. Most were converted for the fighter-reconnaissance role with a camera installation (one vertical and one oblique) becoming FR.47s.

The Mark 47 was the only Griffon-engined Seafire to see operational service. No. 800 Squadron (embarked on HMS *Triumph*) carried out rocket attacks on bandit hideouts in Malaya from October 1949 to February 1950. Later the unit flew 245 offensive patrols and 115 ground attack operations during the Korean War. The Seafire 47 remained in first-line service until replaced by the Supermarine Attacker in 1951.

Seafire XV SW847 is fitted with a sting-type arrester hook and a 50-gallon torpedo overload tank. Lettering on the engine cowling under the exhaust stack reads 'Coffman Starter'. (*Philip Jarrett*)

The ultimate Seafire was the FR.47 with Griffon 85 and contra-rotating propellers. VP447 was used by 800 Squadron aboard HMS *Triumph* and saw anti-bandit action in 1949 in Malaya. (*Philip Jarrett*)

Spiteful and Seafang

The Spiteful, and its naval equivalent the Seafang, were the last developments of the Spitfire line and both featured the same laminar-flow wing. The familiar elliptical wing of the Spitfire was replaced by an entirely new profile with straight leading and trailing edges. Area was reduced to 210 sq.ft (from 248.5 sq.ft of the Spitfire F.21) and the wing was of two-spar construction. Unlike more conventional aerofoils, the laminar-flow wing had a completely different profile in section and was at its thickest at 42% chord which was considerably further aft than on most conventional wings. The main aim was to delay the sharp increase in drag due to compressibility at high speeds by maintaining a smooth (or laminar flow) over a greater portion of the wing. It was hoped that the aircraft could thus fly at higher speeds before suffering compressibility effects. Another design aim with the new wing was a further increase in rate of roll.

Produced to Specification F.1/43, the first Spiteful was a rebuild of Spitfire XIV NN660 and was flown for the first time by Jeffrey Quill

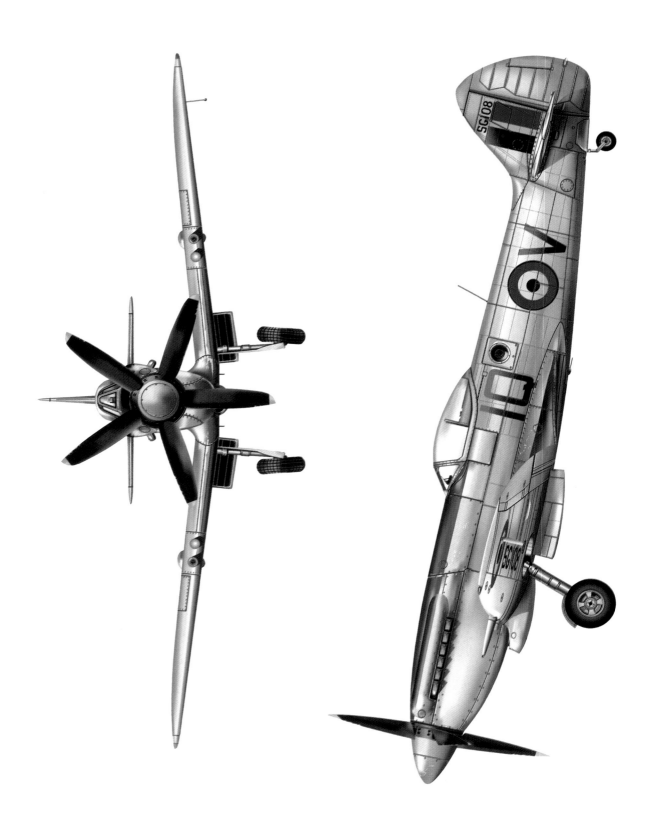

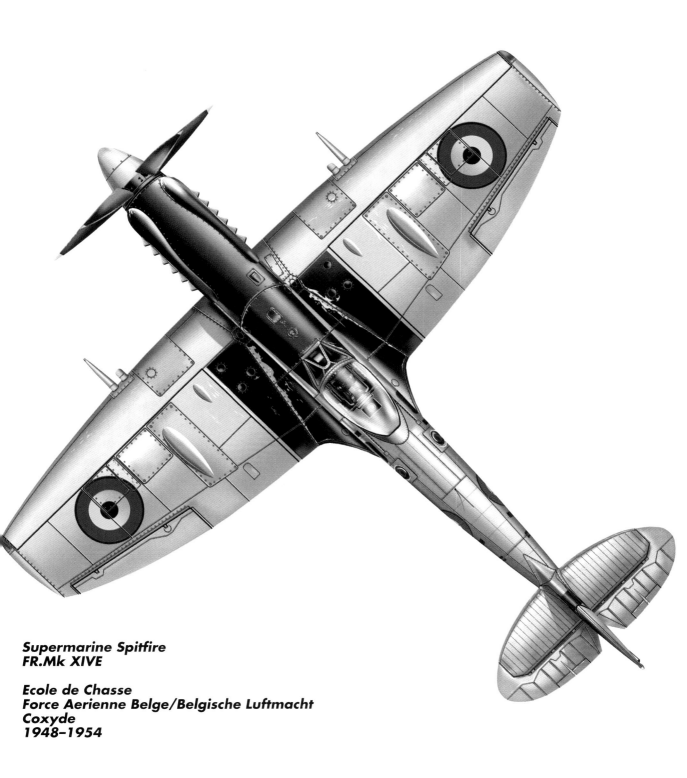

**Supermarine Spitfire
FR.Mk XIVE**

**Ecole de Chasse
Force Aerienne Belge/Belgische Luftmacht
Coxyde
1948–1954**

RB515 was the first production Spiteful and was flown for the first time on 2 April 1945. On 28 September 1945 the constant speed unit failed and its engine exploded after overspeeding. Despite extensive damage, Lieutenant Patrick Shea-Simmonds carried out a successful forced landing at Farnborough. (*Philip Jarrett*)

on 30 June 1944. Its flight characteristics were not good however. It tended to drop a wing at the stall, was prone to flick during a high-speed stall and suffered from aileron snatch. This was in marked contrast to the Spitfire, the wing of which had been designed with washout, whereby the outer portion of the wing had a reduced angle of attack compared to that at the root. This meant that at high angles of attack the wing tended to stall from the root outwards allowing some degree of lateral control. On the laminar-flow wing of the Spiteful there was no washout and the stall appeared to start at the tip and work its way in, the exact opposite of that desired. This characteristic may have been the cause of a crash on 13 September 1944 that claimed the life of Supermarine test pilot Frank Furlong in NN660. The second machine (NN664) flew on 8 January 1945 and was followed by the first production Spiteful (RB515) in April.

Tests with the new wing showed that its supposed advantages were not as great as had been envisaged as it only worked to its theoretical best when kept in pristine condition. Although drag rise due to compressibility was delayed, the slightest debris adhering to the wing surface was likely to produce turbulent flow within the boundary layer, reducing performance significantly.

In the event only 17 Spitefuls were built, initial aircraft featured a Spitfire F.21 tail but later machines had the larger tail surfaces of the Spitfire F.22/24. The Spiteful F.14 was powered by a Griffon 69 with a five-blade Rotol propeller, the F.15 having a Griffon 89/90 and six-blade contra-rotating propeller. The single F.16 had a three-speed, two-stage supercharged Griffon 101.

Overtaken by jets

Although Supermarine had proposed a laminar-flow wing Seafire in October 1943 it was not until 1945 that any official interest was shown and this led to the conversion of Spiteful F.14 RB520 as an interim prototype Seafang with sting-type hook. Nine pre-production Seafang Mark 31s followed this, with five-blade propeller and non-folding wings. The first full prototype was FR.32 VB895 powered by a Griffon 89 with contra-rotating propeller. It also had wing folding and was fitted with one vertical and one oblique camera for its intended fighter-reconnaissance role.

Successful deck landing trials were carried out aboard HMS *Illustrious* in May 1947, but the greater promise shown by the more modern Attacker led the Admiralty to abandon development of the Seafang in favour of its jet-powered stablemate.

2. Operational History

The Spitfire IX entered service with 64 Squadron at Hornchurch in June 1942 and slowly began to supplant the Spitfire V as the RAF's premier day fighter. Its role was identical to that of its predecessor and the familiar sequence of bomber escorts (*Circus* and *Ramrod* operations) together with fighter sweeps (*Rodeos*) were set to continue. A typical operation was that flown by 403 Squadron (part of the Kenley Wing) on 13 March 1943, the escort of 70 B-17 Fortresses of the USAAF Eighth Air Force on a bombing mission to Amiens. The story of the raid is told here by the 403 Squadron diarist:

Ramrod 43

"S/L L.S. Ford led the squadron which, along with 402, acted as high cover to 70 Fortresses bombing Amiens/Longeau marshalling yards. The English coast was crossed at Dungeness at 1430 hrs at 26,000 ft. The bombers were two minutes late, but the Wing had formed up over them by the time Dieppe was reached at the same height. The bombers were strung out over 10-15 miles in several formations so 402 flew in loose fours over and ahead of the leading bombers, while 403 positioned themselves, also in loose fours, on either side and in front of the second half of the formation, 10 miles behind 402.

"The formation proceeded south-south-east after crossing the French coast, passing east of Rouen to Les Andelys where they began a wide turn to port. Here it was understood that the bombers were recalled and some 20 were reported as turning back, but the remainder continued by Beauvais to Amiens. About 12 bombers were seen to bomb Beauvais/Tille aerodrome, hits being seen on the runways. The Kenley Wing was warned by the Controller that time was getting short (fuel supply).

"The bombers escorted by the squadron followed the railway to Poix, bombing railway stations en route and, in particular, a road/rail junction. The whole formation followed the Somme valley out, bombing Abbeville/Drucat aerodrome where direct hits were seen. About 40/50 bombers were seen out in the Somme estuary area and there the Wing lost contact with them, being involved in withdrawal cover actions. At no time were any bombers seen to be in trouble.

Fw 190 shootdown

"Five Fw 190s came up from Rouen direction at 25,000 ft but did not attack and from then on the squadron warded off attacks by 190s in pairs and threes. S/L Ford attacked one of the Fws in one of these groups with several persistent bursts of cannon including SAPI (semi-armour piercing/incendiary) and machine gun closing from 250 to 50 yards. He saw strikes all over, the whole of the cockpit was blown off and a gaping hole appeared behind the cockpit. Bits kept flying off both sides and then there was a big orange explosion in each wing as though the drums had been hit. Everything seemed to crumple up. Half of the starboard wing fell away, the aircraft turned over sideways and dropped straight down, hardly recognizable.

"About this time, Blue section, in the starboard position, was attacked by five Fw 190s from behind. They attempted to engage but the 190s dove away. F/L Magwood saw Sgt Dunbar, who had been alternately lagging and catching up, go down in flames in the vicinity of Grandvilliers. Fw 190s kept badgering the squadron in feints towards the bombers, but never closing in, all the way to the French coast which was crossed at the Somme estuary at 15,000 ft at about 1530 hrs. Near the French

A Spitfire IX carries out fighter affiliation duties over a solid overcast. It is fitted with the streamlined rear view mirror that was introduced in the mid-war period. (*Philip Jarrett*)

coast P/O Cumming reported engine failure and asked for an emergency homing. He evidently decided he could not make it, so turned inland and gave a Mayday fixed some miles east of Berck. This was the last seen or heard of him.

"Owing to shortage of petrol, most of 403 were sent home by S/L Ford except P/O Lane (Red 4). S/L Ford had momentary engine trouble at this time and five Fw 190s dived out of the sun from behind and to port. S/L Ford broke port and P/O Lane broke starboard as the e/a (enemy aircraft) started firing. A considerable dogfight ensued which required an all out effort by both to avoid being shot down. P/O Lane sustained hits on his hood and behind and below his cockpit. The e/a finally gave up and dived away. S/L Ford and P/O Lane both returned to base, crossing the English coast at Hastings."

403 Squadron's composition during this operation was as follows:

Blue section
F/L C.M. Magwood – BS383
Sgt H.E. Morrow – BS110
P/O C.G. Cumming
Sgt R. Dunbar – BS196

Red section
S/L L.S. Ford – BS474
P/O W.J. Cameron – BS549
F/O H.D. MacDonald – BR138
P/O W.T. Lane – BS183

Yellow section
F/L H.C. Godefroy – EN130
Sgt W. McGarrigle – BS534
F/O R. Wozniak – EN129
F/O G.D. Aitken – BR630

First flown on 16 November 1942, Spitfire IX EN133 is seen coded FY-B with 611 Squadron at Biggin Hill. It was lost, together with its pilot Squadron Leader J.H. Slater, during *Rodeo* 188 on 14 March 1943. In the same action with Fw 190s of JG 26, the Biggin Hill Wing Leader, Wing Commander Dickie Milne, was shot down in BS240 to become a PoW. (*Philip Jarrett*)

The Fw 190 shot down by Squadron Leader Les Ford was an A-4 (*Werke* Nr 5615 – White 12) flown by *Oberfeldwebel* Hermann Meyer of 4./JG 26 who was killed. Pilot Officer Cumming and Sergeant Dunbar of 403 Squadron were both killed and Pilot Officer D.J. Crimmon of 402 Squadron was shot down to become a PoW. These were claimed by *Hauptmann* Wilhelm-Ferdinand 'Wutz' Galland, leader of II./JG 26, *Leutnant* Waldemar 'Waldi' Radener of the 4th *Staffel* and *Leutnant* Wiegmann of the 6th *Staffel*.

403 Squadron lost two further aircraft on return owing to fuel shortage, Flying Officer George Aitken force-landing at a disused airfield near Dungeness, Sergeant Morrow coming down at Winchelsea, near Rye. Morrow's aircraft was damaged Cat B, after its wings and tail were ripped off passing over a ditch, a road, through a fence and several small trees. Although it was his first sweep he appeared to be completely unflustered by the experience as he was seen to get out of his machine and saunter off with his hands in his pockets. As five other aircraft of 403 Squadron had to land at the earliest opportunity to refuel, a directive was soon issued reminding all pilots of the correct engine handling techniques for best endurance (see Chapter 4).

Flying bombs

By the following year RAF fighter pilots had a new menace to face, the V-1 flying-bomb. The first V-1 to fall on English soil did so on 13 June 1944 at Swanscombe near Gravesend, the first of nearly 9,000 to be launched from sites in northern France. The most successful Spitfire unit against the V-1 (code-name *Diver*) was 91 Squadron based at West Malling (later Deanland) flying Spitfire XIVs. By the end of the day 91 Squadron had flown 53 anti-*Diver* sorties of which 10 had been successful. All the V-1s were judged to have been travelling around 360-400 mph at a height of approximately 1,500 ft. By early September the Allied armies had overrun most of the launch sites in occupied Europe and the V-1 offensive, with the exception of air-launched bombs, was

No. 91 Squadron, RAF
Diver report No.1 for the 24 hours ending at sunset 18 June 1944

Time	Pilot/Aircraft	Place of Combat	Remarks
1200	Capt J-M. Maridor RB161	5 miles east of base	Attack was made diving from 10,000 ft. *Diver* falling in a field and exploding.
1420	S/L N.A. Kynaston RB185	Outskirts of SE London	Dived from 10,000 ft to attack *Diver*, falling in allotments where it exploded.
1510	S/L P.M. Bond RB161	East of Croydon	Chased from base and attacked east of Croydon where it was shot down, *Diver* falling in a row of houses where it exploded.
2015	F/L A. Smith F/O R.A. McPhie RB182	West of base	Interception made west of base; after attacks *Diver* fell in woods and exploded.
2030	F/L A. Smith F/O R.A. McPhie RB182 S/L P.M. Bond RB161 F/L R.S. Nash RB169	River Thames, E of London	*Diver* overtaken between Gravesend and London where attacked. Pieces seen to fall off starboard wing, *Diver* seen spinning in, between two ships in river.
2210	F/O R.A. McPhie RB182	Croydon	*Diver* chased from Tunbridge to Croydon where attack was made. Jet mechanism fell off and *Diver* fell in woods at Epsom.
2320	S/L N.A. Kynaston RB185	Dungeness	Attack was made at *Diver* coned by searchlights from 5,000 to 1,500 ft at range of 250 yds when, after a short burst, it exploded in air over Dungeness.
2315	F/L R.S. Nash RB169	Beachy Head	Visual made of *Diver* as it crossed coast, attacked and exploded in mid air.
2330	F/L R.S. Nash RB169 + 3 Tempests	Beachy Head	*Diver* attacked by four aircraft as it crossed coast. Strikes seen on it, *Diver* orbited and finally shot down 10 miles north west of Beachy Head.

largely over. By that time 91 Squadron had 184 claims against V-1s, although the hazards of such operations was highlighted on 8 August when *Capitaine* Jean-Marie Maridor was killed when the V-1 he was attacking exploded at close range.

Soon after the invasion of northern Europe the Spitfires of 2nd Tactical Air Force began to encounter a different foe, the Messerschmitt Me 262 jet fighter. The 262 was also used in the bomber role, and was well known to 2 TAF units due to frequent bombing attacks on their home airfields. On 5 October 1944, however, the tables were turned and an Me 262 fell to the Spitfire IXBs of 401 (RCAF) Squadron, the first 262 to be shot down by the Allies. 401 Squadron, led by Squadron Leader Rod Smith from Regina in Saskatchewan, was carrying out a patrol at 14,000 ft in the Nijmegen area when a 262 was seen head-on around 500 ft below.

Spitfire XIV RB146 was used for trials work including evaluating spin recovery at various C.G. loadings for which it was fitted with a tail parachute. It is seen here with a guard for the rudder horn balance to prevent possible fouling. Later it was used to test the piano type aileron hinge of the Spitfire F.21 and was fitted with a Griffon with +25lb/sq.in boost. (*Philip Jarrett*)

Spitfire XIV RM701 flew with 41 and 350 Squadrons before joining the Belgian Air Force in May 1947 as SG-6. (*Philip Jarrett*)

43 Squadron Spitfire LF.IXs at Zeltweg in Austria in September 1945. A little of the pre-war spirit has returned as the unit's black and white check markings can just be seen on the fin of the nearest machine (RK855). 43 Squadron continued to fly Spitfires until it was disbanded in May 1947. *(Philip Jarrett)*

It went into a climbing turn to port with all 12 Spitfires giving chase, then dived down, twisting and turning, and half rolling at high speed. Flight Lieutenant H.J. 'Snooks' Everard (Red 3) fired at the 262 in the dive and again as it levelled out at around 5,000 ft producing a streamer of white smoke. He was followed in turn by his wingman, Flying Officer John MacKay and then by Flight Lieutenant R.M. Davenport (Yellow 1) and Flying Officer A.L. Sinclair (Blue 1), all securing strikes on the engines and fuselage.

Squadron Leader Smith then moved into the attack and fired two 3-second bursts at around 2-300 yards range causing a small fire in the starboard nacelle and a larger one in the port nacelle. Smith broke away to starboard and the 262 turned behind as though intending to ram him, even though it was now well alight. In the event it passed close behind Smith's Spitfire

and crashed in fields about two miles south west of Nijmegen. The Me 262 was probably that flown by *Hauptmann* Hans-Christophe Buttmann of I./KG(J)51.

Due to the urgent need for air support of Allied forces on the ground, the Spitfire's main role in the last months of the war was armed reconnaissance, the seeking out of German armour, motorised transport (MT) and troops for attack. Squadron Leader Art Sager of 416 Squadron (Spitfire IX) describes a typical sortie in his autobiography *Line Shoot – Diary of a Fighter Pilot* (Vanwell Publishing, 2002):

"By the first of September the American army was in Sedan, the British in Amiens and the Canadians east of Dieppe. German forces were reported moving in the open along the whole front and the Wing was ordered to attack those near St Pol, west of Arras. It was mid-afternoon

Spitfire XIV MV259 spent most of its career in Germany with the British Air Forces of Occupation and was flown by 414, 430, 416 and 2 Squadrons before being struck off charge (SOC) in 1949. (*Philip Jarrett*)

and time for two sorties only, 421 going first and 416 an hour later. The C.O. [S/L John McElroy] being still in Paris I was again leading the squadron. After taking off I called S/L Prest, C.O. of 421, now on his return leg. 'Weather's good, but there's a hell of a lot of flak,' he reported.

Avoiding Flak

"We saw the flak as we approached St Pol at 7,000 ft, the sky full of ugly blotches ahead and below us. I dropped the extra fuel tank and signalled the others to do the same. To confuse the German gunners we'd agreed to split up in singles and choose our own targets but before picking mine I ordered the squadron to reform at the same altitude south of the town when I called in about twenty minutes. It was hazy but you could tell there was traffic and armour below as gunfire was coming from all directions.

"Deciding to search a road and railway line north west of St Pol, I flew beyond the flak, turned back, dived and screamed on the deck into a valley leading into the town. Seeing movement ahead, I pulled up to 200 ft, then put the nose down and sprayed everything on the road – mobile guns, lorries, soldiers diving for cover. As I passed a gun opened up on the left

from what looked like a haystack beside a string of railway cars. Twisting and skidding, I climbed back to 7,000 ft where, irrationally angry at the gun in the haystack, I decided to make a second pass and try to get it. This time I went down more slowly, hit the mobile guns and lorries a second time and, turning fast, hammered the haystack with everything. The gun was firing but it stopped abruptly.

"Above at the rendezvous point some of the boys were milling about looking for new targets. By their joking natter on R/T I knew that all had carried out attacks; three were diving onto MT at a crossroads, some of which was already burning. Spotting horse-drawn guns on a road going towards Arras, I skidded down, steep-turned into them and let go with the rest of my ammunition. It was now eight-fifteen and time to pack it up. I called the boys to reform, was relieved to see that no one had been clobbered and we returned to base just before dark."

Having been highly successful in the campaign against the V-1 flying bomb, Spitfire XIVs began to appear in ever increasing numbers with 2 TAF from September 1944 and this variant eventually formed the equipment of 20 squadrons based on the Continent. Flight

Showing its invasion stripes, Spitfire PR.XI PL775 of 541 Squadron carries its individual code letter 'A' just below the serial number. Like most PR variants it has a curved windscreen without bullet-proof glazing. (*Philip Jarrett*)

Lieutenant (later Group Captain) Derek Rake AFC flew with 41 Squadron in the last months of the war:

"My Spitfire XIV operational flying was largely armed recce and our brief was, day after day, to hit anything or person that moved on the German side of the bomb line as the armoured divisions broke out across the North German plain. Sometimes you would find yourself diving to attack our own tanks until you saw the colours of the day displayed. Then it would be a call to Kenway on the control frequency warning them to update the bomb line.

"As part of 125 Wing 2nd TAF, we were given the task of top cover at around 30,000 ft on the day of the crossing of the Rhine (24 March 1945). At briefing we were told that Me 262s would probably try to dive bomb from

high level. When we asked how we would be able to cope with these much faster aircraft the A.O.C. 83 Group, AVM Harry Broadhurst, said that it was essential to stop them interfering with the crossing and that we should attack them head-on, if necessary flying into them. I remember that we only saw one or two 262s all day and by late afternoon I was told to attack some tanks on the bridgehead area near Emmerich at low level. I was hit in the port wing by flak but managed to get back to base (Volkel) landing without flaps and brakes.

"Some of our Spit XIVs had gyro gunsights. I was flying one of these near Delmenhorst on 12 April 1945 when we spotted an Arado 234 which the Luftwaffe used for reconnaissance. I managed to get all the diamonds on the gunsight nicely enclosing his aircraft during a quarter attack and, somewhat to my surprise,

Spitfire PR.XIX PM546 first flew from Benson in July 1945 but was then dispatched to India and was ultimately scrapped in 1947. (*Philip Jarrett*)

he went on fire. Had he seen me first, there is little doubt he could have got away. I destroyed a Ju 188 a few days before the end of the war in Europe and this was the 200th victim of 41 Squadron. I hit him in one engine and he dived to ground level and flew so low that I could not get a proper sighting until he pulled up over an obstacle. It was an exciting chase largely because of the very low flying involved."

Photo Spitfires

From the very beginning it was clear that the Spitfire would make an excellent photo-reconnaissance aircraft and its capabilities were boosted still further with the arrival of the PR.X/XI and the later Griffon-engined PR.XIX. Missions were carried out on a daily basis (weather permitting) to provide up-to-date information on military installations and to assess the amount of damage caused by USAAF Eighth Air Force and RAF Bomber Command raids. Even though the unarmed PR Spitfires were capable of operating close to 40,000 ft, they were not immune from fighter attack and also had to contend with flak, adverse weather and problems caused by a shortage of fuel.

In early 1944 542 Squadron was based at Benson and flying the Spitfire PR.XI. One of its pilots, Flying Officer G.W. Puttick, flew a deep penetration mission on 25 February 1944 to photograph targets attacked by B-17 and B-24 bombers on the final day of the United States Eighth Air Force's 'Big Week'. His report records an eventful trip:

"Another glorious day. I refuelled at Bradwell then took off at 1339 hrs for Stuttgart. I picked up each little waypoint on track all the way to the target where Stuttgart was burning. Flak started bursting all around as I made three runs then set course for Nuremberg. I saw a huge fire burning to my right so immediately weaved towards it. I made three more runs over it then set course for home and mother. On my way back to Frankfurt I passed another burning town which proved to be Nuremberg, making the previous target Regensberg. Made two runs over Nuremberg then I began to realise how short of fuel I was so I cut my revs and descended to 32,000 ft from 37,000 ft. My fuel got lower and lower. I hardly seemed to move over the ground and my hand moved frequently to the gauge button.

"At 10 gallons I called control and kept on till the engine cut, then glided at 130 mph. Broke cloud at 2,500 ft and was told the airfield was behind me. I turned and headed towards it but realised I couldn't make it, so aimed for a field. I was going down fast, then suddenly I had no more height and an orchard rushed up towards me. I pulled back hard on the stick and ditched in the tree tops. I woke up and saw flames in front of me. Startled into rapid

Five (count the tails!) Spitfire VIIIs of the Royal Australian Air Force. These early machines have had the red of the RAF fuselage roundel painted white leaving an oversized centre. Serial numbers from front to back are A58-315, A58-395, A58-405 and A58-409. (*Philip Jarrett*)

activity, I whipped off my straps and dived over the side. Fortunately the fire was soon put out by some villagers. The port wing and engine had departed the fuselage.

"An Army type who appeared helped me with my magazines and took me to Manston where the doc nabbed me and whisked me off to sick quarters. Two stitches in the back of my head, a grazed face and a few bruises were my only hurts, thank God. A night in hospital and the next day I was ready to go back to base. At 6.20 pm I started back with my cameras but we lost our way in the London blackout and fog and arrived at Benson at 2.0 am, cold and tired. We pinched the guard's cocoa that they had just made to warm ourselves a bit!"

Puttick's Spitfire (PA855) was a Cat E write off but he fared better than his comrade Flight Sergeant H.F. Buckingham (BS502) who failed to return from a sortie to photograph the coastline of northern France as part of the

preparations for the forthcoming invasion. 542 Squadron carried out six other sorties on 25 February, three over Germany, with three more over France, including a reconnaissance of *Noball* targets (V-1) around Calais, Dieppe and Cherbourg.

Far East Spitfires

Although most marks of Spitfire saw widespread service in northern Europe, the Spitfire VIII was used almost exclusively in the Mediterranean and Far East theatres. The first examples of the mark began to replace Spitfire VCs of Australian-based squadrons in April 1944. The defence of Darwin was the responsibility of 54 Squadron (together with the newly arrived 548 and 549 Squadrons) which allowed 452 Squadron to be deployed as part of the First Tactical Air Force at Morotai.

Flying Officer J.A. Pretty was quickly off the mark at Morotai, by shooting down a Japanese raider on 24 December 194. By the middle of

Spitfire FR.XVIII SM843 clearly shows the port for the fuselage mounted oblique camera. It survived until December 1953 when it was sold for scrap. (*Philip Jarrett*)

February 452 Squadron had been joined by 457 and 79 Squadrons. Although the main area of operations in the Pacific theatre was now a long way off, some Japanese remained in the region, and the Spitfires' main task was to escort Beaufighters of 30 and 31 Squadrons in attacks against these forces.

By April 1945, 452 Squadron had moved to Tarakan Island, Borneo to cover the P-40 Kittyhawks of No.78 Wing (75, 78 and 80 Squadrons) while 457 Squadron was operating over Labuan with the Kittyhawks of No.81 Wing (76, 77 and 82 Squadrons). Two Spitfires of 457 Squadron shot down a Mitsubishi Ki-46 Dinah on 20 June. After these operations a return was made to Morotai, 452 Squadron losing three Spitfires during ground attack sorties during July. Although a Japanese bomber attacking Balikpapan was shot down on the night of 24/25 July, activity for the final weeks of the war consisted of attacking the few Japanese troops that remained prior to the ending of hostilities on 15 August 1945.

Spitfire VIIIs also saw action in Burma, all squadrons in the area having converted from VCs by the time of the Imphal crisis which began in March 1944 and lasted for 80 days. A Japanese offensive launched on 8 March cut communications with Imphal and all supplies to the beleaguered troops had to be airlifted in. Air defence was provided by 81, 136, 607 and 615 Squadrons, these units rotating through Imphal to protect C-47 Dakotas and C-46 Commandos carrying out air drops. These operations were extremely successful and only three transport aircraft were shot down. During the period of the siege 27 Nakajima Ki-43 Oscar fighters and 3 Dinahs were shot down for the loss of 14 Spitfires to enemy action. Although the Japanese Oscars were highly manoeuvrable, they were generally out-performed by the Spitfire VIII and RAF pilots were able to utilise dive and zoom tactics similar to those perfected by the Luftwaffe over northern Europe.

Drive on Rangoon

After the defeat of the Japanese at Imphal the 14th Army launched its own offensive which ultimately led to the capture of Mandalay in March 1945 and Rangoon two months later. With local air power reinforced by the arrival of 17 and 273 Squadrons, and 1, 2, 3 and 8

Squadrons of the Indian Air Force (all equipped with the Spitfire VIII), Japanese ground forces were under constant pressure and all Spitfire squadrons were heavily engaged at the front line and in attacking pockets of resistance with 500-lb bombs. With 67, 152 and 155 Squadrons also in-theatre, these attacks wiped out large numbers of enemy soldiers, a typical example being that at the village of Pa-en on 1 July 1945 when 273 and 607 Squadrons killed 500 Japanese troops. The last sorties of the campaign were carried out against targets on the Sittang River in typical weather conditions, a cloudbase of around 200 ft and driving rain.

After the war Spitfires were involved in action at various locations throughout the world. The British had the difficult task of policing Palestine until the creation of the state of Israel in May 1948 and part of its air power in the region consisted of the Spitfire FR.XVIIIs of 32 and 208 Squadrons based at Ramat David. On 22 May, shortly before the units were due to re-locate to Nicosia in Cyprus, a Spitfire appeared in the circuit at 0600 hrs and dropped two bombs on parked aircraft before flying off, having also strafed the apron.

Two of 32 Squadron's FR.XVIIIs were set on fire and all but two of the remaining aircraft were holed by shrapnel or bullets. Four of 208 Squadron's Spitfires were scrambled, but no contact was made. On their return it was decided to maintain a standing patrol of two aircraft in case of further attack.

Spitfire versus Spitfire

Two hours later three more Spitfires appeared and immediately turned in towards the airfield, dropping six bombs, one of which fell beside a hangar killing two airmen and injuring several others. A strafing attack was also carried out hitting a Dakota that had just landed to collect stores, killing two of its crew.

The Spitfires were identified as Mark IXs of the Egyptian Air Force and one was brought down by machine-gun fire from an RAF Regiment gunner. Both of the other Spitfires were shot down by 208 Squadron's patrol, Flying Officer Geoffrey Cooper claiming one, the other being shared between Cooper and his No.2, Flying Officer Bowie.

Just after 0900 hrs two more Spitfires were seen and three bombs dropped, one destroying a Dakota that had been loaded with the personal kit belonging to 32 Squadron's ground crew. Both of the Egyptian Spitfires were engaged and shot down by Flying Officer T. McElhaw of 208 Squadron. Standing patrols were maintained for the rest of the day but there were no further attacks. In the early afternoon six replacement aircraft were flown in from Nicosia as the bombing had left 32 Squadron with just two serviceable Spitfires and 208 Squadron with four. The Egyptian authorities later blamed the attacks on a navigational error *and* weather – which at the time was 0/10 cloud and visibility 50 miles. The move to Nicosia was completed two days later.

Dogfights with the Israelis

Seven months later 208 Squadron was based at Fayid in the Suez Canal Zone and was again embroiled in a dogfight with Spitfires, this time of the Israeli Air Force. By early 1949 the Arab-Israeli War of Independence was reaching its climax and on 7 January a section of four Spitfire FR.XVIIIs of 208 Squadron, flown by Flying Officers Cooper and McElhaw with P/Os Sayer and Close as wingmen, took off to reconnoitre the front line. At the same time two Israeli Spitfire XVIs of 101 Squadron flown by John McElroy from Ontario, Canada, and Slick Goodlin, an American, took off from Qastina. McElroy was a 10-kill ace having flown with 249 Squadron in Malta and as C.O. of 416 Squadron. Goodlin had also flown with the RCAF before becoming a test pilot with the Bell Aircraft Company. But for his demand for a bonus, his name would have been written in the history books as the first man to break the sound barrier instead of that of Chuck Yeager.

By an unfortunate twist of fate, the four 208 Squadron Spitfire FR.XVIIIs arrived over the front shortly after a strike by Egyptian Spitfires and were immediately attacked by McElroy and Goodlin who, not surprisingly, thought that the loitering aircraft were responsible for the devastation on the ground. All four of 208 Squadron's aircraft were destroyed, one falling to ground fire, with two shot down by McElroy and one by Goodlin. Of the RAF pilots, Cooper baled out and made it back to base on the back of a camel, McElhaw and Close baled out to

Spitfire IX of 32 Squadron over Palestine in the immediate post war period. 32 Squadron received Spitfire XVIIIs in June 1947 and used these until May 1949 when it converted to Vampire F.3s. (*via Author*)

Israel obtained 59 Spitfire IXs from Czechoslovakia and many were used during the War of Independence. They were gradually replaced by P-51D Mustangs from January 1953 but some remained in service until February 1956. Thirty Spitfires were passed on to the Burmese Air Force in early 1955. (*Philip Jarrett*)

Spitfire F.24 PK682 was first flown by Supermarine test pilot Les Colquhoun on 19 February 1946 and subsequently served with 80 Squadron at Kai Tak, Hong Kong as seen here. It was SOC on 28 August 1951. (*Philip Jarrett*)

become PoWs, but Sayer was killed when his aircraft dived vertically into the desert. The aircraft lost by 208 Squadron were TP340, TP387, TP456 and TZ228.

Spitfire against Tempest

Later in the day more Spitfires of 208 Squadron (together with Tempests of 6 and 213 Squadrons) patrolled the same area in an attempt to find out what had happened to the earlier flight. This only led to further loss however, a Tempest of 213 Squadron being shot down by Ezer Weizmann, later to be commander of the Israeli Air Force. With both sides now on high alert a major escalation was averted only by frantic diplomatic activity, locally based RAF units being told in no uncertain terms that retaliatory action was out of the question.

The final operational uses of the Spitfire in a combat role took place in the Far East during the initial stages of Operation *Firedog* in Malaya, and in Hong Kong in response to local communist-inspired uprisings. Nos. 28 and 60 Squadrons based at Sembawang in Malaya flew Spitfire FR.XVIIIs, carrying out cannon and rocket attacks on Communist Terrorist (CT) camps in jungle hideouts, the reconnaissance role being undertaken by Mosquito PR.34s and Spitfire PR.XIXs of 81 Squadron at Seletar.

28 Squadron moved to Hong Kong in May 1949 and the final Spitfire ground attack sorties were carried out on 1 January 1951, 60 Squadron then re-equipping with Vampire FB.5s. No. 81 Squadron continued to operate the Spitfire PR.XIX until 1954, the last sortie being flown by the unit's C.O., Squadron Leader W.P. Swaby in PS888 on 1 April.

In Hong Kong, 80 Squadron (Spitfire F.24)

Spitfire PR.XIX 31001 in Royal Swedish Air Force service. This is former PS935 which was delivered on 7 October 1948 carrying the class-B registration G.15-12. In Swedish service the PR.XIX was designated S.31 and was flown by F.11 at Nykoping for reconnaissance flights over the Baltic. (*Philip Jarrett*)

In 1951 the Burmese Air Force acquired 20 de-navalised Seafire XVs including UB403, the former SR642. Delivery was carried out using the class-B registration G.15-214. (*Philip Jarrett*)

In addition to purchasing 30 refurbished Spitfire FR.XIVs in 1950-51, the Royal Thai Air Force also bought four PR.XIXs in 1954 including PS888. This aircraft flew the last operational sortie by an RAF Spitfire on 1 April 1954 with 81 Squadron in Malaya. It is seen here in a poor state, the paint finish has weathered appreciably and it has a flat tyre. (*Philip Jarrett*)

arrived at Kai Tak in July 1949 to join 28 Squadron (FR.XVIII). Duties included ground attack, day interception at all levels and anti-piracy patrols. With the outbreak of civil war in China in 1949 increased tension in the area led to a number of interceptions being made, mainly civil aircraft that were 'lost'.

28 Squadron continued to fly Spitfire FR.XVIIIs until it converted to Vampire FB.5s in March 1951 and 80 Squadron received de Havilland Hornets in January 1952, eight of its Spitfire F.24s being passed to the Hong Kong Auxiliary Air Force. A detachment of two Spitfire PR.XIXs of 81 Squadron led by Flight Lieutenant E.C. Powles AFC carried out 107 photographic sorties over Chinese territory from Kai Tak in 1951 and 52.

In addition to the air forces of Commonwealth countries, late mark Spitfires were flown by a number of other air arms throughout the world. In Europe, Belgium retained 51 Spitfire IXs and 25 Mark XVIs after World War Two and later received 132 Spitfire XIVs, Czechoslovakia using 73 Mark IXs until coming under communist control. Denmark took delivery of 41 Spitfire IXs and one PR.XI in 1947-8 and France acquired 172 Mark IXs,

mainly for use in North Africa and French Indo-China. Having flown Spitfire Vs, Greece replaced these older aircraft with 74 Mark IXs and 54 XVIs and Holland took 55 ex-RAF Mark IXs. Italy also flew the Spitfire IX as part of its rebuilt air force and two squadrons of the Norwegian Air Force (331 and 332) were equipped with Mark IXs until 1952-53. Sweden also took delivery of 50 PR.XIXs for use by F11 at Nykoping-Shavsta.

In the Middle East, 37 Spitfire IXs were operated by the Royal Egyptian Air Force and 10 F.22s were supplied to Syria. As already recorded the Israeli Air Force flew Spitfire IXs and XVIs, 50 being acquired from Czechoslovakia in 1948. Elsewhere, Burma took 20 de-navalised Seafire XVs, the Irish Air Corps 6 two-seat Tr.9s and Thailand 30 FR.XIVs and 4 PR.XIXs.

The Soviet Air Force flew large numbers of Spitfire IXs during the Second World War, 1,188 being delivered in all, plus five PR.IXs and two PR.XIs. Some Spitfires were resold several times, an example being the Burmese Air Force which acquired a number of ex Israeli Mark IXs in 1955. These were the last Spitfires to see operational use in the late 1950s.

3. Engineers and Aces

Reginald J. Mitchell will be forever remembered as the creator of the Spitfire. However, his early death on 11 June 1937, at the age of 42, meant that the subsequent success of the aircraft was then in the hands of Joe Smith, his replacement as Chief Designer, and the rest of the team at Supermarine. Smith was born in 1887 and, after attending Birmingham Municipal Technical School, served in the Royal Navy in the First World War. He became an apprentice in the aircraft department of the Austin Motor Company and joined Supermarine in 1921. His qualities were such that by 1926 he had risen to be Chief Draughtsman and, as already noted, Chief Designer after Mitchell's death. Joe Smith's priorities were to develop the prototype Spitfire (K5054) into a weapon of war and prepare the aircraft for mass production. This was no easy task as the need to produce large numbers of the fighter, and quickly, had not been a design consideration.

Having worked closely with Mitchell for 11 years, Smith knew the Spitfire better than anyone and was fully aware of its capabilities. He also recognised that it would need to be constantly developed to take full advantage of more powerful versions of the Rolls-Royce Merlin engine. Significantly, he began to look at the possibility of fitting the larger Griffon into a Spitfire in 1939, a task that many thought impossible. Smith's temperament was ideally suited to the task of improving the Spitfire. He had great determination and strength of purpose, but these qualities were mixed with an innate caution which ensured that all revisions to the basic design were thoroughly considered from all angles before being put in practice. As J.D. Scott wrote in his history of Vickers, 'If Mitchell was born to design the Spitfire, Joe Smith was born to develop it.'

Other important members of the team involved with the Spitfire included Alan Clifton, Head of the Technical Office, Ernie Mansbridge whose job it was to arrange flight test schedules and collate data obtained in the air, and Alf Faddy who, under Joe Smith, was responsible for much of the detail design of the structure.

There was also Arthur Shirvall, Head of the Project Office, and Beverley Shenstone, a Canadian aerodynamicist who had joined Supermarine from Junkers in 1931. Although Shenstone left the company in 1938, he was involved with Mitchell in the evolution of the Spitfire wing and some credit is due to him for the elliptical planform and thin section which, more than any other factor, contributed to the Spitfire's greatness.

The Test Pilots

Throughout the Spitfire's long development period company test pilots carried out a vital role in ensuring that maximising the aircraft's performance did not come at the expense of a deterioration in handling characteristics. Jeffrey Quill was involved from the very beginning and, together with the likes of Alex Henshaw and George Pickering, made sure that all aircraft delivered to the RAF and Fleet Air Arm were thoroughly tested.

The huge task of checking the performance and handling characteristics of each Spitfire produced was eased by the seconding of service pilots as development test pilots. Altogether around forty pilots carried out these duties including Flight Lieutenants Tony Bartley and Clive Gosling and Squadron Leader R.E. 'Tich' Havercroft from the RAF, with Lieutenants Frank Furlong and Patrick Shea-Simmonds and Lieutenant Commander Mike Lithgow from the Royal Navy.

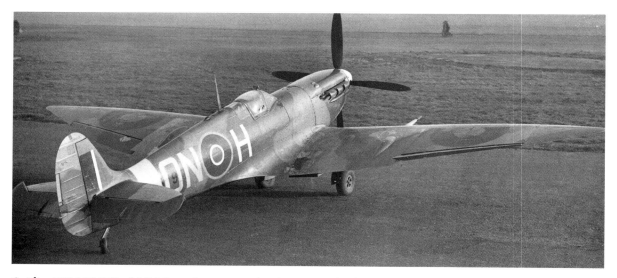

Spitfire HF.VI BR579 of 124 Squadron pictured in late 1942 displays the extended wing tips that increased span to 40 ft 2 in. It was passed to 234 Squadron on 13 February 1943 and also served with 66, 313, 310 and 504 Squadrons before ending its days at Farnborough in 1945. (*Philip Jarrett*)

The Aces

In marked contrast to the early war period, pilots of late mark Spitfires had less opportunity to accumulate high scores. The large-scale battles that had taken place over south-east England in 1940 and over Malta in 1942 would not be repeated and the gradual decline of the *Luftwaffe* meant that very few pilots commencing their operational careers after 1942 got into double figures. Even so 115 pilots 'made ace' or, in other words, achieved at least five victories flying the later Spitfires. Of this total no less than 50 were Canadians with 24 British, 13 Norwegians, 9 New Zealanders, 6 French, 5 Americans, 3 Australians and one each from Czechoslovakia, Denmark, Poland, Rhodesia and South Africa.

The British

One pilot stands out above all others in terms of aerial success in late mark Spitfires irrespective of nationality, and that was Group Captain J.E. 'Johnnie' Johnson DSO DFC. By the time that Johnson came to fly Spitfire IXs as leader of the Canadian Wing at Kenley in March 1943 he was already an ace with 7 kills (plus 2 shared) and over the next six months he would claim another 14 victories with 5 more

shared. With the exception of two Fw 190s shot down when flying MA573, all of these kills were achieved flying his regular Spitfire IX EN398 coded JE-J. Following a rest period at 11 Group HQ, he returned to operations in March 1944 as leader of Number 144 Wing (RCAF). Further combat success followed with another 13 victories, the last three at the head of Number 127 (Canadian) Wing. His last victory occurred on 27 September 1944, by which time his overall total stood at 34 with 7 shared, making him the top-scoring British pilot of the war. He eventually retired from the service in 1966 with the rank of Air Vice-Marshal, his last post being that of AOC, Air Forces Middle East in Aden.

The most successful pilot to fly the Griffon-engined Spitfire XII was Wing Commander Raymond Harries from South Wales. His first combat successes had been achieved on Spitfire VBs, initially as a Flight commander on 131 Squadron and later as leader of 91 Squadron, but when the unit re-equipped with the Mark XII in May 1943 the change was dramatic and Harries shot down 10 German aircraft with one shared in the next five months. One further Spitfire IX kill on 25 July 1944 as leader of Number 135 Wing brought his wartime total to 15 with 3 shared. Another high-scoring pilot in

AB450 was built as a Mark V before being converted into the prototype Spitfire VII with a Merlin 61 in August 1942. It is seen here in late 1942 with the Special High Altitude Flight at Northolt with upper surfaces painted in PR blue and deep sky undersides. (*Philip Jarrett*)

the late war period was Squadron Leader Harry Walmsley who flew Spitfire XIVs as a Flight commander with 130 Squadron and then as C.O. of 350 Squadron. Six victories in April 1945 brought his final tally to 11 with one shared, all but one having been achieved on late mark Spitfires. Only one other British pilot achieved double figures on the later Spitfires, Squadron Leader S.W. 'Dan' Daniel from Slough who served with 72 Squadron in the Mediterranean and Italy and destroyed 10 with one shared (16 + 1 in total).

Mediterranean Ace

The top scoring RAF pilot in the Mediterranean theatre was Squadron Leader Neville Duke whose wartime total of 26 victories (plus 2 shared) included 2 Savoia S-82s destroyed with 92 Squadron in April 1943 (Spitfire IX) and 4 Bf 109Gs and 2 Fw 190s shot down when flying Spitfire VIIIs with 145 Squadron. In the course of three tours he flew nearly 500 sorties and

accumulated over 700 hours on operations. After the war his fame reached new heights as Chief Test Pilot at Hawker Aircraft and holder of the World Airspeed Record in the Hunter.

Flight Lieutenant Jack Hussey of 72 Squadron was another high-scoring Mediterranean ace. From Wells in Somerset, Hussey joined the unit in 1942 before it left the U.K. for Bone in North Africa where it became part of 324 Wing. With two victories on Spitfire VCs, Hussey had considerable success after 72 Squadron converted to the Mark IX in February 1943 and shot down another 8 with 4 shared. Following a rest period he returned to operations with 19 Squadron on Mustang IIIs but was killed on 20 February 1945 when his aircraft spun in on approach to land.

A total of four pilots achieved six victories on late mark Spitfires, including Wing Commander Geoffrey Page who had recovered from severe burns received when his 56 Squadron Hurricane was hit by return fire from

Another view of AB450, this time after being fitted with two Hispano cannon. The extended wing tips and underwing radiators are shown to advantage. AB450 was flown at Boscombe Down in 1942 for cockpit carbon monoxide contamination tests and on trials work with various propeller reduction gear ratios. (*Philip Jarrett*)

a Do 17 on 12 August 1940 during the Battle of Britain. By early 1944 Page was C.O. of 132 Squadron and led an attack on Deelen airfield in Holland on 29 April during which he shot down the Bf 110G of night-fighter ace *Major* Hans-Joachim Jabs of NJG 1. However this was only after the German had shot down two of 132 Squadron's Spitfires (Jabs survived the subsequent crash-landing).

Page was further injured in a crash in September by which time his tally was 6 plus 3 shared (10 plus 5 shared in total). Also with six victories were Flight Lieutenant Ron Hagger (81/72 Squadrons), Flight Lieutenant Ian Ponsford (130 Squadron) and Squadron Leader John Shepherd (610/41 Squadrons).

Of the pilots claiming five victories, Wing Commander Don Kingaby achieved the first combat success in a Spitfire IX when he shot down an Fw 190A near Boulogne on 30 July 1942. At the time Kingaby was a Flight commander with 64 Squadron and he went on to be one of the RAF's top marksmen with 22 victories in total.

Kingaby had a reputation for being extremely aggressive in the air as many of his squadron colleagues found out during practice dogfights. Flight Lieutenant (later Lieutenant General) Michael Donnet recalled his impressions of Kingaby in his book *Flight to Freedom* (Ian Allan, 1974):

'Kingo' in action

"He was quite a small man but wiry and with quick, adept movements. He had no less than eighteen confirmed 'kills' to his credit and on training flights we soon found out the reason. Twist, dive, turn and spin as we would, in a few minutes the propeller of Kingo's Spitfire would be right on our tail. We were glad he

Squadron Leader Neville Duke of 92 Squadron standing in front of Spitfire IX EN152 QJ-3. 92 Squadron flew the Mark IX in North Africa for a short time in 1943 before receiving Spitfire VIIIs. The aircraft identifier during this period was a white painted numeral rather than the more normal code letter, and the squadron QJ code was in a toned down grey. (*Neville Duke via Author*)

was on our side!"

Kingaby's last victory occurred on 8 March 1943 by which time he was commanding 122 Squadron. His combat report highlights the increased operational flexibility of the Spitfire IX and shows that pilots could get themselves out of trouble much more easily and re-engage if an opportunity presented itself:

"The Squadron flew in two sections. I was Red Leader. Shortly after the bombers [B-24s of the 44th BG, Eighth Air Force] had turned for home Red section was attacked by 6-8 Fw 190s and Me 109s from the starboard quarter. I ordered the section to break right and climb, and as the enemy aircraft went past I stall turned down behind the last one and chased him down from 24,000 ft to 19,000 ft but could not catch him. I tried to climb up again but was attacked from above and behind by 5-6 more Focke-Wulfs. As I was climbing and they had the speed on me, they out-climbed me when I broke into them, so I went into an aileron turn and dived down at full throttle. The aileron turn threw them off

and with over 500 mph on the clock I climbed up like a rocket at +18 lbs boost and 2,900 revs in a steep climbing turn.

"I arrived slightly below and just behind the bombers as a Focke-Wulf finished an attack on them. I came up right underneath, rolled out of my turn finishing about 150 yards behind. He evidently did not see me owing to my unusual approach and I opened fire with 2 seconds cannon and machine-guns and saw strikes on the tail end of the fuselage. Then one elevator buckled up and tore away. The enemy aircraft flicked into a vicious spin and the other elevator departed. I did not follow him down as I was getting a long way from the bombers but I saw a parachute open beneath me a few moments later. I opened up to full bore again, caught up with the bombers and accompanied them home."

Other pilots to achieve five kills were Flying Officer Pat Coleman (41 Squadron), Squadron Leader Graham Cox (229/92 Squadrons), Flying Officer Desmond Ruchwaldy (129

Spitfire HF.IX PT465 shows typical Mark IX features, four-blade propeller, multi-ejector exhausts and a rounded, streamlined rear-view mirror. This aircraft was shipped to the Middle East via Casablanca in August 1943 and was lost on operations on 24 April 1945. (*Philip Jarrett*)

Squadron), Squadron Leader R.W. 'Paddy' Turkington (43/241 Squadrons) and Squadron Leader W.M. 'Babe' Whitamore of 81 Squadron.

The Canadians

The top scoring Canadian with 14 destroyed and 2 shared (all on Spitfire IXs) was Squadron Leader Don Laubman. From Edmonton, Alberta, Laubman spent a year as an instructor at 31 EFTS, De Winton, before coming to the U.K., where he joined 412 Squadron at Staplehurst in August 1943. After a slow start he shot down two Fw 190s near Caen on 2 July 1944 and scored regularly throughout his tour, his final victories being another pair of Fw 190s on 28 October. After a rest period he returned to operations just before the end of the war as C.O. of 402 Squadron but was shot down by flak on 14 April 1945 and taken PoW until the end of hostilities. In the post war years Laubman rejoined the RCAF and retired with

the rank of Lieutenant General in 1972, one of his last posts being commander of No.1 Canadian Air Division at Lahr in Germany.

Laubman's wartime record was closely matched by that of Squadron Leader Billy Klersy with 14 victories and one shared. Klersy came from Brantford in Ontario and, like his compatriot, arrived in the U.K. in mid-1943 joining 401 Squadron, also at Staplehurst. His first victim was an Fw 190 that fell to his guns on 7 March 1944 but he had to wait until after D-Day to increase his score. He became an ace on 2 July with the destruction of a Bf 109G and by the end of his tour in September had destroyed two more. Following his return to 401 Squadron as its C.O. in January 1945 he shot down another 7 with one shared before losing his life in a flying accident shortly after the end of the war.

Klersy did not have it all his own way in 401 Squadron as he was pushed hard by Flight

Official records state that former 312 and 485 Squadron Spitfire IXE NH491 was damaged beyond repair in a wheels up landing near Hamble on 13 September 1944, however a lack of leaves on the trees in the background and a fall of snow suggest this date might not be accurate. (*Philip Jarrett*)

Lieutenant John MacKay who joined the unit in August 1944 and was to end the war with 10 victories plus 2 shared. One of MacKay's claims to fame is that he was noted for destroying German aircraft without firing his guns! On three separate occasions he caused his opponents to lose control at low level and crash, a Bf 109G and an Fw 190 on 1 January 1945 and another 190 on 13 January. On each occasion he had run out of ammunition. After the war he remained in the RCAF and commanded 416 Squadron before being seconded to the 39th Fighter Interceptor Squadron of the 51st Fighter Interceptor Wing, USAF in Korea where he claimed a MiG-15 on 30 June 1953.

Although the opportunities for multiple scoring were not as good as earlier in the war, it was still possible as Flight Lieutenant Dick Audet of 411 Squadron proved on 29 December 1944 when he became an ace in a day. In his first ever dogfight with enemy fighters he shot down two Bf 109Gs and three Fw 190s covering Me 262 fighter-bombers taking off from Rheine airfield near Osnabruck. Audet was the only Spitfire pilot to shoot down five in one sortie. He returned to the Osnabruck area on 23 January and had further success as recorded in his combat report:

"1st Combat – While flying as Yellow 1 in 411 Squadron over the aerodrome west of Rheine I sighted aircraft lined up for take off. I dived to attack but meanwhile a tractor had hooked on to the Me 262 and pulled it towards the side of the 'drome. I opened fire from about 1,000 yards at 90 degrees to the direction it was moving. There were many strikes and the aircraft burst into flames about the starboard wing root. I fired again from about 300 yards,

EN221 was the first production Spitfire XII and was sent to Boscombe Down for trials on 5 November 1942. It was one of the first Spitfires to have flush riveting to the fuselage and, together with EN222, undertook an intensive flying trial in late 1942 amounting to 150 hours flying time. Clearly visible in this view is the circular Mark V oil cooler under the port wing. (*Philip Jarrett*)

there was a sheet of flame all about the fuselage. This aircraft continued to burn and 30 minutes later while passing over I could still see smoke and smouldering embers coming from the wreck.

"2nd Combat – Returning from an armed recce in the Osnabruck area I sighted an aircraft at about 4,500 ft in a diving turn over an aerodrome north east of Rheine. I dived to attack and recognised an Me 262. The pilot lowered wheels, then raised them as I closed from the port side. At about 300 yards and 15 degrees I opened fire and saw strikes on the fuselage. The e/a immediately burst into flames and spiralled into the deck and blew up about a mile and a half from the airfield."

This proved to be Audet's last victory as he was killed on 3 March 1945 when his Spitfire LF.IX (MK950) was hit by flak during a strafing attack on a train. His final tally stood at 10 destroyed with one shared.

The fifth highest scoring Canadian ace was Flight Lieutenant Wilfred Banks of 412 Squadron. Banks came from Saskatchewan and was another to have accumulated several hundred hours flying time as an instructor before becoming operational. He put this experience to good use in the latter half of 1944 claiming nine victories, the final one being a Ju 88 shot down near Dortmund on 1 January 1945.

A total of seven pilots achieved eight kills on late mark Spitfires including Squadron Leader Hugh Trainor of 411 Squadron whose combat success was achieved in the space of just five weeks commencing with a Bf 109G shot down on 28 June 1944. Flight Lieutenant George Johnson from Hamilton, Ontario was another to have flown with 411 Squadron, his first combat victory (a Bf 109G) being recorded on 7 June 1944. His final claims were made with 401 Squadron.

Wing Commander R.W. 'Buck' McNair and

Spitfire XII prototype DP845. Although it has a retractable tail wheel, at one point in its career DP845 had this removed and replaced with a fixed wheel. It has the pointed, broad-chord rudder and clipped wings. Judging by the scuff marks on the wing root and leading edges it has seen much use. (*Philip Jarrett*)

Spitfire FR.XIV RN218 of 273 Squadron escorts the aircraft carrying Air Chief Marshal Sir Keith Park to Singapore. 273 Squadron operated the Mark XIV for three months prior to disbandment at Tan Son Nhut (Saigon) in January 1946. Previously it had flown Spitfire VIIIs during the Burma campaign. (*Philip Jarrett*)

Spitfire XIVE RM784 took part in trials in late 1944 with a metal rudder in place of the normal fabric covered surface. In March 1945 it was passed to Boscombe Down for assessment of spin recovery with the low-back fuselage. Compared to standard fuselage aircraft a delayed response was noted. It was sold to the Belgian Air Force in 1949 becoming SG-100. (*Philip Jarrett*)

Squadron Leader Wally McLeod had both become aces over Malta in 1942 before extending their scores over northern Europe. McNair's later victories were achieved with 421 Squadron but he had to retire from operational flying towards the end of 1943 due to the after effects of a bale out on 20 July in which he suffered burns. His overall victory tally was 16 destroyed. McLeod recorded eight victories on Spitfire IXs with 443 Squadron before being shot down and killed during a dogfight with Bf 109Gs on 27 September 1944. At the time of his death McLeod had destroyed a grand total of 21 German aircraft. Three other Canadian pilots achieved eight kills - Flying Officer David Jamieson of 412 Squadron, Wing Commander George Keefer who recorded four kills as leader of 126 Wing (Spitfire IX) and another four as leader of 125 Wing (Spitfire XIV) and Flight Lieutenant Andy MacKenzie who served with 421 and 403 Squadrons.

The Norwegians

Thirteen Norwegian pilots achieved ace status on late mark Spitfires, the top scorer being Captain Svein Heglund of 331 Squadron with 11 victories plus one shared. Like many of his countrymen he learned to fly in Canada at the Little Norway base near Toronto and became operational in May 1942 on Spitfire VBs, his first victory occurring on 19 August during the Dieppe Raid. 331 Squadron began to fly Spitfire IXs in October 1942 and continued with this mark for the rest of the war. Heglund's tour ended in November 1943, his last Spitfire victory being a Bf 109G shot down when flying MA568 FN-L on 24 October. After a rest period he returned to operations flying Mosquitos of 85 Squadron and was credited with destroying three Bf 110 night-fighters during bomber support duties.

The second top-scoring Norwegian with

The Egyptian Air Force took 20 Spitfire F.22s, 681 being the first to be delivered on 14 June 1950 under the class-B registration G.15-88. Used until 1955, they were replaced by Vampire FB.5s. (*Philip Jarrett*)

9 victories was Captain Helmer Grundt-Spang DFC, also of 331 Squadron, who joined the unit as a Sergeant pilot in mid-1942. Following a break from operations he returned as a Flight commander in November 1944 by which time the unit was flying Spitfire IXBs and based at B.60 Grimbergen as part of 132 Wing, 2 TAF. His most successful day occurred on 29 December 1944:

"I was flying Blue 1 on the fighter sweep led by Major Gran. Having reached a height of about 16,000 ft over Arnhem the squadron started a shallow dive towards the Enschede area in order to sweep at the highest possible cruising speed. Soon after we had left the Arnhem area the Ops controller of LONGBOW 6 gave us information of two Hun formations, one north of Rheine flying south and one north of Enschede flying in a southerly direction. Immediately after a Hun formation was reported by Blue 4 at 8 o'clock above. I gave the orders to Blue section to jettison tanks and followed the squadron in a climbing turn to port.

109s behind
"The e/a, which by this time had been identified as Me 109Gs, turned in behind us and manoeuvred into sun about 2,000 yards away. Both the Hun and our formation now started to manoeuvre for a favourable tactical position. The Huns were in a left orbit and were twice into the sun for us, and we were climbing hard, also in a left-hand circuit with everything forward. At about 16,000 ft the Hun formation totalling 30 aircraft stretched over more than half a circle, with 2 aircraft straggling a bit. Major Gran picked one of these two, I the other and both went down in flames. I opened fire at about 250-300 yards range, using the gyro (gunsight) nearly fully open. The e/a took evasive action, kicking rudder then reversing bank. In doing so he was hit in the engine,

Spitfire F.22 PK407 of 608 (North Riding) Squadron at Thornaby in 1948. It was later flown by 602 Squadron before being sold for scrap on 8 September 1954. (*Philip Jarrett*)

white smoke poured out and a second after he started to burn. I did not see him bale out.

"I was in return attacked from starboard by two 109s and turned into the attack. I was turning with these two aircraft for about 3 minutes, the fighting now taking place a bit south of Enschede. The Hun always kept 500 ft above me trying to attack me in turn, I managed fairly well turning into each attack squirting at one without hitting, until 5 more 109s arrived and joined in. With full boost and throttle 'through the gate', I called for assistance and went into a climbing corkscrew turn with nose so high that the ASI went down to 90 mph and keeping left rudder on all the time. After a minute of this I was not yet hit when two 109s attacked head-on from above and from opposite directions.

"I gave them a burst"

"They came in very close to each other both firing and I gave them a 1-2 second burst shooting off a big piece of the starboard wing of one of the Me's and possibly hitting the other in the engine. They collided just in front of me and in order to avoid collision myself I had to yank the stick hard back causing my aircraft to go

into an inverted spin which immediately corrected itself to a normal spin. I let the aircraft spin a few thousand feet and noticed that 4-5 109s had followed me. I also saw the two 109s I had fired at, one going down in flames and one spinning down with about half its right wing missing. At 10,000 ft I took the aircraft out of the spin but allowed it to continue downwards in big aileron turns gathering speed to about 450 mph. I straightened out at 6,000 ft and in a shallow dive set course for Arnhem. The 109s followed but could not close the gap and turned back."

The above engagement also resulted in a triple success for 331 Squadron's C.O. Major Martin Gran who shot down two Bf 109Gs and an Fw 190 to bring his score to 7 with another 2 shared. His final victory of the war was another Bf 109G dispatched near Osnabruck on 14 January 1945. 331 Squadron (132 Wing, 2 TAF) also produced several other aces including Captains Nils Jorstad and Ragnar Dogger, both with 6 kills, and Major Arne Austeen, Lieutenants Fredrik Fearnley and Helge Sognnes all with five. Top scorers with 332 Squadron (the second Norwegian fighter

First production Spitfire F.22 PK312. This view shows the four 20 mm Hispano cannon and blisters over the ammunition feed drums. Following manufacturers trials at High Post and service trials at Boscombe Down, PK312 was fitted with a Griffon 85 and contra-rotating propellers. (*Philip Jarrett*)

squadron and also part of 132 Wing) were Captain Marius Eriksen with 6 victories and Major Werner Christie with 5 plus one shared. A sad loss for the Norwegians, and a needless one, was that of Lieutenant Colonel Rolf Arne Berg, leader of 132 Wing, who was killed during a strafing attack on the airfield at Eelde in Holland on 3 February 1945. With 6 kills to

his name (including one on Spitfire VBs) Berg was to have been rested, but decided to fly one more operation. He died in his personal Spitfire IX PV181 which was coded 'RAB'. It was also adorned with the Norwegian colours in stripes on the outer wings and vertically on the broad-chord rudder. These colours were also applied to the spinner.

A low-back Spitfire F.22 leading two standard fuselage F.21s. The revised wing planform of the later Spitfires is clearly visible as is the layout of the armament. Inboard of the cannon blisters is the fairing over the main wheel bay. (*Philip Jarrett*)

The New Zealanders

Already an ace on Spitfire VBs, Wing Commander Bill Crawford-Compton was the highest scoring New Zealander on late mark Spitfires with 15 victories. He first flew the Spitfire IX in August 1942 as a Flight commander with 611 Squadron, his first confirmed kill with this mark being an Fw 190 shot down near Fauville on the 24th. In December 1942 he was posted to 64 Squadron as its C.O., a role he fulfilled until the end of his tour in March 1943. He returned to operations in April 1944 as leader of 145 Wing, 2 TAF and further increased his score, his last victory being a Bf 109 shot down on 9 July in Spitfire

LF.IX NH590 bringing his overall total to 21 destroyed with one shared. He remained in the service after the war and retired with the rank of Air Vice-Marshal.

Wing Commander Johnny Checketts was born in Invercargill (as was Crawford-Compton) and joined 485 (New Zealand) Squadron in November 1941 on Spitfire VBs. He was wounded in combat on 4 May 1942 and returned to operational flying with 611 Squadron in January 1943, claiming his first victory on 30 May. In July he moved back to 485 Squadron as its leader and had considerable combat success during the summer of 1943, including three Bf 109s shot down on 9 August.

A Westland-built Seafire XVII (SX273) low over the sea. This variant introduced the low-back fuselage and teardrop canopy to Naval service. The Seafire XVII remained in use until 23 November 1954 when the last examples were retired from No.764 Training Squadron at Yeovilton. (*Philip Jarrett*)

Having destroyed an Fw 190 on 6 September, he was himself shot down in EN572 but despite suffering burns, managed to evade capture with the help of the Resistance . In June 1944 he returned to operations as leader of the Spitfire Wing at Horne during which he achieved the unique feat of shooting down two V-1 flying bombs when flying a Spitfire VB. His final tally on late mark Spitfires was 13 destroyed.

The top-scoring New Zealander with 27 victories plus 2 shared, Wing Commander Colin Gray, achieved 7 kills on Spitfire IXs as leader of 81 Squadron and 322 Wing in the Mediterranean. His final operational posting was as leader of the Spitfire XIV Wing at Lympne, comprising 41, 130 and 610 Squadrons. Others of note include Flight Lieutenant Ray Hesselyn of 222 Squadron who shot down 6 aircraft plus one shared, Flight Lieutenant David Livingstone of 111 Squadron (5 plus one shared), Flight Lieutenant Alan Peart of 81 Squadron (5 plus one shared), and Flying Officer Jack Rae of 485 Squadron (5 plus one shared).

The French

Six Free French pilots became aces on late mark Spitfires, Lieutenant Robert Gouby leading the way with 8 kills. Although he had begun training with the *Armee de l'Air* before the war, Gouby did not attain operational status before the fall of France and made his way to England via Morocco. He was posted to 340 Squadron in October 1942 and soon established a reputation for being something of an Fw 190 specialist as all his victories were over the Focke-Wulf

Spitfire XI LV-NMZ was used for photography in Argentina after the war and was modified by Vickers with two additional 20-gallon wing tanks. It is seen here fitted with a 170-gallon slipper tank that brought total fuel capacity to 428 gallons. It was flown across the South Atlantic in 1947 from Senegal to Brazil, a distance of 1,800 miles. Flight time was 8 hours 40 minutes. (*Philip Jarrett*)

fighter, commencing with a 190 shot down on 2 November in Spitfire IX BS394. In late 1943 he joined 165 Squadron, subsequently moving to 611 Squadron but was killed on 14 August 1944 when his aircraft (MA755) was hit by flak during a ground attack sortie.

Although there is controversy over the total number of aircraft that Flight Lieutenant Pierre Clostermann destroyed (estimates vary from 11-18), it appears that he shot down seven during his career as a Spitfire IX pilot with 341 and 602 Squadrons. He subsequently converted to Tempests and had further success with 274, 56 and 3 Squadrons. Also with seven victories, Lieutenant Pierre Montet of 341 Squadron flew under the nom de guerre Christian Martell (due to links with the Resistance) and recorded all of his kills in the summer of 1943. He took over as leader of 341 Squadron in April 1944 but died the following year after a flying accident at Ouston.

The Free French Squadrons (340 and 341) produced two more aces, Lieutenant Michel Boudier and *Capitaine* Marcel Bouguen. Boudier destroyed 6 aircraft in Spitfire IXs (8 in total) and survived the indignity of being shot down by P-47 Thunderbolts on 9 July 1944. Bouguen claimed 5 victories (all Fw 190s) but was killed on 9 March 1944 during a practice bombing sortie when his bomb hung up and exploded under his aircraft. Capitaine Jacques Andrieux claimed 3 kills flying Spitfire XIIs with 91 Squadron and another 2 on Spitfire IXs with 341 Squadron.

The Americans

Although most American pilots serving in Fighter Command transferred to the USAAF in 1942, a few elected to stay in the RAF. These included Lance Wade whose first tour was on Hurricanes with 33 Squadron in North Africa. He returned to the action in February 1943 with 145 Squadron, initially as a Flight commander, the unit converting to Spitfire IXs (from VBs) two months later, by which time Wade had been made its C.O. With 17 victories plus 2

Three two-seat Tr.9s delivered to the Royal Netherlands Air Force on 23 March 1948. The aircraft carry their former identities on the fin. H-97 was MK715 in RAF service and flew with Nos. 56, 402 and 1 Squadrons. H-99 was converted from BS147 and later carried the Dutch civil identity PH-NFN. H-98 is former BF274, an incorrect serial number applied in 1942 – it should have been BS274 but was never changed. (*Philip Jarrett*)

shared already to his credit, Wade added 3 more on the Mark IX plus another 2 after the unit received Spitfire VIIIs. He was killed in January 1944 when the Auster he was flying spun in at low level.

Among the number of US pilots trained in Canada and serving in Canadian squadrons was Flight Lieutenant Don Pieri who joined 442 Squadron on Spitfire IXEs in December 1944, later serving with 412 Squadron. In a short career he claimed 5 German aircraft shot down with 2 shared, but was hit by ricochets during a strafing attack on 2 May 1945. Although he baled out his body was never found. Squadron Leader Henry Zary joined 421 Squadron in April 1943 and on 25 July 1944 accounted for three Bf 109s, two with gunfire and one by forcing its pilot to lose control. He took command of 403 Squadron in February 1945 and 'made ace' on 21 April when he destroyed a Bf 109 in Spitfire XVI TB752. Flight Lieutenant Paul Johnson also flew with 421 Squadron and shot down 5 German aircraft before crashing to his death on 18 July 1944 after hitting a tree

during a strafing attack in Spitfire LF.IX MK809.

The Rest

Of the three Australian late mark Spitfire aces, the top scorer was Squadron Leader Tony Gaze whose overall total of 11 destroyed with 3 shared was achieved using five different marks of Spitfire. He shot down an Fw 190 and a Do 17 flying with 616 Squadron (Spitfire VI) in 1942 and the following year destroyed another Fw 190 in Spitfire IX MA621 of 129 Squadron. His final kills were recorded in 1945 with 610 and 41 Squadrons (Spitfire XIV) and comprised a Ju 52, two Fw 190Ds and an Me 262. Flying Officer Bobby Bunting scored 5 kills with 93 Squadron on Spitfire IXs and Flying Officer Larry Cronin, from Canterbury in Victoria, also secured 5 victories with 81 Squadron, 3 in the Mediterranean and 2 over Burma.

Flight Lieutenant William Maguire from Salisbury, Southern Rhodesia scored 12 of his 13 victories on Spitfire IXs with 81 and 154 Squadrons in North Africa and Italy, and South African Squadron Leader J.J. 'Chris' Le Roux,

Spitfire F.22s of the Southern Rhodesian Air Force. These were the first combat aircraft received by the SRAF after the Second World War and 22 were delivered in 1951. (*Philip Jarrett*)

already with 12 kills to his name, secured another 6 victories flying Spitfire IXBs with 602 Squadron. He was also responsible for attacking the staff car in which General Erwin Rommel suffered a fractured skull on 17 July 1944. Le Roux went missing over the Channel five weeks later when flying back to the U.K. in marginal weather. The top-scoring pilot from Eastern Europe was Czech Squadron Leader Otto Smik with 8 destroyed and 2 shared achieved with 222 and 310 Squadrons.

The V-1 Aces

Many Spitfires IXs, XIIs and XIVs were involved in anti-*Diver* operations (together with Tempest Vs, Mustang IIIs and Mosquitos) and destroyed around 500 V-1s, approximately 25% of those destroyed by fighters. The top-scoring Spitfire pilot was Squadron Leader Norman Kynaston from Chester who shot down 22 V-1s flying Spitfire XIVs with 91 Squadron. Kynaston's performance was closely matched by that of Flying Officer R.F. Burgwal of 322 Squadron who recorded 19 kills with another 5 shared (also on Spitfire XIVs). His best day occurred on 5 July 1944 when he shot down four. Squadron Leader R.S. Nash, another 91 Squadron pilot, was the third top scorer on Spitfires with 17 plus 3 shared.

Although the highest scores were achieved by pilots flying Griffon-engined Spitfires, the Mark IXs of Numbers 1 and 165 Squadron also made a valuable contribution, shooting down 47 and 50 respectively. Flight Lieutenant D.H. Davy with 6 destroyed and one shared was the top scorer for 1 Squadron, with Flying Officer C.M. Lawson having that honour on 165 Squadron with 6 kills.

The record for the shortest successful sortie went to Flying Officer McIntosh of 1 Squadron who took off from Lympne in the early evening of 28 June 1944 and saw a V-1 to his left as he was raising his undercarriage. A quick turn downwind allowed him to open fire with a deflection shot which resulted in the V-1 blowing up in a huge fireball. McIntosh kept his turn going and was back on the ground 1 minute after taking off!

4. Accomplishments

Perhaps more than any other Second World War fighter the Spitfire is everything to everyone. For spectators at an airshow its finely sculpted contours and the noise from its Rolls-Royce engine combine to produce perfection in sight and sound, perhaps even leading some to become a little misty eyed. The pilot, on the other hand, is likely to experience emotions of a completely different sort as his senses are assailed by the cacophony produced by twelve stub exhausts a few feet in front of him, the unique cockpit aroma, and gut-wrenching accelerations, courtesy of an engine producing 1,500-2,000 hp depending on the version he happens to be flying. Either way, the end result is probably the same. For those on the ground the sight of a Spitfire will most likely have been the highlight of the show. For the pilot, the chance to fly a Spitfire will have been the highlight of a career.

Putting emotion aside though, what are the chief claims to fame of the Spitfire? Its fine handling characteristics, in particular its superiority in the turn, were discussed in Spitfire Marks I-V in the Combat Legend series, and despite increases in all-up weight and wing loading, this capability was maintained with the late mark machines. One of the Spitfire's other outstanding features was its ability to accept more development than virtually any other contemporary fighter. The only other aircraft that came anywhere near it was the Fw 190, but as this did not fly until 1939, it can be considered as belonging to the second generation of monoplane fighters so a comparison with the Spitfire is a little unfair.

The prototype Spitfire (K5054) was flown for the first time on 5 March 1936 and was powered by a Merlin Type 'C' engine of 990 hp driving a two-blade fixed-pitch wooden propeller. Its maximum speed was 348 mph, it weighed 5,332 lbs and had a wing loading of 22 lbs/sq.ft. In contrast the Spitfire F.21 featured a Griffon 61 of 2,050 hp driving a five-blade variable-pitch propeller. Maximum speed was 454 mph, loaded weight 9,305 lbs and wing loading 38 lbs/sq.ft. Service ceiling of the F.21 was 43,000ft (an increase of over 10,000ft on the early Spitfires) and its initial rate of climb at 4,900 ft/min, was more than double that of the Spitfire I.

Ultimate Spitfire

Even so, the F.21 was not quite the end of the line as the Seafire FR.47 with its Griffon 85 and contra-rotating propellers weighed 11,615 lbs with a full load of fuel and external stores, more than double that of K5054. The use of more powerful engines, improved controls and heavier weaponry kept the Spitfire at the forefront of piston-engined fighter technology throughout its long service career. To emphasize the level of development that was applied to the basic Spitfire airframe a closer look is going to be taken at the F.21, a variant that had more than its fair share of troubles.

The major improvements made with the Spitfire F.21 have already been recorded in Chapter 1 but some led to quite serious handling deficiencies. To compete with other fighter types the Spitfire needed the biggest, most powerful engine that it could accommodate, the Rolls-Royce Griffon. By careful design the increase in dimensions of the forward fuselage was kept to a minimum but this, together with an increase in blade area needed to absorb the extra power, led to a destabilising effect and consequent deterioration in directional and longitudinal handling. Compared with the Spitfire XIV, the

Spitfire F.21 prototype PP139 was first flown in July 1943 and is seen here with pointed wings and a standard Mark XIV tail. In its original form it had a straight leading edge to the fin. Note also the hinged landing gear door that covered the main wheel when retracted. This aircraft had a compromised serial number as PP139 also appeared on a Sunderland III flying-boat. (*Philip Jarrett*)

F.21 had an even bigger propeller but it retained the earlier aircraft's tail. Use of the new propeller raised top speed by about 10 mph, but its increase in diameter (from 10 ft 5 in to 11 ft) was one of the major factors behind the over-control that was being experienced. In contrast, lateral control was greatly improved due to the strengthened wing and use of larger tab-balanced ailerons. Roll rates in the order of 120 degrees/sec were achieved at 300 mph, an increase of around 33 per cent.

An early production F.21 (LA201) was tested by the Central Fighter Establishment (CFE) towards the end of 1944 and for once the Spitfire did not receive top marks. In terms of flying controls and general handling it was described as follows:

"The aircraft is unstable in the yawing plane, especially at altitude and at high speeds. The rudder is extremely sensitive to small movements and very careful flying is necessary to avoid skidding and slipping. Aileron control is light and positive at all speeds up to 350 mph ASI. Above this speed the ailerons tend to stiffen, the deterioration being more rapid above 400 mph ASI but nevertheless they are the best yet encountered on any mark of Spitfire.

Constant corrections

"Although the elevator control is positive in action and the aircraft is stable in pitch, constant correction is necessary, particularly at low speed and at high altitude at all speeds. Trimming tabs are provided for rudder and elevators. Trimming is at all times extremely critical, and harsh use of the trimming tabs is to be avoided. Reaction to acceleration in the dive, deceleration in the climb and change of throttle, is marked.

"Whilst this aircraft is not unstable in pitch, above 25,000ft the instability in yaw makes it behave as if it were unstable about all three axes. Because of its higher wing loading, the high speed stall comes in earlier than with

Spitfire F.21 LA188, pictured in late 1944, was used for high-speed trials. In 1946 it had its guns removed and a Griffon 65 installed for compressibility dives at Farnborough during which it reached Mach 0.89. (*Philip Jarrett*)

other marks of Spitfire and in a steep turn the general feeling of instability, combined with its critical trimming qualities, is unpleasant. The control characteristics are such that this aircraft is most difficult to fly accurately and compares most unfavourably with other modern fighters."

The solution was simple enough: the Spitfire F.21 needed a bigger tail. However, due to the demands of the RAF, any slackening of production to accommodate the testing of an enlarged tailplane was out of the question. Supermarine were well aware of what was required and the larger vertical and horizontal tail surfaces of the Spitfire 22 and 24 restored the aircraft's handling qualities in pitch and yaw. The problem of what to do with the F.21s coming off the production line was solved by several small fixes which had a big effect on the aircraft's characteristics. The over-sensitive rudder was cured by removing the balance action of the rudder trim tab. At the same time the elevator trim tab gearing was reduced by 50%, a metal-covered elevator was used and the

horn balance was made slightly smaller. It was also given a rounded inboard edge.

A modified Spitfire F.21 (LA215) was tested at CFE in March 1945 and the subsequent report concluded that the critical trimming characteristics had largely been eliminated by the modifications carried out. It was considered acceptable for both instrument and low flying and a suitable aircraft for the average pilot to fly in combat, which was something of a climb down considering that just four months before CFE had stated that no further attempts should be made to perpetuate the Spitfire family! This change in attitude was reinforced in May 1945 when pilots from CFE began testing a Spitfire F.21 fitted with contra-rotating propellers. The trial was highly successful, so much so that a more comprehensive test was carried out towards the end of 1945 using LA215 and LA217. The following is taken from the CFE report:

Description

"The aircraft is identical to the normal Spitfire 21 except for the contra-rotating propeller

AB505 was built as a Spitfire V and first flew on 25 January 1942 before being converted to an HF.IX and delivered to 64 Squadron. It was subsequently fitted with a Merlin 77 and contra-rotating propellers as seen here. After trials it was converted back to standard F.IX configuration and flew with 611 and 312 Squadrons but was damaged beyond repair when it collided with MH357 in December 1944. (*Philip Jarrett*)

mechanism which reduces maximum power available by some 135 thrust hp but does not in any way complicate engine handling. The aircraft were not representative of proposed production aircraft which will incorporate a larger tail unit and cutaway hood to overcome the de-stabilising influence of the contra-rotating propeller at high speeds. This will remove the present speed limitation of 470 mph ASI. During trials LA215 flew 30 hours and LA217 41 hours. No difficulties were experienced.

Fore and Aft Stability

"The aircraft appears to be stable fore and aft at all speeds from 120-450 mph ASI at low and medium altitude and at 30,000 ft down to 140 mph ASI. There is no tendency to tighten up in turns although the aircraft can easily be held in the turn with light stick forces. Large forward stick forces are only required in a prolonged dive if no trimming is used. It appears that the contra-rotating propeller Spitfire 21 is definitely more stable than the five-blade 21 and is not as a result handicapped when manoeuvring.

Lateral Stability

"At low altitude the aircraft is just stable in the rolling plane but at 30,000 ft is just unstable. The ailerons are light and effective over the whole speed range and speed does not affect the lateral stability ie, for all practicable purposes the contra-rotating propeller has no effect on the lateral stability of the Spitfire 21.

Despite initial problems with the development of contra-rotating propellers, they were used successfully on the Seafire 46 and 47. This view of Seafire 46 LA542 emphasizes the variant's long nose (fuselage length of the F.46 was 33 ft 7 in). LA542 was used for manufacturers trials in connection with the carriage of wing combat tanks and rocket projectiles. (*Philip Jarrett*)

Forward View

"The increased density of the propeller disc has no detrimental effect on the forward view and there is no appreciable difference between it and other conventional propellers, either by day or night. Some concern has been expressed by Fighter Command at the 'ghost images' which are clearly visible to people located at the rear of the aircraft when it is on the ground, particularly when the engine is at low revolutions, but throughout the trial no pilot reported adversely on the phenomenon and unless it is specifically brought to his attention he is unlikely to notice it.

Aerobatics

"All forms of aerobatics are greatly enhanced by the contra-rotating propeller due to the complete absence of change of directional trim with speed or throttle setting, and a uniform rate of roll in either direction.

Instrument Flying

"The excellent general handling characteristics of the aircraft greatly simplify instrument flying by eliminating the need for any change of directional trim.

Operational Ceiling

"The height at which the climb fell below 1,000ft/min was 4,000 ft lower than for a Spitfire 21 with five-blade propeller tested at the same time. This is mainly due to the decreased diameter of the propeller.

Night Flying

"As in instrument flying, the qualities of the contra-rotating propeller are accentuated at night, particularly during take off when the absence of swing and the improved stability at low speed are a great advantage.

Sighting Platform

"A considerable programme of cine gun air-to-air and air-to-ground firing, and cannon firing from air-to-ground has been done. Pilots unanimously consider that the aircraft is an excellent sighting platform because the tendency to skid during the attack is largely eliminated provided no stoppages occur, and it is easy to hold the sight on another aircraft which is taking evasive action."

During the trial the contra-prop Spitfire was compared with a standard F.21 using +18

59

The use of contra-rotating propellers greatly eased deck operations as there was no swing due to engine torque. Seafire FR.47 PS948 was the first to have powered wing folding and was used for deck landing trials and RATOG trials at Farnborough in 1947. (*Philip Jarrett*)

Close up of the contra-rotating propeller installation on Seafang 32 VB895. This aircraft was demonstrated to the Dutch military by Mike Lithgow in August 1946 but did not find favour. (*Philip Jarrett*)

The Spitfire PR.XI was also used by the USAAF for PR duties. This is a machine of the 14th Photo Squadron, 7th Photographic Group based at Mount Farm in Oxfordshire. By the summer of 1944 the 14th PS had 14 Spitfire PR.XIs on strength and these were used for deep penetration sorties over Germany. (Philip Jarrett)

lbs/sq.in boost. In terms of range and endurance, speed and dive performance the two were virtually identical. The contra-prop F.21 had a slightly reduced rate of climb in the order of 100ft/min at sea level, increasing to 300ft/min at 21,500ft, and was also not quite as good in acceleration tests, both as a result of its reduced propeller diameter. Rate of roll was difficult to assess, the general consensus being that the standard aircraft was slightly better below 300 mph with the contra-prop having the edge at speeds above 300 mph. The contra-prop F.21 also had an improved turning circle, particularly at high altitude and in turns to the left, and the improved 'feel' of the aircraft was most marked when carrying out tight turns.

Despite enthusiastic reporting on LA215 and LA217, the contra-prop Spitfire was never used by the RAF, although the similar Seafire FR.47 did see active service with the Royal Navy. With its lack of torque, and absence of directional trim problems, it was the equivalent of the early jet fighters in terms of performance

(but without the lag in throttle response). However, as jet engines were already offering around 5,000 lbs thrust with the prospect of much more to come, it was clear that the future lay with the turbo-jet rather than advanced versions of piston-engined fighters, however good they might be.

Another aspect of performance in which the Spitfire reigned supreme over its contemporaries was its high compressibility Mach number (the Mach number at which compressibility causes significant control problems and possible loss of control). Diving tests were carried out by RAE Farnborough from May 1943 using a Spitfire PR.XI (EN409) and a Mustang I (AG393) to determine overall drag and longitudinal trim changes at high Mach numbers. The pilot throughout the trial was Squadron Leader J.R. Tobin AFC and the results were compared with data supplied by the USA on diving trials with a P-47 Thunderbolt. Although all three aircraft showed a rise in drag coefficient at Mach

Spitfire PR.XI PA892 of the 14th PS, USAAF. The caption on the back of the original print states that the overall colour scheme was silver with dark blue spinner, a red panel around the exhaust and an olive green rudder. PA892 survived the war and was struck off charge on 14 September 1945. (*Philip Jarrett*)

numbers in excess of 0.7, their characteristics at higher values varied greatly.

The technique used was to accelerate to maximum level speed at the highest altitude the aircraft could achieve before pushing into a 45-degree dive. Before commencing the dive the pilot was warned of the possibility of large trim changes in the nose-down direction and of the possible ineffectiveness of the elevator trim tab. The pilot trimmed into the dive at the beginning, but when the nose-down change appeared near maximum Mach, he made no attempt to correct on the trimmer but held the aircraft by stick force alone. The dives were continued for a few seconds after maximum Mach number was reached before starting a gentle (2 to 3g) pull out.

The trials showed that due to its thinner wing, the Spitfire was superior to both American aircraft. As the Mustang had the low-altitude rated Allison engine, flights were made without guns and radio, but even so dives could only be commenced at around 28,000 ft. The Spitfire PR.XI in contrast could be dived from 40,000 ft. A Mach meter was fitted in both aircraft but as this was only calibrated to Mach 0.80 it proved useful during dives in the Mustang but not in the Spitfire, as for most of the time it was off the scale.

Despite the fact that the Mustang was fitted with a semi-low-drag wing (laminar-flow), its overall drag coefficient was greater than that of the Spitfire, which had a conventional wing of roughly 2212 section. This showed that the overriding factor was wing thickness, that for the Spitfire being 13% thickness/chord ratio at the wing root and only 7% at the tip. Comparable figures for the Mustang were 16% and 11%.

The results of the P-47 Thunderbolt trials showed it to be the worst of the three aircraft and RAE calculated that a pull of 200 lbs would still not be enough to counteract the nose-down

RAe Farnborough dive tests
May 1943

Aircraft	Start Height	Maximum Mach Nr	Pull Out Height
Mustang I	28,000ft	0.80 at 17,000ft	10,000ft
Spitfire XI	32,000ft	0.85 at 20,000ft	10,000ft
Spitfire XI	36,000ft	0.87 at 25,000ft	15,000ft
Spitfire XI	40,000ft	0.89 at 29,000ft	20,000ft

The ultimate PR variant of the Spitfire was the PR.XIX. PS925 wears the markings of the Photographic Reconnaissance Development Unit. This aircraft survived until 1 July 1949 when it crashed on approach to Leuchars during service with 237 OCU. (*Philip Jarrett*)

moment in the dive, even assuming a pilot was capable of exerting such a force. In the same situation it was estimated that the Spitfire needed a pull of 50-60 lbs to maintain trim at Mach 0.89 at 30,000 ft. It was likely that the P-47 would be out of control until reaching denser air at lower levels when the Mach number began to decrease. Even here, however, there was danger as the slackening of the nose-down pitching moment, together with a strong pull force on the stick, could lead to excessive accelerations and possible structural failure, an eventuality even more likely if the pilot had been foolish enough to apply nose-up trim to assist with the pull out.

Although the Spitfire was capable of flying at higher Mach numbers than any other piston-engined fighter, it was not immune to disaster as Squadron Leader Tony Martindale discovered during a high-speed dive in EN409 on 27 April 1944. The following is his report on the flight:

"I took off and climbed to 40,000 ft with the altimeter at 1,013mb. At ceiling I began to feel slightly anoxic due to the low oxygen flow and flew level for a time at 2,850 rpm full throttle and worked the ASI round to 170 mph. I then most carefully set the rudder and elevator trims, selecting an intermediate position on the latter between the extremes I have tried. I switched on the camera and dived the aeroplane. I bunted steadily keeping the 'g' low so as to reduce drag and closed the throttle slightly. When I was down to 32,000 ft the altimeter was spinning merrily and the dive was very steep and I was pulling back on the stick in the usual way due to the change of trim at the shock stall.

"I glanced at the altimeter and saw it drop from 28,000 to 27,000 ft and I knew I was past the high speed. I began to think of pulling out of the dive when there was a fearful explosion and the aircraft became enveloped in white smoke. I incorrectly assumed that a structural failure had occurred as I knew this to be the danger. The aircraft shook from end to end and

Spitfire PR.XIX PS890 of 81 Squadron having its cameras removed (PS888 in background). Along with three other PR.XIXs, PS890 was sold to the Royal Thai Air Force in 1954 where it became U14-26/97. It was presented to Ed Maloney (founder of The Air Museum in the USA) by the King of Thailand in 1962. It took to the air again in 2002 at Chino in California having been rebuilt with clipped wings, a Griffon 58 engine and contra-rotating propellers. (*Philip Jarrett*)

I knew I could not bale out at such speed so sat still. The aircraft was doing nothing startling but the screen and hood were now quite black and I could see nothing. Automatically I eased the stick back and discovered by looking backwards through the oil film that I was climbing. The airspeed was falling as the noises were dying down. I realised I could now bale out and opened the hood, but the aircraft was under partial control at least and so I switched off the camera and began to think I might be able to get the aircraft down and save the film and other apparatus. I still did not know what had happened as I could not see through the windscreen.

"I pointed the aircraft towards base and called up on the radio. As I tried to look round the screen my goggles were whipped away, but the engine clearly was not going and I could see no propeller. Bits of engine were sticking out and it seemed to have moved sideways. I reported this to base. I consulted the Chief Test Pilot as to the advisability of lowering the wheels, supposing they would go down. The

hydraulics were u/s and I had pressure for flaps. The CTP advised a wheels down landing and I glided 20 miles or so and saw I could reach base. This I reached at 6,000 ft, the aircraft gliding very nicely without its propeller. On landing I saw that the propeller and engine reduction gear had gone and a main engine bearer had buckled."

Ten days later Martindale was flying Spitfire XI PL827 in a dive when the supercharger burst and the engine set on fire. The fire soon went out but once again his windscreen was covered in oil that prevented him from seeing high-tension cables on his approach to land in a field near Woking. As a result he crash-landed and suffered back injuries but still had the presence of mind to collect the valuable recording camera from his burning machine, an act for which he was later awarded the Air Force Cross (AFC).

The Spitfire was by no means perfect, but it probably came as close to perfection as any. However, Mitchell's brief had been to design a

Spitfire VIII JF463 shown after roll out with long span wings and Merlin 63. It was shipped to Casablanca in June 1943 for service in North Africa. (*Philip Jarrett*)

short-range interceptor so fuel capacity was limited to reduce weight and thus optimise performance. This proved to be rather an embarrassment when the aircraft was asked to do offensive work later in the war and many pilots ran out of fuel on the way back from France, resulting in a large number of write offs and no few fatalities. The following guidelines were issued to pilots of 403 Squadron after the *Ramrod* operation on 13 March 1943 as described in Chapter 2.

INSTRUCTIONS TO PILOTS ON THE HANDLING OF ENGINES

"The number of forced landings due to fuel shortage is unnecessarily high. Employment of fighter aircraft on escort or offensive operations necessitates that the most economical engine running conditions which can be employed, having regard to the circumstances, must be used. Wasteful methods will result in limiting the scope of operations or risking losses of aircraft and pilots. In many of the recent accidents it is noted that pilots are not using weak mixture and are running engines at higher speeds than those recommended for economy.

"Many pilots have complained that Merlin engines do not run smoothly at the weak mixture setting. This matter has been under investigation. A large number of tests have been carried out under varied conditions. It has been found that provided limits of R.P.M. and boost for weak mixture setting are not exceeded, no rough running will occur in weak mixture.

"A reduction in fuel consumption amounting to approximately 25% is obtained by using weak mixture setting provided boost is below +3.75 lbs/sq.in. It cannot be too strongly emphasised that pilots should make a habit of using the weak mixture setting whenever possible.

"Pilots should realise that if they inadvertently leave the mixture control in weak setting when opening up the throttle, the mixture strength becomes automatically rich when the boost pressure reaches +5 lbs/sq.in. In the range +3.75 to 5 lbs/sq.in boost the mixture is slightly weak but provided rough running does not occur, no damage can be done to the engine.

"Should rough running occur in this range it is suggested that, if possible, the pilot should

Spitfire XII DP845 pictured in early 1942. This machine was well liked by Jeffrey Quill who rated it amongst his favourite Spitfires. He flew it at Farnborough on 22 July 1942 in a speed trial with a Typhoon, flown by Hawker test pilot Ken Seth-Smith, and an Fw 190 flown by W/Cdr H.J. Wilson, O.C. Aerodynamics Flight, RAE. The Spitfire won, followed by the Typhoon and the Fw 190 – the reverse of what had been expected! (*Philip Jarrett*)

move the throttle to get out of the phase of rough running. If this is not possible the mixture control should be moved to rich position. The mixture control must be in rich position for take off.

"Maximum fuel economy for any given airspeed will be obtained by a combination of low R.P.M. and relatively high boost. It is appreciated that the use of higher R.P.M. than is necessary for economical running is sometimes justified by virtue of increased flexibility obtained and the consequent improvement in the handling qualities of the aircraft.

"It must be realised, however, that in order to obtain the lowest fuel consumption practicable, use of high R.P.M. should be avoided unless contact with the enemy is imminent and full manoeuvrability and performance must consequently be immediately available.

"At low altitudes maximum fuel economy will be obtained with c.1900 R.P.M. At higher altitudes, higher R.P.M. will be necessary. It is suggested that for fuel economy the A.S.I. should be kept between 160 and 180 (at all altitudes) and the lowest R.P.M. which will maintain this airspeed be used in combination with the upper limit of boost pressure."

Free hunters

Towards the end of the war, the *Luftwaffe* fighter force was put under increasing pressure by the overwhelming numerical superiority of the Allied air forces, allowing greater tactical freedom for Spitfire squadrons based in the U.K. With the Germans pulling back to defend the homeland, full use could be made of the 90-gallon slipper tank allowing operations further into occupied territory, even to the extent of escorting bombers to the Ruhr and back. By August 1944, Flight Lieutenant Tony Cooper was flying Spitfire LF.IXs with 64 Squadron as part of the Harrowbeer Wing under Wing Commander Harold 'Birdie' Bird-Wilson. His logbook for the period records seven operations in excess of 3 hours duration including sweeps to the south of the River Loire, 150 miles from the French Channel coast. By September, 64 Squadron had moved to Bradwell Bay in Essex and were operating over Holland and Belgium,

Spitfire XII MB878 at Boscombe Down in October 1943 (note Sea Otter in background). It was there for speed trials with a 500-lb bomb mounted on a Universal Mark III rack. Top speed with bomb fitted was 363 mph (383 mph clean). MB878 joined 41 Squadron on 14 July 1944 and was damaged during operations on 26 August. After repair it flew with the Fighter Leaders School at Milfield. (*Philip Jarrett*)

with occasional bomber escorts into Germany. On 27 September it was tasked with escorting 175 Halifax and Lancaster bombers of 6 and 8 Groups during an attack on a synthetic oil plant at Bottrop in the Ruhr. For Tony Cooper it would be the last time that he flew his beloved MK805 'Peter John III':

"There was a lot of flak over the target and several of the bombers were hit. On the way back at about 15,000 ft over the North Sea without warning my engine suddenly stopped dead (possibly due to flak damage). I had no idea where I was so called up on the radio for a fix and it appeared that I was nearer the Dutch coast than the English. I turned back with my No.2 (Warrant Officer G.R. Maunders) and we glided down through 9-10,000 ft of cloud. Due to the very slow speed I was gliding at, my No.2 lost contact with me and I came out at about 1,500 ft. I looked for somewhere to land and saw what appeared to be an airfield. When I was on the downwind leg and starting to turn crosswind I noticed that it was covered in shell holes and impossible to land on so I extended my glide crosswind and headed for a ploughed field, straight ahead.

"With wheels up and a stationary prop it was a very long glide and I was surprised to see how far the aeroplane floated. In the end I had to put the nose down as there was a farmhouse ahead. Luckily the field was pretty soft, there was a lot of mud and stuff flying around but apart from banging my head on the gunsight, I was quite ok. I had no idea where I was so prepared to burn the aircraft and blew up the IFF (Identification Friend or Foe). A group of farmers who came up turned out to be Flemish, quickly followed by a British army half-track commanded by a Captain who informed me that if I had come down on the same spot two days before I would have been behind enemy lines!"

Cooper had come down at Moerbecke in Belgium and was taken to a nearby chateau owned by a member of the Belgian government. As it had been an early 'show' (take off at 0715 hrs) he was given breakfast and a shirt in place of the pyjamas he was still

Spitfire F.24 VN324 was test flown by Les Colquhoun on 13 July 1946 and used for gyro gunsight vibration tests in June 1947 when it was flown by John Derry. Early in 1948 it was used at Boscombe Down for gunnery acceptance trials with the Mark V Hispano cannon, and was sold for scrap in June 1956. (*Philip Jarrett*)

wearing under his battledress! After a night in Ghent, he was back on operations the next day having flown back to the U.K. in a VIP Dakota. Although MK805 was not new when he began flying it, Tony Cooper recalls that it was in magnificent state and rates it as the best Spitfire of the many he has flown. His ground crew kept it in top condition, even polishing it with Simoniz wax to add a few more mph. He was very sad to lose it but amazed to find it again 39 years later.

After its unscheduled arrival in a Belgian field MK805 was returned to the U.K. where it was repaired. In May 1945 it was delivered to 145 Squadron at Treviso in Italy. It was sold to the Italian Air Force in 1946 along with 136 other Spitfire IXs and was given the serial number MM4084. Its history in Italian service is obscure but it was withdrawn from use around 1952 and placed on display at Nettuno.

Here it became increasingly derelict and it was not until 1976 that the airframe was earmarked for display in the Italian Air Force Museum at Lecce. The aircraft's true identity was not revealed until 1983 when its RAF serial number was discovered during the restoration process, allowing Tony Cooper to be contacted and informed that 'his' Spitfire had survived (the only one of the Italian Spitfires to have done so).

A living legend

Maybe the Spitfire's true claim to fame is its enduring appeal which is as strong now as it was in the war years. Once a weapon of war, its current role is one of education, reminding succeeding generations of past conflicts, and bringing like-minded individuals from all over the world together. The fact that Tony Cooper's Spitfire is now proudly displayed wearing the markings of a former enemy state and is venerated as much as it would be in the U.K. is, perhaps, an indication that the sacrifices of sixty years ago were not in vain.

5. Variants

The Spitfire was produced in numerous different variants and in this chapter these are recorded in number sequence rather than chronological order.

Spitfire VI

The Spitfire VI was the first serious attempt by Supermarine to turn the Spitfire into a true high-altitude fighter and featured a pressure cabin and extended wingtips which increased span to 40 ft 2 in and wing area to 248.5 sq.ft. A Marshall Mark IXA blower was mounted on the starboard side of the engine and was fed by an air intake below the exhaust stack resulting in a distinctive elongated blister. Power came from a 1,415 hp Merlin 47, effectively a Merlin 46 with Merlin XII crankcase and Coffman starter drive (the shaft of which drove the blower) and a four-blade de Havilland or Rotol constant-speed propeller. The canopy could not be opened in flight and was locked in position by ground crew prior to take off, although it could be jettisoned by the pilot in case of emergency. Apart from its extended tips, the wings of the Spitfire VI were standard 'B' Type with two 20 mm Hispano cannon and four 0.303 in Browning machine-guns. Fuel was carried in two fuselage tanks mounted forward of the cockpit, the upper tank holding 48 gallons and the lower 37 gallons. All-up weight with full war load was approximately 6,738 lbs (around 180 lbs heavier than a Spitfire VB) resulting in a wing loading of 27 lbs/sq.ft.

Spitfire VII

Designed to fulfil the same high-altitude role as the Mark VI, the Spitfire VII featured a heavily revised airframe and was powered by a two-speed, two-stage supercharged Rolls-Royce Merlin. Its wing was a modified 'C' Type, with additional fuel tanks holding 14 gallons in each leading edge. Due to the use of the larger Merlin with intercooler, rectangular section radiators were used under both wings. The fuselage fuel capacity was raised to 96 gallons by increasing the size of the lower tank to 49 gallons. The ailerons were reduced in span by 8 in to 6 ft 3 in as a precaution against flutter and the fuselage was fully stressed to cater for the increased weight and power of the engine. The tail wheel was also retractable. As a result of the longer nose dimensions a pointed broad-chord rudder was fitted to restore directional stability, overall length now being 31 ft. Fully loaded weight was 7,990 lbs and wing loading was 32 lbs/sq.ft.

Like its predecessor, a pressure cabin was fitted, air being supplied by a Marshall Mark XII blower (similar to the Mark IXA but with a higher gear ratio). Most aircraft also featured a revised 'Lobelle' hood that slid on rails like a normal canopy and could be opened for take off and landing. The first Spitfire F.VIIs were fitted with either a Merlin 61 or 64 (SU carburettor) whereas later HF.VIIs had a Merlin 71 with injection carburettor. Two Spitfire HF.VIIs (EN465 and EN470) were modified by Heston Aircraft to test a system of liquid oxygen injection to increase rate of climb to intercept high-flying intruders. The LOX was contained in the starboard wing fuel tank and although flight trials were largely successful, problems were encountered with ground handling and the idea was eventually abandoned.

Spitfire VIII

The Spitfire VIII was developed in tandem with the Mark VII, the only major difference being the lack of a pressure cabin. The Spitfire VII and

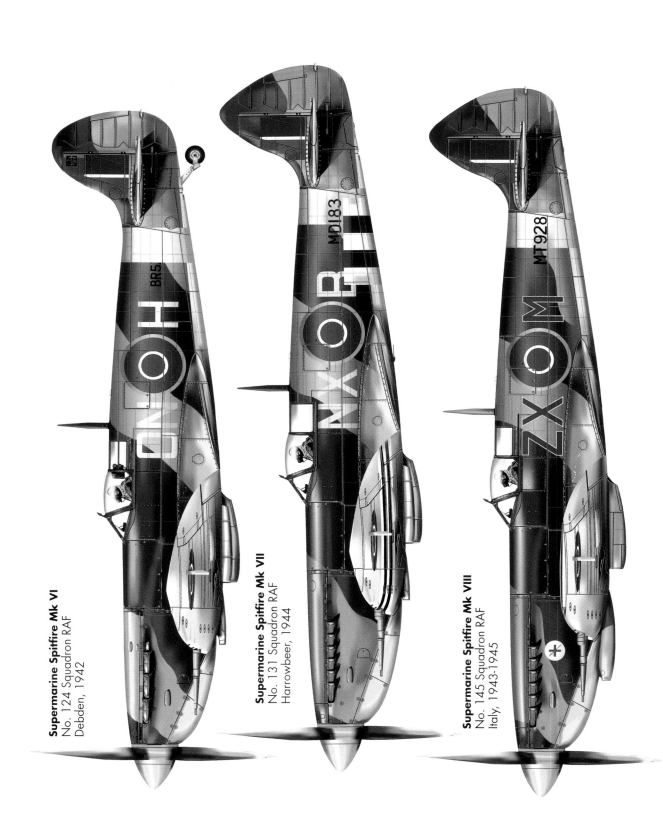

Supermarine Spitfire Mk VI
No. 124 Squadron RAF
Debden, 1942

Supermarine Spitfire Mk VII
No. 131 Squadron RAF
Harrowbeer, 1944

Supermarine Spitfire Mk VIII
No. 145 Squadron RAF
Italy, 1943-1945

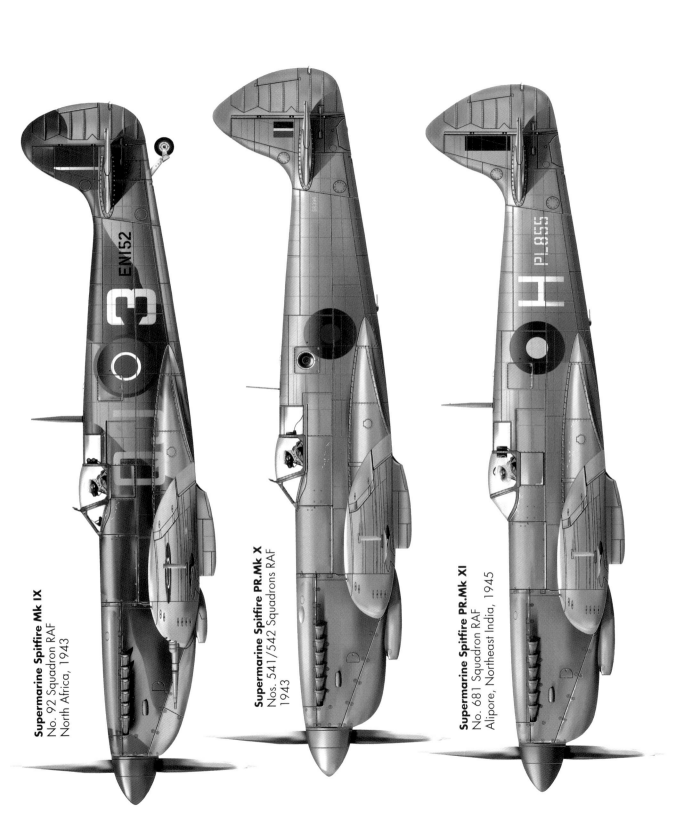

Supermarine Spitfire Mk IX
No. 92 Squadron RAF
North Africa, 1943

Supermarine Spitfire PR.Mk X
Nos. 541/542 Squadrons RAF
1943

Supermarine Spitfire PR.Mk XI
No. 681 Squadron RAF
Alipore, Northeast India, 1945

Photographed at Duxford in June 1942, Spitfire VI BR289 was used by the Air Fighting Development Unit for tactical trials before serving with 616 Squadron. It was struck off charge on 14 March 1945. (*Philip Jarrett*)

VIII represented a complete re-think of the basic Spitfire airframe, the aim being to increase its performance so that it could compete with the Fw 190A and Bf 109G. The Spitfire VIII was built in three different versions, the low-altitude LF.VIII with a 1,705 hp Merlin 66, the F.VIII medium-altitude fighter powered by a 1,560 hp Merlin 61 and the high-altitude HF.VIII with a 1,655 hp Merlin 70, the latter normally having extended wings of 40 ft 2 in span. The other sub-variants usually flew with a wing of standard planform and later examples were fitted with a pointed, broad-chord rudder. Unlike the Mark VII, the Spitfire VIII had a tropical filter, the Vokes 'Aero-Vee', a particularly neat design which did not detract from performance like the 'chin-type' filter of the Spitfire VC (trop).

Several Mark VIIIs were used to develop features that were used on later variants of the Spitfire. JF299 was the first Spitfire to fly with the cut-back rear fuselage and teardrop canopy and it was also fitted with a curved windscreen in front of the bullet-proof glazing. Another Spitfire VIII (JK535) took part in trials work at Rolls-Royce, Hucknall with a Merlin 63 and six-blade contra-rotating propellers. A total of seven Mark VIIIs (JF316-321 and NH636) took part in the Griffon engine programme. The most outlandish proposal for the Spitfire VIII

was that by Flight Lieutenant Malianowski to increase its ferry range by using the towed wing principle. He proposed mounting twin booms to the Spitfire wing's trailing edge to which was fixed a flying wing. The wing contained 450 gallons of fuel, sufficient to give a range of 2,100 miles, and the booms were to have been fixed by two universal joints to the upper surfaces of the Spitfire's wings with further fixings connected to the main spar. No Spitfire was ever modified as such, although the system was tried behind a Miles Magister.

Spitfire IX

Although it followed the Spitfire VII and VIII in number sequence, the Mark IX preceded both and was an adaptation of the Mark VC airframe to accept a Merlin 61. This engine was first flown in Spitfire III N3297 on 27 September 1941. Apart from the longer nose and four-blade propeller, the other main recognition feature was the revised radiator layout with rectangular ducts under each wing. Low, medium and high-altitude variants (LF, F and HF) were produced as for the Spitfire VIII, with the same engines as noted above, except that some F.IXs were powered by a 1,760 hp Merlin 63 or 63A. Early Spitfire IXs were fitted with 'C' Type wings but later versions appeared with the 'E' Type wing which could accommodate

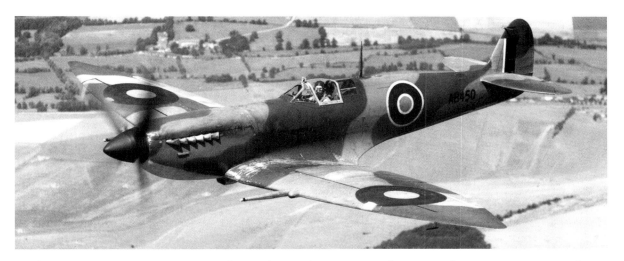

Spitfire VII AB450 in its original camouflage scheme after conversion from a Mark V in August 1942. It has a modified Mark V fuselage, retractable tail wheel, Merlin 61 engine and four-blade propeller, a 'universal' wing with extended tips, 'B' armament and rectangular section radiators under each wing. A horn balance guard has been fitted for an anti-spin parachute. (*Philip Jarrett*)

Spitfire VIII JG204 went to Farnborough in September 1943 for synthetic tropical trials before being modified to evaluate the wing of the Spitfire F.23. The wing leading edge was raised by 1 in and the contour adjusted, it had revised root fillets and the ailerons were fitted with piano hinges and trim tabs. During trials at Boscombe Down in 1944 the aircraft proved to be longitudinally unstable. (*Philip Jarrett*)

two 20 mm Hispano cannon and two 0.5 in Browning machine-guns. Mark IXs also appeared with the pointed, broad-chord rudder and two additional fuel tanks of 75 gallons capacity in the rear fuselage. Those with a cut-back rear fuselage and teardrop canopy however, had reduced rear tankage of 64 gallons. A significant improvement introduced around mid-1944 was the gyro gunsight which began to replace the old GM 2 reflector sight.

Many aircraft allocated to the low level role had clipped wings.

The Spitfire IX was quickly adapted to the reconnaissance role, 15 aircraft being modified as PR.IXs with two vertical cameras in the rear fuselage, the removal of all armament and the installation of a larger oil tank under the nose. A number of others became FR.IXs with a single oblique camera viewing through the port side, but due to their low level role, armament

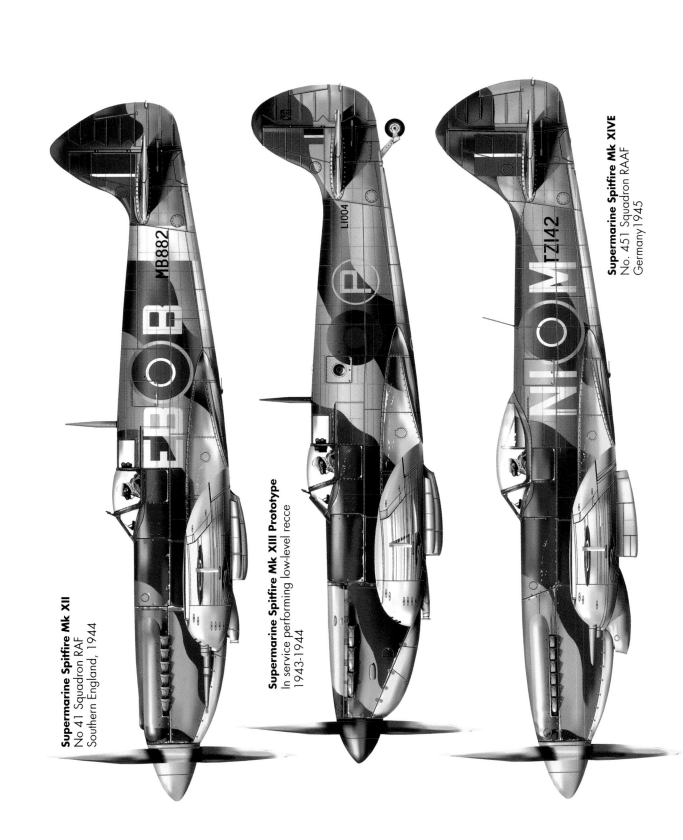

Supermarine Spitfire Mk XII
No 41 Squadron RAF
Southern England, 1944

Supermarine Spitfire Mk XIII Prototype
In service performing low-level recce
1943-1944

Supermarine Spitfire Mk XIVE
No. 451 Squadron RAAF
Germany 1945

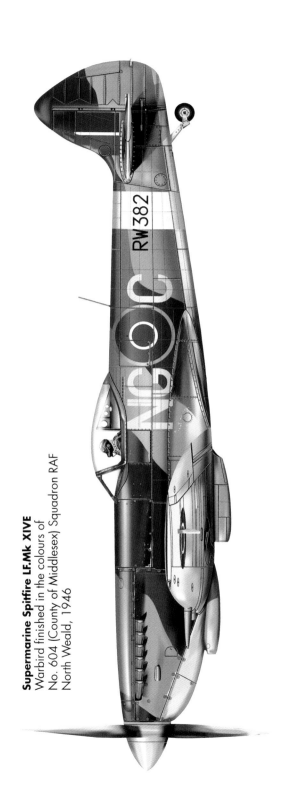

Supermarine Spitfire LF.Mk XIVE
Warbird finished in the colours of
No. 604 (County of Middlesex) Squadron RAF
North Weald, 1946

RW382

NG·C

Supermarine Spitfire Mk XIV
No. 610 (County of Chester) Squadron
Lympne, 1944

RB159

DW·D

Spitfire IX BS456 is seen in the markings of 316 Squadron coded SZ-Z. It was lost on 22 August 1943 when shot down by Fw 190s. Its pilot, F/Lt L. Kurylowicz, was rescued after spending five days in his dinghy. (*Philip Jarrett*)

was retained. Experimental versions of the Mark IX included five aircraft fitted with Merlin 77 and contra-rotating propellers. Some trouble was experienced with the translational bearing that changed the pitch of the rear propeller to match that of the front airscrew. Occasionally the bearing would fail, which usually resulted in the rear disc going into full fine pitch. This acted like a huge airbrake and even with full power selected, airspeed fell away rapidly to around 140 mph IAS. At least one contra-prop Spitfire IX (MA587) also featured a Mark XIV tail and retractable tail wheel.

Trials were carried out on several Spitfire IXs to test different overload tanks. MA210 was flown at Wright Field, Ohio with two 62-gallon Mustang drop tanks under the wings which, together with a further 43 gallons in the rear fuselage, brought total capacity up to 284 gallons, sufficient for it to fly across the Atlantic via Iceland in 1944. EN314 was also used to test a 200-gallon torpedo shaped tank that was carried under the centre section. Neither system was used operationally. One Spitfire IX (MJ892) was converted as a floatplane in 1944 - flight trials were successful but no further examples were produced.

Spitfire PR.X

Only 16 PR.Xs were built, all being originally scheduled as Mark VIIs. The first PR.X (MD192) entered service on 4 April 1944 and this variant was flown by 541 and 542 Squadrons. Although externally similar to the PR.XI, the PR.X had a pressure cabin and could be distinguished by the air intake for the blower under the starboard exhaust stack and by the heavier runners for the 'Lobelle' hood. The Spitfire PR.X was powered by a Merlin 64/77 of 1,655 hp.

Spitfire PR.XI

The PR.XI was produced in greater number than any other reconnaissance variant and eventually 476 were built. Compared with the PR.IX, it carried more fuel, the fuselage tanks of 48 gallons (upper) and 37 gallons (lower) being supplemented by leading edge tanks each capable of holding 66 gallons. Range could be extended further by the use of a 30, 45 or 90-gallon slipper tank under the centre section. An enlarged oil tank of 14 gallons was fitted under the nose resulting in a deeper profile. Armament and bullet-proof glazing to the windscreen were removed to increase performance.

Spitfire PR.X, probably MD196. This variant was powered by a Merlin 64 of 1,710 hp and was flown by 541 and 542 Squadrons at Benson until September 1945. (*Philip Jarrett*)

The deeper nose profile of the Spitfire PR.XI due to the enlarged oil tank is well shown in this view of EN654. To allow for increased sortie times, oil capacity was increased to 14.4 gallons as compared with 7.5 gallons for the Spitfire IX. (*Philip Jarrett*)

Various camera combinations were used, latterly in a universal installation in which cameras could be quickly inter-changed. Normal sets included one of the following installations : two F.52 vertical (36 in focal length), two F.8 (20 in), one F.52 (20 in) vertical, or two F.24 (14 in) vertical and one F.24 (14 in or 8 in) oblique viewing to port. Each camera had its own duct for hot air which was passed from the radiator via a heater box in the cockpit. Later some PR.XIs were modified to carry a 5 in

focal length F.24 camera in an underwing blister just beyond the wheel well for low to medium level tactical reconnaissance. The lens was splayed outboard 10 degrees and was heated by warm air taken from the adjacent radiator.

Although early PR.XIs had the standard fin and rudder, later machines were fitted with the pointed, broad-chord rudder. All had a retractable tail wheel. Power came from a 1,561 hp Merlin 61, 1,760 hp Merlin 63/63A or a

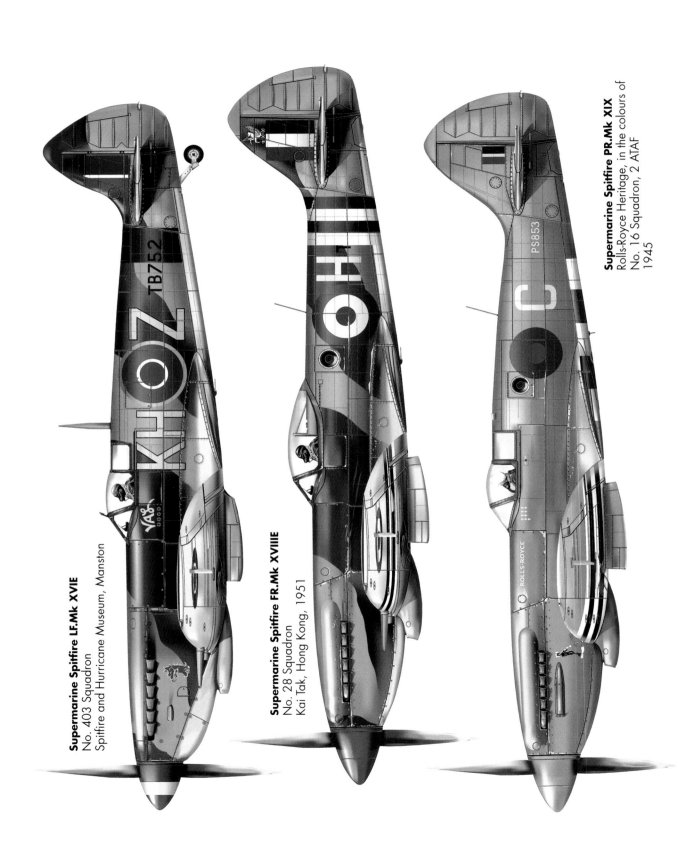

Supermarine Spitfire LF.Mk XVIE
No. 403 Squadron
Spitfire and Hurricane Museum, Manston

Supermarine Spitfire FR.Mk XVIIIE
No. 28 Squadron
Kai Tak, Hong Kong, 1951

Supermarine Spitfire PR.Mk XIX
Rolls-Royce Heritage, in the colours of
No. 16 Squadron, 2 ATAF
1945

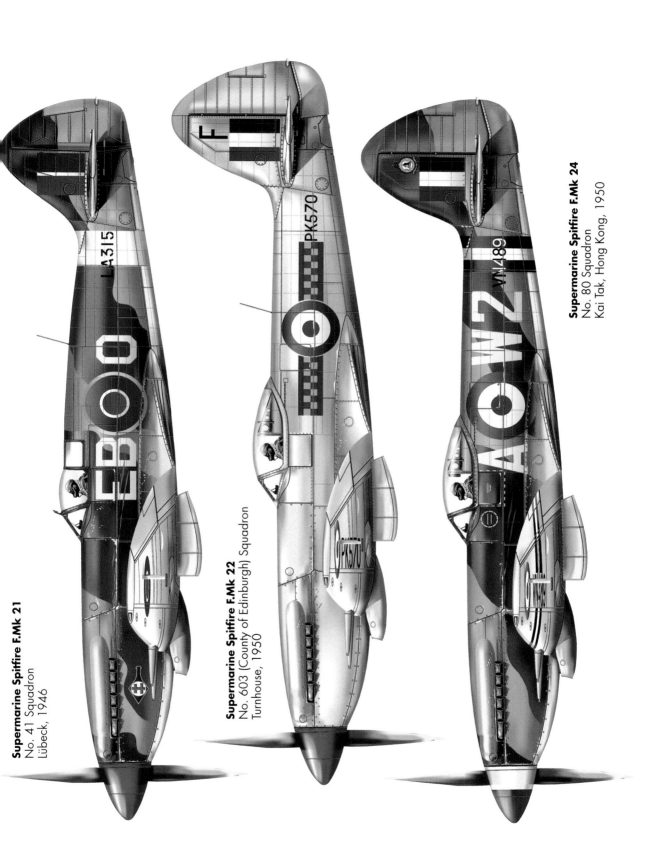

Supermarine Spitfire F.Mk 21
No. 41 Squadron
Lübeck, 1946

Supermarine Spitfire F.Mk 22
No. 603 (County of Edinburgh) Squadron
Turnhouse, 1950

Supermarine Spitfire F.Mk 24
No. 80 Squadron
Kai Tak, Hong Kong, 1950

Spitfire XII prototype DP845 at Boscombe Down in September 1942. In this view the aircraft has a fixed tail wheel. Note flaps and the small indicator protruding through the upper surface of the wing. (*Philip Jarrett*)

Merlin 70 of 1,655 hp. The PR.XI weighed only slightly less than the PR.X and was cleared to a fully loaded weight of 8,040 lbs which resulted in a wing loading of 32 lbs/sq.ft.

Spitfire XII

First of the Griffon-engined Spitfires, the Mark XII was developed from the Mark IV/XX and was powered by a 1,735 hp Griffon III/IV with a four-blade Rotol constant-speed propeller. The prototype (DP845) had a retractable tail wheel, although as early Spitfire XIIs were adapted from VC airframes they had fixed wheels. Later aircraft were, however, fitted with a retractable tail wheel. As the early Griffon engines were rated at a relatively low altitude, all examples of this variant had clipped wings to improve low-level manoeuvrability. Other noticeable features were an elongated spinner and a pointed, broad-chord rudder.

Unlike all other late model Spitfires, the Mark XII retained the smaller, circular oil cooler of the Mark V under the port wing. The repositioning of the oil tank from underneath the engine (as on all Merlin-engined variants) to the forward bulkhead resulted in a smaller top fuselage fuel tank with a capacity of 36 gallons. Armament comprised two 20 mm Hispano cannon and four 0.303 in Browning machine guns.

Spitfire PR.XIII

The PR.XIII was a conversion of former Spitfire I/V airframes with a low-altitude Merlin 32, the deletion of cannon armament and the provision of two vertical F.24 cameras (5 and 24 in focal length) and an F.24 for oblique photography as used in the PR.IG (PR.VII). In all 25 PR.XIIIs were converted, these aircraft serving with 4, 400, 541 and 542 Squadrons. Twelve were passed to the Royal Navy for use from shore bases.

Spitfire XIV

Following on from the Spitfire XII, the Mark XIV was powered by a two-speed, two-stage Griffon 61/65 driving a five-blade Rotol propeller with Jablo or Hydulignum blades. It was based on the Mark VIII airframe, but because of its extended nose and larger blade area, the XIV needed larger vertical tail surfaces. For the first time in the Spitfire's development, fin area was extended, together with an increase in the size of the rudder. As the Griffon 61 employed an intercooler, rectangular radiator ducts were located under both wings, similar to Marks VIII/IX, but of slightly deeper section. A coolant radiator was located in each duct together with the intercooler radiator under the starboard wing and oil cooler under the port wing. The first

This Spitfire FR.XIVE has a cut-back rear fuselage, teardrop canopy, five-blade Rotol propeller, 'E' Type clipped wing and an armament of two 20 mm Hispano cannon and two 0.5in Browning machine-guns. It is also fitted with a 90-gallon slipper tank. (*Philip Jarrett*)

Spitfire XIVs emerged with the 'C' Type or 'universal' wing but this was soon changed to the 'E' wing with two 20 mm Hispano cannon and two 0.5 in Browning machine-guns.

Like the Mark VII/VIII, the Spitfire XIV had fuel capacity in the wings and 13 gallons could be carried in each leading edge. The FR.XIV featured an F.24 camera for oblique photography, clipped wings and a rear-mounted fuel tank of 33 gallons capacity which was pressurised and had its own individual contents gauge. Late production examples of this variant were delivered with cut-back rear fuselages and teardrop canopies. With its increased fuselage dimensions, length of the Mark XIV was 32 ft 8 in, fully loaded weight was around 8,400 lbs and wing loading 34.7 lbs/sq.ft.

A number of Spitfire XIVs were used for experimental work. RM650 and RM689 were fitted with curved windscreens and NH717 tested a cowling manufactured in Elektron magnesium alloy which was 30 lbs lighter than the standard item. This unfortunately suffered from excessive cracking. Several Mark XIVs were tested with six-blade, contra-rotating propellers including the sixth prototype JF321 and RB144.

Spitfire XVI

The Spitfire XVI was closely related to the LF.IXE, the only principal difference being the fitting of a Merlin 266, an engine built by the Packard Motor Car Company of Detroit, USA and equivalent to the low-altitude rated Merlin 66. Apart from slight differences in dimensions, the only major alteration was the use of an electro-hydraulic supercharger gear change in place of the former electro-pneumatic system. Packard-built Merlins suffered from reliability problems in service, 127 Wing, 2nd Tactical Air Force (403, 416, 421 and 443 Squadrons) experiencing 34 engine failures in the first three months of 1945 alone.

Spitfire XVIs were produced alongside Mark IXs at the factory at Castle Bromwich in one of three configurations:– 1) standard cockpit, clipped wings and 'C' Type wing; 2) standard cockpit, clipped wings and 'E' Type wing or 3) teardrop canopy and cut-back rear fuselage, clipped wings and 'E' Type wing. Rear fuselage fuel tanks were fitted as on late model Mark IXs, these feeding straight to the engine and controlled by a fuel cock on the port side of the cockpit. The positioning of these tanks meant that the elevator and rudder cables had to pass

Spitfire XVIII TP265 spent the whole of its active life in India, initially with the RAF and then with the Indian Air Force. (*Philip Jarrett*)

through the lower tank on their way to the tail surfaces.

Spitfire XVIII

The Spitfire XVIII was a development of the Mark VII/VIII/XIV and saw action after the war with 28 and 60 Squadrons against Malayan guerrillas and also with 32 and 208 Squadrons in Palestine in 1948. In external appearance it was similar to late production Mark XIVs with a cut-back rear fuselage and teardrop canopy. Its wing and undercarriage were strengthened to cater for two 33-gallon fuel tanks positioned behind the pilot to supplement the 12.5 gallon tanks in each wing.

Of the total production run of 300 aircraft, 200 were used in the fighter-reconnaissance role with two vertical F.24 cameras and one F.24 oblique (or one vertical F.52). This installation came at the expense of one of the rear fuel tanks. Standard armament of two 20 mm Hispano cannon and two 0.5 in Browning machine-guns was retained on the FR version. Power came from a 2,035 hp Griffon 65 or a 2,340 hp Griffon 67 driving a five-blade Rotol propeller.

Spitfire PR.XIX

The Mark XIX was the ultimate PR version of the Spitfire. It had performance similar to the Mark XIV, even greater range than the PR.XI and as most aircraft were equipped with a pressure cabin, the more comfortable cockpit conditions of the PR.X. No armament was carried and the camera fit could consist of two F.52, two F.8 or two F.24 vertical cameras. With the latter installation an oblique F.24 could also be carried viewing to port.

In addition to the 66-gallon leading edge tanks, from the 25th production machine 19-gallon inter-spar tanks were fitted outboard of the wheel wells. This brought internal fuel capacity to 254 gallons (three times that of the Spitfire I). Slipper tanks of 30, 45 and 90 gallons were also frequently used on operations, even the oversized 170-gallon tank was used on occasion.

Initial Spitfire PR.XIXs were fitted with a Griffon 65, subsequent aircraft receiving a Griffon 66 which allowed the use of a Marshall Mark XIV blower to pressurise the cabin. Contrary to previous practice the blower and its associated air intake were located on the port side of the nose. A spill valve allowed air from the blower to be bypassed when not required and there was also a cock which controlled the air supply to the hood seal. The PR.XIX out-performed all other Spitfires with a maximum speed of 460 mph, a service ceiling of 43,000 ft and range of 1,550 miles.

The Spitfire PR.XIX entered service with 542 Squadron in May 1944 and was the RAF's premier photographic reconnaissance aircraft in the immediate post war period. With its pressure cabin, the PR.XIX was capable of operating at heights up to 49,000ft. Equipped with a 90-gallon slipper tank, range was around 1,400 miles. (*Philip Jarrett*)

Spitfire XX

See Spitfire XII.

Spitfire F.21

Initially known as the 'Victor', the F.21 featured a new wing that was much stronger and was of revised planform due to the use of larger ailerons to improve the rate of roll. Although the first few aircraft had pointed wingtips similar to the high-altitude Mark VII, subsequent machines had rounded tips giving a span of 36 ft 11 in. There were also two leading edge fuel tanks in each wing, one of 13 gallons and one of 5.5 gallons. The engine used was a Griffon 61 attached to a five-blade Rotol propeller, the diameter of which was increased to 11 ft (7 in greater than the Spitfire XIV). As a result the undercarriage had to be extended to maintain ground clearance and the opportunity was also taken to widen track. The wheels were also fully enclosed when retracted by inward-folding doors hinged outboard of the wheel wells.

Another new feature seen on later machines was the use of metal elevators and rudder in place of fabric covered surfaces. A revised elevator horn balance went a long way to curing the adverse handling characteristics noted on early production aircraft. Armament on the F.21 comprised four 20 mm Hispano cannon. Two ammunition boxes, one for each gun, were housed outboard of the guns and aft of the main spar holding 175 rounds (outboard) and 150 rounds (inboard). During trials with LA187 at Boscombe Down in 1945 fully loaded weight was measured at 9,305 lbs resulting in a wing loading of 38 lbs/sq.ft. This compares with figures of 5,935 lbs and 24.5 lbs/sq.ft measured during tests with Spitfire I K9793 in 1939. A number of Spitfire F.21s were fitted with Griffon 85 engines and either Rotol or de Havilland six-blade contra-rotating propellers.

Spitfire F.22

The Spitfire F.22 was closely related to the F.21 but featured the cut-back rear fuselage and teardrop canopy. It also introduced 24-volt electrics, all previous Spitfires having had a 12-volt system. The first Spitfire F.22 was PK312 which flew in March 1945. Initially it had the same tail dimensions as the F.21, but towards

PK312 was the first Spitfire F.22, seen here with the original F.21 tail. An enlarged tail was fitted towards the end of 1945. The F.22 was used by 73 Squadron in the Middle East and by nine squadrons of the Royal Auxiliary Air Force until 1950/51 when they converted to Vampire F.3/FB.5s and Meteor F.4s. (*Philip Jarrett*)

the end of the year it received the enlarged Spiteful-type tail developed to restore adequate controllability in pitch and yaw. All subsequent Spitfire 22s were delivered with these revised surfaces which increased tailplane/elevator area by 27% and fin/rudder area by 28% compared with the F.21. Armament was four 20 mm Hispano cannon plus wing pick up points for zero-length rocket projectile launchers. Some F.22s were also fitted with a Griffon 85 and contra-rotating airscrews in place of the standard Griffon 61 (five-blade Rotol).

Spitfire F.23

Just as the name 'Victor' was at first applied to the F.21, the F.23 was initially referred to as the 'Valiant'. Two machines (Mark VIII JG204 and PP139, the F.21 prototype) were modified with a high-speed aerofoil with a raised leading edge, new root fillets, and tab-assisted ailerons with piano hinges. A curved windscreen and balloon hood were fitted but the aircraft proved to be longitudinally unstable and the project was abandoned. Future work on high-speed flight concentrated on the laminar-flow wing Spiteful.

Spitfire F.24

The final Spitfire variant was adapted from the F.22. It featured increased internal fuel tankage, two additional fuel tanks each containing 33

gallons being mounted in the rear fuselage. Armament differed from the Mark 22 in that the four 20 mm Hispano cannon were of the short-barrelled Mark V type. In 1947 flight trials were carried out using VN302 under various loading conditions. With four 300-lb rocket projectiles and a full 90-gallon slipper tank, all-up weight was 12,120 lbs. This represented a wing loading of approximately 50 lbs/sq.ft, or more than double that of the Spitfire prototype. Even at this extreme weight handling qualities were deemed acceptable although it was recommended that take off be made on paved runways instead of grass surfaces, as bumps were liable to launch the aircraft into the air too soon resulting in excessive strain to the undercarriage. The only unit to fly the Spitfire F.24 was 80 Squadron, initially from Gutersloh in Germany (1948) and from Kai Tak, Hong Kong (1949-52). When 80 Squadron converted to the de Havilland Hornet, some of its aircraft were taken on by the Hong Kong Auxiliary Air Force which used them until 1955.

Two-seat Spitfires

Due to the greatly increased performance of the Spitfire compared with that of the RAF's inter-war biplane fighters, the idea of a two-seat version was put forward in 1941. In the event the desperate need for single-seat operational machines, together with the fact that new pilots

This view of a Spitfire Tr.9 before delivery to the Indian Air Force shows to advantage the domed canopy of the second cockpit. To facilitate the additional position, the front cockpit was moved forward by 13 inches which meant that the fuselage fuel tank had to be reduced in size to 39 gallons. To compensate, two extra fuel tanks, each of 14 gallons, were carried in the cannon bays. (*Philip Jarrett*)

were converting successfully to the Spitfire via the Harvard/Master advanced trainers, meant that an official two-seat variant of the Spitfire did not appear during the war years. There were, however, at least two examples of Spitfires being modified locally as two-seaters. A Spitfire VC (ES127) was converted by 261 Squadron in Sicily to have a second seat forward of the cockpit in place of the main fuel tanks. It was fitted with a windscreen (but no canopy) and was used as a hack. A more professional job was carried out by the Soviet Air Force which converted a number of Spitfire IXs to the training role by incorporating a second seat, covered by a standard canopy, behind the main cockpit.

In 1946, Spitfire VIII MT818 was converted by Supermarine to two-seat configuration by reducing the capacity of the fuselage fuel tanks to 39 gallons and moving the cockpit forward by 13.5 in. This allowed a rear cockpit to be installed with raised seat, its own windscreen and balloon hood. It was also fitted out with full controls. The cannons were deleted and additional fuel (14 gallons on each side) took their place. Initially numbered N32, it was registered G-AIDN and was the only Mark VIII to be converted. It survives in the USA.

Having proved the concept with G-AIDN, Supermarine offered a two-seat conversion of the Spitfire IX which was taken up by the air forces of India (10), Holland (3), Egypt (1) and the Irish Air Corps (6). The cockpit layout of the Tr.9 was identical to that of the Tr.8 but as the Mark IX lacked leading edge fuel tanks, two separate wing fuel tanks (13 and 14.5 gallons) were added to each wing outboard of the wheel wells and to the rear of the main spar. Four 0.303 in Browning machine-guns were retained for gunnery training. More two-seat Tr.9s have survived than any other variant, in particular those supplied to the Irish Air Corps, four of which are still airworthy (see Appendix 4).

Seafire XV

The Seafire XV was developed from the Seafire III and featured the required fuselage strengthening to accept a 1,750 hp Griffon VI and other airframe modifications. Although early aircraft were fitted with an A-frame arrester hook, later machines had a sting-type hook which was spring loaded and, on release, extended aft by about 18 inches. In the lowered position it was prevented from bouncing on hitting the deck by an oleo-pneumatic damper. It could also pivot laterally through about 30 degrees. To prevent the tail wheel being fouled by the arrester wires, it was protected by a tubular guard. Unlike the Spitfire XII, the under-wing radiators were full-size even

Seafire XVII SX311 of 1832 Squadron RNVR on HMS *Illustrious* in the summer of 1951. In 1947 this aircraft was used for assisted take off and intensive landing trials on HMS *Triumph* until damaged during a low approach when it hit the round down. Its final service use was at RNAS Stretton and it was struck off charge on 2 October 1956. (*Philip Jarrett*)

though the single-stage Griffon VI did not have an intercooler. The starboard duct carried a coolant radiator with a further coolant radiator in the port duct, together with the oil cooler. A cut-back rear fuselage and teardrop canopy appeared on the last few Seafire XVs to be produced.

Seafire XVII

In appearance the Seafire XVII was difficult to distinguish from the later Seafire XVs. The biggest difference lay internally and was the change from a 12-volt to a 24-volt electrical system. For extra range a 33-gallon fuel tank was mounted in the rear fuselage, this being replaced by two F.24 cameras for vertical and oblique photography on the FR.XVII. The Seafire XVII was capable of using rocket-assisted take off (RATOG), two rocket motors being carried adjacent to the wing/fuselage fillet. Firing time was four seconds and the rockets were jettisoned when safely airborne. For improved deck handling the Seafire XVII

had a long-stroke undercarriage, the shock-absorber struts having a travel of 8 inches.

Seafire F.45

The Seafire F.45 was the Naval equivalent of the Spitfire F.21 and was powered by a two-stage Griffon 61 driving a five-blade Rotol propeller. As the wings were standard Spitfire F.21, this variant did not have wing folding. Armament comprised four 20 mm Hispano cannon, the first Seafire to be so equipped. A number of Seafire F.45s were fitted with the Griffon 85 and contra-rotating propellers, the engine/propeller combination of the definitive Seafire F.47.

Seafire F.46

Unlike the Seafire F.45, the F.46 was of low-back configuration and was similar to the Spitfire F.22. Early aircraft tended to have the original empennage, whereas later machines had the Spiteful-type tail. The first examples were powered by a Griffon 61 with five-blade propeller, later aircraft having a Griffon 87 with

SPITEFUL F MK XIV
GRIFFON

The wide-track undercarriage of the Spiteful is evident in this view of RB518. Built as an F.14 (Griffon 69 and five-blade propeller), it was converted in 1947 to be the sole F.16 with a three-speed, two-stage Griffon 101. On trials it reached 494 mph, the fastest speed ever achieved by a British piston-engined fighter. (*Philip Jarrett*)

six-blade contra-rotating propellers. Once again no wing folding was incorporated. Only 24 Seafire F.46s were produced, a few being designated FR.46 with the installation of an F.24 oblique camera.

Seafire F.47

The first Seafire F.47 (PS944) was flown on 25 April 1946, after which another 13 aircraft in the PS serial batch were produced, all powered by a Griffon 87 with contra-rotating propellers. These were followed by others serialled VP427-VP465, VP471-VP495 and VR961-VR971 with the Griffon 88 which had a Rolls-Royce developed fuel injection and transfer pump instead of the Bendix-Stromberg induction-injection carburettor used on previous versions of the Griffon engine. Although this added 70 lbs to all-up weight, power was maintained under all conditions of 'g'. Wing folding was

incorporated with a single break point outboard of the cannon installation.

The main recognition feature of the F.47 was its extended air intake under the nose. For reconnaissance, two electrically-heated cameras (one vertical and one oblique) were mounted in the rear fuselage. The aperture for the vertical camera had a spring-loaded flap for protection when on the ground. With a 33-gallon rear fuselage fuel tank, leading edge tanks (plus 90-gallon drop tank and 23-gallon under-wing blister tanks), total fuel capacity amounted to a prodigious 287 gallons, sufficient for a range of around 1,000 miles. The F.47 was flown at the highest all-up weight of any Spitfire/Seafire and RATOG trials were carried out using VP437 with a full war load at an all-up weight of 12,450 lbs. Even heavier loads could be lifted, the F.47 being cleared for gentle flying when overloaded to 12,900 lbs.

VG471 was the first production Seafang and was delivered to Farnborough on 15 January 1946. It was not fully representative however, as it did not have wing folding and was fitted with a five-blade propeller instead of the six-blade contra-prop. Note the guard in front of the tail wheel, which is designed to prevent it being fouled by arrester wires on landing. (*Philip Jarrett*)

Spiteful

The Spiteful was in many respects a step too far in the development sequence of the Spitfire. It featured a laminar-flow wing of which much was expected, but in practice the benefits were rather disappointing and the Spiteful was soon to become an irrelevance with the end of the war and the levels of performance generated by the early jets. Although the fuselage was still that of a Spitfire, its wing was entirely different with almost straight leading and trailing edges and squared-off tips. Wing area was 210 sq.ft compared with 243.6 sq.ft for the Spitfire F.21.

Following three interim prototypes (NN660, NN644 and NN667) just 16 production Spitefuls came off the line, the first, designated F.14 (RB515), powered by a 2,375 hp Griffon 69 with five-blade propeller. The F.15 was fitted with a Griffon 89/90 driving a six-blade contra-rotating Rotol propeller and the one-off F.16 (RB518) had a three-speed, two-stage supercharged Griffon 101 with +25 lbs boost. RB518 set a speed record for British piston-engined aircraft at 494 mph, but only at the expense of a number of engine failures and a total of seven forced landings! Even then the

aircraft was only written off when it was dropped from a crane while being moved after its last premature return.

Seafang

As possible RAF orders for the Spiteful dried up the Fleet Air Arm began to show interest in a navalised variant which became the Seafang. Just two versions saw the light of day before it too was abandoned, the Mark 31 with Griffon 61 and five-blade propeller and the FR.32 with Griffon 89, contra-rotating propellers, and hydraulically-operated wing folding. Armament comprised four 20 mm Hispano Mark V cannon, the same as on the Spiteful. Provision was also made for one vertical and one oblique camera. During deck landing trials the Seafang 32, due to its lack of engine torque, was shown to be ideally suited to the naval role but despite this it did not proceed. An interesting project that never got beyond the drawing board was a development of the Seafang with completely revised fuselage and Rolls-Royce 46H (Eagle) engine driving contra-props. Known as Supermarine Type 391 it had a projected top speed in excess of 500 mph.

Appendix 1
Specifications

Spitfire Mark IXE

Dimensions: Span 36 ft 10 in; Length 31 ft 0.5 in; Height 11 ft 8 in
Wing area: 242 sq ft
Wing loading: 30.6 lbs/sq.ft
Weights: Empty 5,800 lbs; Loaded 7,500 lbs
Performance: Maximum speed 408 mph at 25,000 ft
Initial rate of climb: 3,950 ft/min
Service ceiling: 43,000 ft
Normal range: 434 miles
Armament: Two 20 mm Hispano cannons; Two 0.5 in Browning machine-guns; Provision for 2 x 250-lb and 1 x 500-lb bombs or rocket projectiles
Powerplant: Rolls-Royce Merlin 61 of 1,515 hp or Merlin 63/63A of 1,710 hp

Spitfire F.21

Dimensions: Span 36 ft 11 in; Length: 32 ft 8 in; Height: 11 ft 9.75 in
Wing area: 243.6 sq ft
Wing loading: 38 lbs/sq.ft
Weights: Empty 6,923 lbs (7,137 lbs with contra-prop); Loaded 9,182 lbs (9,411 lbs with contra-props)
Performance: Maximum speed 450 mph at 19,000 ft
Initial rate of climb: 4,900 ft/min
Service ceiling: 43,000 ft
Normal range: 580 miles
Armament: Four 20 mm Hispano cannons
Powerplant: Rolls-Royce Griffon 61 of 2,050 hp (five-blade Rotol) or Griffon 85 (six-blade contra-rotating propellers)

Appendix 2
Weapons and Systems

Spitfire VI/VII
Armament on the pressurised Spitfire VI and VII was identical to that fitted to the Mark V and comprised two 20 mm Hispano cannon and four 0.303 in Browning machine-guns. The Hispano was the primary armament of all late mark Spitfires. Although it initially suffered from a high stoppage rate its reliability was gradually improved. In the 12 months up to May 1945 the average stoppage rate in 2nd Tactical Air Force squadrons was one per 1,562 rounds, half of these being caused by the feed mechanism, not the gun itself.

Spitfire VIII
The Spitfire VIII was fitted with the 'C' Type wing, standard armament still being two 20 mm Hispano cannon and four 0.303 in Browning machine-guns. Each cannon had 120 rounds of ammunition, the Brownings each having 350 rounds. Alternatively, the four 0.303 in machine-guns could be deleted and replaced by two additional cannon, although this arrangement was rarely used due to the problem of asymmetric recoil should a cannon suffer a stoppage. This produced a strong yawing tendency which made aiming virtually impossible. With a mix of cannon and machine-guns the pilot was able to select machine-guns only via a thumb operated selector on the spade grip of the control column. The Spitfire VIII could also be operated in the ground attack role with two 250-lb bombs under the wings and one 500-lb bomb under the fuselage.

Spitfire IX
Along with the Spitfire V, the Mark IX was delivered in large numbers and was in production from June 1942 until the end of the war. Such longevity resulted in greater weapons variety than most Spitfire variants, although compared to equivalent German fighters of the period, this still did not amount to all that much. The Spitfire F.IX (Merlin 61) had the 'C' Type wing, as did the LF.IX (Merlin 66) and HF.IX (Merlin 70). In 1944 the LF.IXE began to appear with the 'E' Type wing which introduced the 0.5 in Browning heavy machine-gun. In this installation the two 20 mm Hispano cannon were moved to the outer cannon bays, the 0.5 in guns being mounted immediately inboard. Not only did the larger Browning have a heavier weight of fire than the rifle calibre weapon, its inboard position did away with aiming problems caused by wing flexing under 'g' during tight turns. This had particularly affected the outer 0.303 in guns on earlier Spitfires. Although the 'E' wing could also

accept four 20 mm cannon, this configuration was still not popular.

The Spitfire IX was capable of carrying two 250-lb bombs under the wings and a 500-lb bomb under the fuselage and was also used to fire rocket projectiles (RP), albeit in very limited numbers. The installation used by 74 Squadron towards the end of the war consisted of a 60-lb rocket on a single launcher under each wing, with a 500-lb bomb on the centreline. Spitfire IXs supplied to the Royal Hellenic Air Force during 1944 were later modified to carry rocket projectiles under the wings. Various other installations were tested including the American M10 three-tube cluster rocket launcher. This fired a 4.5 in rocket, one being fitted under each wing, but the system was never used in action.

In the reconnaissance role, the FR.IX retained its normal armament and was fitted with a 14 in F24 oblique camera. It was operated by 16 Squadron and painted in a pale pink colour scheme. A few PR.IXs were flown by 541 and 542 Squadrons, these had armament removed and a pair of 36 in F52 cameras mounted in the rear fuselage for vertical photography.

Spitfire PR.X/XI

As dedicated photo-reconnaissance machines the PR.X and PR.XI were not armed. Camera installation was either two 36 in F52, or two 20 in F8 for vertical photography, plus one 14 in F24 for oblique views. Later PR.XIs had a 5 in F24 in each wing for wide-angle verticals.

Spitfire XII

The Spitfire XII carried the standard armament of two 20 mm Hispano cannon and four 0.303 in Browning machine-guns. A single example (MB787) was tested at Boscombe Down in September 1943 with a 500-lb bomb under the fuselage.

Spitfire XIV

Early production examples of the Spitfire XIV had the same armament as the Mark XII, later machines being fitted with the 'E' Type wing with two 0.5 in Browning machine-guns in place of the four 0.303 in guns. The FR variant was fitted with a single F24 camera for oblique low-level photography.

Spitfire XVI

As the Spitfire XVI was built at Castle Bromwich on the same production line as the Mark IX the two variants were closely linked. Armament on the Mark XVI was the same as the IX and depended on whether 'C' or 'E' Type wings were fitted. It was also used extensively for ground attack with two 250-lb and one 500-lb bombs.

Spitfire XVIII

Fitted with the 'E' Type wing, the Mark XVIII had two 20 mm Hispano cannon and two 0.5 in Browning machine-guns as standard. It could also carry up to 1,000 lbs of bombs or rocket projectiles, the latter being used to good effect by 60 Squadron during the Malayan emergency in 1948-51. The FR variant retained its guns and was fitted with two 20 in F24 vertical cameras and one 14 in F24 oblique which could be positioned to view from either side of the fuselage.

Spitfire PR.XIX

The last PR Spitfire was unarmed and could be fitted with one of four vertical camera installations: two 36 in F52, two 20 in F52, two 20 in F8 or two 14 in F24. In addition an 8 in or 14 in F24 oblique camera was fitted, viewing to port.

Spitfire F.21/F.22/F.24

The final fighter variants of the Spitfire were fitted with four 20 mm Hispano cannon with 175 and 150 rounds for the inboard and outboard guns respectively. The guns could be fired selectively. Pressing the top of the button on the control column fired the inboard cannon, pressing the bottom fired the outboard guns and all four fired simultaneously if the centre of the button was pressed. Later Spitfire F.24s were fitted with the short-barrelled Mark V Hispano cannon. The wings were stressed to carry a bomb of up to 500 lbs or rocket projectiles.

Seafire XV

First Griffon-engined Seafire was armed with two 20 mm Hispano cannon and four 0.303 in Browning machine-guns.

Seafire XVII

Armament as for the Seafire XV but with provision for carrying eight 60-lb rocket projectiles under the wings.

Seafire F.45/F.46

Both the F.45 and F.46 were fitted with four 20 mm Hispano cannon and could also accommodate one 500-lb bomb under the fuselage.

Seafire FR.47

Armament for the FR.47 comprised four 20 mm Hispano cannon plus up to three 500-lb bombs or eight 60-lb rocket projectiles. The camera fit comprised one F24 vertical and one F24 oblique.

Appendix 3: Production

Spitfire VI
97 aircraft built by Supermarine
AB176, 200, 211, 498, 503, 506, 513, 516, 523, 527-530, 533-534. **BR**159, 162, 164, 167, 171-172, 174, 178, 181, 186, 189, 191, 193, 197, 200, 205, 243, 247, 250, 252, 255, 286-287, 289, 297-298, 302, 304, 307, 309-310, 314, 318-319, 326, 329-330, 563, 567, 569, 571, 575, 577-579, 585, 587-588, 590, 593, 595, 597-599, 979, 983-984, 987. **BS**106, 108, 111, 114-115, 117, 124, 133-134, 141, 146, 149, 228, 245, 436-437, 442, 448, 453, 460, 465, 472. **EN**176, 189.

Spitfire VII
141 aircraft built by Supermarine
BS121, 142, 229, 253, 427. **EN**178, 192, 285, 297, 310, 457, 465, 470, 474, 494-497, 499, 505-506, 509, 511-512. **MB**761-769, 806, 808, 820-828, 883-887, 912-916, 929-935. **MD**100-146, 159-190.

Spitfire VIII
1,654 aircraft built by Supermarine
JF274-300, 316-364, 392-427, 443-485, 501-528, 557-592, 613-630, 658-676, 692-716, 740-789, 805-850, 869-902, 926-967. **JG**104-124, 157-204, 239-275, 312-356, 371-387, 404-432, 465-500, 527-568, 603-624, 646-695. **LV**643-681, 726-756. **MB**959-976. **MD**214-256, 269-303, 315-356, 369-403. **MT**502-527, 539-581, 593-635, 648-689, 703-748, 761-802, 815-846, 872-915, 925-969, 981-999. **MV**112-156, 169-208, 231-245, 321-329, 342-346, 398-441, 456-487, 499-514. **NH**614-636.

Spitfire IX
5,663 aircraft (557 built by Supermarine, 5,117 built at Castle Bromwich)
BR581, 592, 594, 596, 600-605, 977-978, 980-982, 985-986. **BS**104-105, 107, 109-110, 112-113, 116, 118-120, 122-123, 125-132, 135-140, 143-145, 147-148, 150-152, 157, 159, 167, 170, 172, 176-177, 179-180, 183, 185, 189, 192, 194-196, 198, 200, 202, 227, 239-244, 246-252, 254-255, 292, 294, 296-297, 299, 301-304, 306-319, 383-411, 428-435, 438-441, 443-447, 449-452, 461-464, 466-471, 473-474, 506-515. **EN**122-148, 152, 156, 171-175, 177, 179-188, 190-191, 193-207, 259, 261, 265-270, 286-296, 298-309, 311-315, 329, 333-336, 339-340, 344-345, 349-350, 390, 392-394, 397-406, 444-456, 458-464, 466-469, 471-473, 475-476, 478-483, 490-493, 498, 500-502, 510, 513-514, 617. **JK**395, 611, 641, 650, 770, 796, 881-884, 980. **JL**134-138, 177-180, 226-230, 252-256, 375-377, 383-384. **LZ**816, 831-833, 836-843, 861, 888-899, 915-925, 947-956, 989-998. **MA**221-260, 299-315,

369, 398-428, 443-487, 501-546, 559-601, 615-642, 683, 687, 690, 693, 705-713, 726-767, 790-819, 831-849, 854, 860, 878-9, 884. **MB**807. **MH**312-336, 349-390, 413-456, 470-512, 526-563, 597-599, 601-604, 606-623, 635-636, 647-678, 691-738, 756-796, 813-856, 869-912, 924-958, 970-999. **MJ**114-156, 169-203, 215-258, 271-314, 328-369, 382-428, 441-485, 498-536, 549-555, 557-589, 602-646, 659-698, 712-756, 769-801, 814-858, 870-913, 926-967, 979-999. **MK**112-158, 171-213, 226-268, 280-326, 339-379, 392-428, 440-486, 499-534, 547-590, 602-646, 659-699, 713-756, 769-812, 826-868, 881-926, 939-969, 981-999. **ML**112-156, 169-216, 229-277, 291-323, 339-381, 396-428. **NH**148-158, 171-218, 230-276, 289-326, 339-381, 393-438, 450-496, 513-558, 570-611. **PK**991-998. **PL**123-169, 185-228, 313-356, 369-408, 423-466, 488-499. **PT**355-380, 395-436, 451-498, 523-567, 582-627, 639-683, 697-738, 752-795, 818-859, 873-915, 929-970, 986-999. **PV**115-160, 174-215, 229-270, 283-287, 289-294, 296-305, 308-326, 341-8, 350-9. **RK**798-819, 835-839, 841, 843-848, 850-858, 860-864, 867, 884-887, 889-890, 894, 898-901, 906-909, 911-912, 914-917, 919-920, 922-924. **RR**181-211, 228, 231-232, 235, 237-239, 241, 244, 246, 251-254, 258-260, 262, 264. SL594-595, 625-635, 648-665. **SM**135-150, 170-177, 240, 425, 441-463, 486, 504-506, 508-510, 513-515, 517-537, 539-548, 563-597, 610-645, 647, 663, 666, 668-669. **TA**738, 740, 742-758, 760-780, 793-808, 810-840, 844, 850-851, 854-888, 905-948, 960-999. **TB**115-129, 133-135, 142-150, 168-193, 195-197, 213-231, 233-236, 238-243, 249, 251, 253, 393, 413-450, 464-474, 477, 479, 482-491, 499-500, 503, 516, 518, 523-524, 527, 529-548, 563-571, 573, 575-577, 579, 584, 586-587, 638, 640-659, 674, 676-701, 703, 708, 710-712, 717-718, 736, 740, 771-808, 824-827, 830, 837-857, 909, 914, 918, 920, 924-5, 938-959, 971-988, 992, 994. **TD**155, 175, 178-183, 192-213, 287, 290-2, 294-315, 352-368, 370-371, 373-374, 378-379, 395, 399, 952-958, 970-999. **TE**115, 117-118, 121-158, 197, 205, 211, 213, 215, 230-234, 236, 238, 289-290, 292-299, 301, 303-309, 312-313, 315, 329, 331, 333, 336-337, 343, 493-535, 549-578.

Spitfire PR.X
16 aircraft built by Supermarine
MD191-199 and **SR**395-400

Spitfire PR.XI
476 aircraft built by Supermarine
BS497-499, 501-502. **EN**149-151, 153-154, 260, 263, 330-332, 337-338, 341-343, 346-348, 385,

391, 395-396, 407-430, 503-504, 507-508, 652-685.
MB770-793, 888-911, 936-958. **PA**838-871, 884-913, 926-951, 959-961. **PL**758-799, 823-866, 881-925, 949-998. **PM**123-160.

Spitfire XII
100 aircraft built by Supermarine.
EN221-238, 601-637. **MB**794-805, 829-863, 875-882.

Spitfire XIV
957 aircraft built by Supermarine
MT847-858. **MV**246-273, 286-320, 347-386.
NH637-661, 685-720, 741-759, 775-813, 831-846, 857-871, 892-929, 973-975. **NM**814-823. **RB**140-189. **RM**615-625, 648-656, 670-713, 726-770, 783-825, 839-887, 901-943, 957-999. **RN**113-160, 173-221. **SM**812-842, 876-899, 913-938. **TP**236-240.
TX974-998. **TZ**102-149, 152-176, 178-199.

Spitfire XVI
1,053 aircraft built by Castle Bromwich
MJ556. **PV**288, 295, 307, 327, 349. **RK**840, 842, 849, 859, 865-866, 868, 883, 888, 891-893, 895-897, 902-905, 910, 913, 918, 921, 925-926. **RR**205, 212-213, 226-227, 229-230, 234, 236, 240, 242-243, 245, 247-250, 255-257, 261, 263, 265.
RW344-359, 373-396. **SL**541-565, 567-571, 573-579, 596-602, 604-605, 607-611, 613-618, 620-624, 666, 668-676, 678-681, 685, 687-690, 713, 715, 717-721, 724-725, 727-728, 733, 745. **SM**178-213, 226-239, 241-258, 273-316, 329-369, 383-424, 426-427, 464-485, 487-488, 503, 507, 511-512, 516, 538, 646, 648, 664-665, 667, 670-671. **TA**739, 741, 759, 809. **TB**130-132, 136-141, 232, 237, 244-248, 250, 252, 254-256, 269-308, 326-349, 352-392, 394-396, 475-476, 478, 480-481, 492-498, 501-502, 515, 517, 519-522, 525-526, 528, 549, 572, 574, 578, 580-583, 585, 588-598, 613-637, 639, 675, 702, 709, 713-716, 733-735, 737-739, 741-759, 828-829, 831-836, 858-868, 883-908, 901-903, 915-917, 919, 921-923, 989-991, 993, 995-999. **TD**113-154, 156-158, 176-177, 184-191, 229-267, 280-286, 288-289, 293, 316-325, 338-351, 369, 372, 375-377, 400-408. **TE**116, 119-120, 174-196, 198-204, 206-210, 214, 228-229, 235, 237, 239-259, 273-288, 291, 300, 302, 310-311, 314, 328, 330, 332, 334-335, 338-342, 344-359, 375-385, 387-408, 434-471, 473-480.

Spitfire XVIII
300 aircraft built by Supermarine
NH847-856, 872. **SM**843-845, 939-956, 968-997.
TP195-235, 257-298, 313-350, 363-408, 423-456.
TZ200-205, 210-240.

Spitfire PR.XIX
224 aircraft built by Supermarine
PM496-519, 536-637, 651-661. **PS**831-6, 849-893, 908-935. **RM**626-647.

Spitfire F.21
120 aircraft built at Castle Bromwich and Supermarine, South Marston
LA187-236, 249-284, 299-332.

Spitfire F.22
263 aircraft built at Castle Bromwich and South Marston.
PK312-356, 369-412, 426-435, 481-525, 539-582, 594-635, 648-677, 680, 684, 715.

Spitfire F.24
78 aircraft (completed at South Marston)
PK678-679, 681-683, 685-689, 712-714, 716-726.
VN301-334, 477-496.

Seafire XV
450 aircraft (PR and SP serials Cunliffe-Owen Aircraft Ltd, SR and SW serials Westland Aircraft Ltd)
PR338-379, 391-436, 449-479, 492-522. **SP**136-168, 181-197. **SR**446-493, 516-547, 568-611, 630-645.
SW781-828, 844-879, 896-921.

Seafire XVII
216 aircraft (SP serials Cunliffe-Owen Aircraft Ltd, SW and SX serials Westland Aircraft Ltd)
SP323-327, 341-355. **SW**986-993. **SX**111-139, 152-201, 220-256, 271-316, 332-370, 387-389.

Seafire F.45
50 aircraft (built at South Marston)
LA428-457, 480-499.

Seafire F.46
24 aircraft (built at South Marston)
LA541-546.

Seafire F.47
89 aircraft (built at South Marston)
PS944-957, **VP**427-465, 471-495, **VR**961-971.

Appendix 4
Museum Aircraft and Survivors

Airworthy Survivors

Mark VIII
MT719 – Ex YB-J of 17 Sqn (Burma campaign) and flown by Indian Air Force post war. Acquired by Ormond Haydon-Baillie in 1977, sold to Franco Actis in Italy after rebuild. Currently with Cavanaugh Flight Museum, Dallas, Texas.

MT818 – Tr.8 with Jack Erickson, Tillamook Naval Air Station Museum, Oregon. First Vickers two-seater, flown as N32 and later as G-AIDN.

MV154 – With Robs Lamplough at Filton. First post-restoration flight 28 May 1994 in markings of 'MT928' ZX-M of 145 Sqn.

MV239 – David Lowy, exhibited at the Temora Aviation Museum, NSW, Australia.

NH631 – Preserved by the Indian Air Force Historic Flight at Palam, Delhi.

Mark IX
MA793 – Ex SAAF and Museum of Flying, Santa Monica, California where it was flown painted as 'EN398' JE-J. Purchased by Rolls-Royce and presented to Brazilian airline TAM at San Carlos.

MH434 – Flown in WWII by 222 and 350 Sqns, this aircraft was subsequently used by 322 Sqn of the RNethAF in Indonesia and later with COGEA as OO-ARA. Bought by Tim Davies in 1963 and registered G-ASJV, it was later acquired by Adrian Swire and is currently with the Old Flying Machine Company at Duxford.

MJ627 – Maurice and Peter Bayliss, Bruntingthorpe. Ex 9G-Q of 441 (RCAF) Sqn. Converted to Tr.9 in 1950/51 for Irish Air Corps as 158.

MJ730 – With Jerry Yagen, Tidewater Technical Institute, Virginia, formerly registered to David Pennell as G-HFIX and flown from Staverton.

MJ772 – Tr.9 with Champlin Fighter Museum. Mesa, Arizona. Ex Irish Air Corps 159.

MK356 – Joined the Battle of Britain Memorial Flight at Coningsby in 1997 in the 443 (RCAF) Sqn colours it wore in WWII coded 2I-V.

MK732 – RNethAF Historic Flight, Gilze-Rijen. Ex 485 (RNZAF) Sqn coded OU-Q, MK732 was allocated after the war to the Netherlands where it was flown by the Fighter School at Twente as H-25 and later by 322 Sqn as 3W-17. After spending time in the UK, it was returned to Holland and restored.

MK912 – Imported to the U.K. from Belgium in 1989, MK912 was restored by Historic Flying at Audley End and flies as SH-L of 64 Sqn. Based at Duxford.

MK923 – Ex 126 Sqn, MK923 is currently based at Boeing Field, Seattle, with the Museum of Flight.

ML407 – Tr.9 based at Duxford and operated by Carolyn Grace. Saw combat during WWII with 485 (RNZAF) Sqn. Converted to two-seater for Irish Air Corps as 162.

ML417 – Converted to two-seat configuration for the Indian Air Force, ML417 was rebuilt as a single-seat LF.IXC by Steven Grey in the 1980s. Now with Tom Friedkin and

based at Chino, California.

NH238 – Based at North Weald with Flying 'A' Services, ex RNethAF (H-60, later H-113) and Belgian Air Force (SM-36).

PL344 – Ex Kermit Weeks, now owned by Tom Blair and based in Florida.

PT462 – Flown by 253 Squadron as SW-A, PT462 later served with the air forces of Italy and Israel before being converted to two-seat Tr.9 configuration in the 1980s. Based in North Wales with Anthony Hodgson.

TE213 – SAAF Museum Flight, Lanseria, South Africa. Under restoration to fly following a landing accident in April 2000.

TE308 – Formerly with Don Plumb at Windsor, Ontario, TE308 is ex Irish Air Corps 163 and is based at Aspen, Colorado. Owned by Bill Greenwood.

TE554 – Israeli Air Force Museum, Beersheba, Israel. Ex RAF, Czech Air Force and Israeli Air Force 20-57.

Mark XI
PL965 – Served with 16 Sqn during WWII. PL965 took to the air again in December 1992 after restoration by the Medway Aircraft Preservation Society. Flown for a number of years by the Real Aeroplane Company from Breighton, it moved to the Leeward Air Ranch, Ocala, Florida in 2001.

Mark XIV
MV293 – Preserved at Duxford by The Fighter Collection, the first post-restoration flight took place in August 1992 in an overall silver colour scheme with the code OI-C of 2 Sqn.

NH749 – Ex Indian Air Force. Restored at Cranfield by Craig Charleston and flown on 9 April 1983 in SEAC colours, coded 'L'. Sold to David Price in 1985 and based at Santa Monica, California.

NH799 – Under restoration in New Zealand following an accident in January 1996 in which its owner, Sir Tim Wallis, was badly injured.

NH904 – Owned by Bob Pond and resident at Planes of Fame East at Chino, California, NH904 was formerly operated by Spencer Flack in the U.K. as G-FIRE. During WWII it was flown by 414 Sqn and post war by 610 Sqn.

RN201 – Ex 350 Sqn Belgian Air Force (SG-31). Restored by Historic Flying, made its first flight at Duxford on 24 April 2002.

SM832 – Restored to fly in May 1995 as YB-A of 17 Sqn. Subsequently flown by Christophe Jacquard at Dijon.

TZ138 – Currently owned by Robert Jens and based in Vancouver.

Mark XVI
SL721 – Former personal aircraft of ACM Sir James Robb and restored to his light blue colour scheme and J-MR codes. Based in Ottawa.

TB863 – Owned by Sir Tim Wallis' Alpine Fighter Collection and based at Wanaka, New Zealand.

TD248 – Based at Duxford with Historic Flying and painted in the silver and red colour scheme as used by 41 Sqn on one of its Spitfire F.21s for the Blackpool Air Races in 1947.

TE184 – Ex FJT-A of CGS, Leconfield, TE184 has French markings and is owned by Alain de Cadanet.

TE356 – Restored by Trent Aero in the 1980s after long-term display on the parade ground at RAF Leeming, North Yorkshire. Sold to the USA in 1990 and currently with Evergreen Aviation, Oregon.

TE384 – Sold to Australia in 1972 and flown for the first time following restoration in October 1988. Now owned by Ken McBride in San Jose, California and the subject of further restoration work.

TE392 – Operated by the Lone Star Flight Museum, Galveston, Texas, and flown in the colours of 145 Sqn coded ZX-Z.

TE476 – A former gate guardian, TE476 was bought by Kermit Weeks from Historic Flying and restored by Personal Plane Services. It went to Florida in 1995 and flies from Polk City.

Mark XVIII

SM845 – Ex HS867 of the Indian Air Force. Restored by Historic Flying in the 1990s and made its first flight in July 2000. Based at Duxford.

SM969 – Ex HS877 of the Indian Air Force. Acquired by Doug Arnold and restored, first flown in October 1985. Now in store with Flying 'A' Services at North Weald.

TP280 – Ex HS654 of the Indian Air Force. Restored by Historic Flying and flown in July 1992. Owned by Rudy Frasca at Urbana, Illinois.

Mark XIX

PM631 – Based at Coningsby with the Battle of Britain Memorial Flight.

PS853 – Initially allocated to CPRU at Benson, served with 16 Sqn at Melsbroek, Eindhoven and Celle. One of three PR.XIXs used by THUM Flight for gathering meteorological information 1951-57. Ex BBMF, now with Rolls-Royce at Filton.

PS890 – Formerly with the Royal Thai Air Force, PS890 made its first post-restoration flight at Chino in May 2002 modified with contra-rotating propellers, Griffon 58 and clipped wings. Owned by Planes of Fame.

PS915 – Based at Coningsby with the Battle of Britain Memorial Flight.

Recent Losses

TE566 (Mark IX) – Crashed on landing at Wonderboom Airport in South Africa on 25 April 2002 killing its owner Mike Snoyman.

PL983 (Mark XI) – Crashed during an attempted forced landing at Rouen 4 June 2001. Pilot Martin Sargeant killed.

Museum Aircraft

Mark VII

EN474 – Smithsonian National Air and Space Museum, Washington, DC.

Mark VIII

JF294 – National Museum of Military History, Saxonwold, South Africa.

JG267 – Darwin Aviation Museum, Australia.

NH631 – Indian Air Force Museum, Palam.

Mark IX

BS464 – Musee de l'Air, Le Bourget.

EN145 – Israel Air Force Museum, Beersheba.

EN199 – Malta Aviation Museum.

MH350 – Royal Norwegian Air Force Museum, Bodo.

MJ143 – Royal Netherlands AF Museum, Soesterberg.

MJ271 – National Aerospace Museum Aviodrome, Schiphol.

MJ755 – Hellenic War Museum, Athens.

MJ783 – Musee de l'Armee, Brussels.

MK805 – Italian Air Force Museum, Lecce.

ML255 – Museo do Ar, Alverca Ribatejo, Portugal.

ML427 – Birmingham Museum of Science and Technology, U.K.

NH188 – Canada Aviation Museum, Rockcliffe, Ottawa.

NH417 – Egeskovmuseum, Denmark.

TE565 – Museum of Aviation and Space, Prague, Czech Republic.

Mark XI

PA908 – USAF Museum, Wright-Patterson AFB, Dayton, Ohio.

PL979 – Royal Norwegian Air Force Museum, Gardermoen.

Mark XIV

MT847 – Manchester Museum of Science and Technology, U.K.

MV246 – Musee de l'Armee, Brussels.

MV370 – Gunter Leonhardt Museum, Hanover.

RM921 – Belgian Air Force Museum, Florennes.

SM914 – Royal Thai Air Force Museum, Bangkok.

Mark XVI

RR263 – Musee de l'Air, Le Bourget.

RW388 – Potteries Museum, Hanley, Stoke-on-Trent.

RW393 – Royal Air Force Museum, Cosford.

SL574 – San Diego Aerospace Museum, California.

SM411 – Polish National Museum, Krakow.

TB752 – RAF Manston Memorial Building.

TE214 – Canadian Warplane Heritage Museum, Mount Hope, Ontario.

TE288 – Royal New Zealand Air Force Museum, Wigram.

TE456 – War Museum, Auckland, New Zealand.

TE462 – Museum of Flight, East Fortune, Scotland.

Mark XVIII

SM986 – Indian Air Force Museum, Palam.

TP285 – Dutch War Museum, Overloon, Holland.

Mark XIX

PM627 – Swedish Air Force Museum.

Mark F.21

LA198 – Restored at Museum of Flight, East Fortune, due to be exhibited at the Kelvingrove Museum, Glasgow.

LA255 – RAF Wittering, preserved by 1 Sqn.

Mark F.22

PK355 – Zimbabwe Military Museum, Harare.

PK481 – RAAF Association, Bull Creek, Western Australia.

Mark F.24

PK683 – Hall of Aviation, Southampton, U.K.

PK724 – Royal Air Force Museum, Hendon.

VN485 – Imperial War Museum, Duxford.

Appendix 5: Spitfire Models

Academy
2130   Spitfire XIV, 1:72; RB159 DW-D of 610 Sqn
2157   Spitfire XIV, 1:48; RM619 AP-D of 130 Sqn
2161   Spitfire XIVE, 1:48; NH895 NI-K of 451 Sqn

Airfix
2081   Spitfire IX, 1:72; JE-J of W/C J.E. Johnson, 1943
5107   Spitfire VIII, 1:48; UM-C of 152 Sqn
7105   Spitfire F.22/24, 1:48; 603 Sqn Turnhouse 1951, F.22
        of 73 Sqn Malta or F.24 of 80 Sqn Hong Kong 1951
7106   Seafire 46/47, 1:48; FR.46 of 1832 NAS 1947
        or FR.47 of 800 NAS HMS Triumph, Korea 1950

CzechMaster
1097   Spitfire F.22/24, 1:72; 5-blade and contra prop,
        decals for 2 a/c (resin kit)

Fujima
72132   Spitfire PR.19, 1:72

Hasegawa
AP042   Spitfire IX, 1:72; JE-J of W/C J.E. Johnson
9424   Spitfire IX, 1:48; a/c 'Z' of 73 Sqn
9408   Spitfire VII, 1:48
ST019   Spitfire VI, 1:32; ON-H of 124 Sqn
JT079   Spitfire IX, 1:48; SZ-G of 316 Sqn + a/c of 443 Sqn
JT081   Spitfire VIII, 1:48; a/c of 145 Sqn

Heller
0282   Spitfire XVI, 1:72; GE-D of 349 Sqn

ICM
48062   Spitfire VII, 1:48; 131 Sqn
48063   Spitfire IX, 1:48; Israel AF

48064   Spitfire IX, 1:48; DU-A of 312 Sqn or Czech AF
48065   Spitfire VIII, 1:48; USAAF markings
48068   Spitfire IX, 1:48; GW-D of 340 Sqn Free French
48069   Spitfire IX, 1:48; Italian AF
48076   Spitfire IX, 1:48; Dutch AF
48078   Spitfire IX, 1:48; DU-N of F/L O. Smik, 312 Sqn
48079   Spitfire IX, 1:48; Danish AF

Italeri
094   Spitfire IX, 1:72; LO-D of 602 Sqn

KP
3115   Spitfire IX, 1:72; 145 Sqn (W/C S. Skalski)
3116   Spitfire IX, 1:72; JH-M of 317 Sqn
3160   Spitfire VIII, 1:72; DG-R of 155 Sqn
3161   Spitfire XVI, 1:72; AU-Y of 421 Sqn

MPM
48040   Spitfire IX, 1:48; Decals for six different a/c
72086   Spitfire PR.XI, 1:72; USAAF, RAF Europe or SEAC

Occidental
0202   Spitfire IX, 1:48; 132 Sqn
0212   Spitfire IX, 1:48; JE-J of W/C J.E. Johnson

Silver Cloud
4802   Seafang F.32, 1:48; Limited edition, pewter metal
castings

SMER
0891   Spitfire VI, 1:72; ON-H of 124 Sqn

Appendix 6: Spitfire Books

Andrews, C.F. and Morgan, E.B.,
Supermarine Aircraft Since 1914 (Putnam, 1981)

Bracken, Robert,
Spitfire – The Canadians (Stoddart Publishing, 1995)

Dibbs, John and Holmes, Tony,
Spitfire – Flying Legend (Osprey, 1996)

Dick, AVM Ron,
Spitfire, RAF Fighter (Airlife Publishing)

Franks, Norman,
Buck McNair – Canadian Spitfire Ace (Grub Street, 2001)

Henshaw, Alex,
Sigh For A Merlin – Testing The Spitfire (Crecy, 1999)

Houlton, Johnnie,
Spitfire Strikes – A New Zealand Fighter Pilot's Story
(John Murray, 1985)

Jackson, Robert,
Spitfire – The Combat History (Airlife Publishing)

Morgan, Eric B. and Shacklady, Edward,
Spitfire – The History (Key Publishing, 1987)

Price, Alfred,
The Spitfire Story (Arms and Armour Press, 1986)
Spitfire – A Documentary History (Macdonald and Jane's, 1977)
Spitfire At War (Ian Allan, 1974)
Spitfire At War – 2 (Ian Allan, 1985)
Late Mark Spitfire Aces (Osprey, 1995)

Quill, Jeffrey,
Spitfire – A Test Pilot's Story (Crecy, 1998)

Rae, Jack,
Kiwi Spitfire Ace, (Grub Street, 2001)

Robertson, Bruce,
Spitfire – The Story of a Famous Fighter (Harleyford)

Sager, Arthur,
Line Shoot – Diary of a Fighter Pilot (Vanwell Publishing, 2002)

Scutts, Jerry,
Spitfire In Action No.39 (Squadron/Signal, 1980)

Index

ANGLER'S MAIL

HOW TO SUCCEED AT
COARSE
FISHING

HOW TO SUCCEED AT
COARSE
FISHING

DAVE COSTER

Consultant Editor: Roy Westwood

HAMLYN

All photographs by Roy Westwood

First published in Great Britain in 1994
by Hamlyn
an imprint of Reed Consumer Books Limited
Michelin House, 81 Fulham Road,
London SW3 6RB
and Auckland, Melbourne, Singapore and Toronto

ISBN 0 600 58075 X

A catalogue record for this book is available from the British Library

Printed in Spain

CONTENTS

REWARDS AND OPPORTUNITIES

Take up coarse fishing and you're normally hooked for life. Many millions of anglers will testify to that fact but ask them to explain the chief reason for their compulsion and you'll receive as many answers as there are rivers.

One of the major attractions must be the mystery element. Wherever you fish, another world lies beneath the surface and it's impossible to predict what might come along next.

But the magnetism of fishing does not simply stem from its unpredictability. The thrill of a good fish streaking off with your bait, the sudden arc of the rod, the resultant thump which transmits into your hands, this is an experience not to be missed!

Angling in any of its multiple forms has an uncanny knack of heightening the senses. It could be that unseen quarry attached to your line, or just the feeling of expectation as a float is towed away into the depths. Whatever the cause, it most definitely grips your imagination to the exclusion of everything else. No wonder many anglers admit they experience a marvellous sense of peace while sitting at the waterside.

There are still many unspoilt areas of the country where coarse fishing will undoubtedly take you, but even industrialised areas of canal and river possess their own particular magic. No matter where you go coarse fishing, it will always give you time to reflect and that's surely a benefit worth seeking when most of us live and work in the fast lane.

The beauty of coarse fishing is that it remains relatively inexpensive for newcomers. There are certain junior fishing kits on the market for under £20 which include enough gear to give a flavour of the sport...and to catch that all important first fish.

But a more realistic estimate for a basic starter outfit would be around £100. There's enough good budget tackle around nowadays to be able to test the water, before committing yourself too heavily.

Once you have got yourself kitted out, it shouldn't prove too difficult to find some good fishing. Numerous commercially run, small stillwaters have opened in recent seasons. They are often highly stocked and for the price of a day ticket, offer the beginner a great chance of bagging a big fish – or good catches of smaller ones.

Then there are many hundreds of prolific and well managed club waters, where you don't necessarily have to be an expert to catch some fish.

Once on the bank, the first major challenge to confront any angler, whether novice, or highly experienced, is how to approach and make the best of the swim.

There are numerous critical decisions to take including choice of suitable tackle, baits and methods and the need to identify which part of the swim should be concentrated on. As experi-

ence is gained, this task becomes slightly easier, but the answers are never cut and dried.

Water and weather conditions are constantly changing and a successful formula one day may fail miserably the next.

All this is part and parcel of the sport, a fascinating aspect in fact, which is another reason why anglers are held spellbound all their lives.

SEPARATE GROUPS WITHIN THE SPORT

Coarse fishing embraces several quite distinct categories of angler. The majority are pleasure anglers, who basically go out for their own enjoyment, either individually or in company. Many become very proficient, and sometimes progress into the more competitive spheres of the sport.

Club anglers usually go on regular group outings to a variety of waters. A more competitive aspect enters here. There are often small sweepstakes with cash prizes for the anglers taking the heaviest catches. And, at the end of the season, trophies may be awarded for the top specimen fish, biggest catches and the most consistent points scorers.

Club fishing offers various social functions and regular meetings. It's a very good way for the beginner to learn quickly.

Matchmen often emerge direct from the club scene. Competitive angling has become very professional and some of the top performers are almost making a living from their match winnings. Sponsorship deals from tackle companies may also be involved.

A mature Hertfordshire gravel pit dug during the Second World War to build fighter plane runways. The coloured water suggests there's a good stock of bottom stirring feeders like carp and bream.

Quivertipping on the tidal Yare in Norfolk. The rod is raised high to keep as much of the line as possible clear of the strong flow.

Match fishing revolves around team events and Open competitions for individuals. Team fishing is extremely popular and there are many leagues, including National Championship Divisions and the *Angler's Mail* Super League series. Open matches are listed every week in the *Mail* and offer a unique opportunity for even the raw beginner to line up alongside leading international stars.

Specialists, or specimen hunters as they are commonly called, are dedicated to the pursuit of specimen-sized fish, most notably carp, pike and barbel. These anglers might set themselves tough personal targets and some spend months in search of a specific, known fish.

Heavyweight carp are the most popular species for the majority of specimen anglers. The capture of one fish may entail many hours, even weeks, camped out by the waterside.

CHOOSING A VENUE

There's a vast network of gravel pits and lakes available to the coarse angler along with thousands of miles along rivers and canals. Local clubs and associations control much of this fishing and they issue season or day tickets. There are also private syndicate waters where membership and access is restricted and, at the other extreme, commercially-run complexes where the

---

FIRST BUY A ROD LICENCE

All anglers aged 12 and over must purchase a rod licence issued by the National Rivers Authority. A single national licence covers the entire country but does not actually confer the right to fish anywhere. Very few stretches of water are free and you'll normally have to buy a day or season ticket in addition to the national rod licence.

The cost of the rod licence has been the subject of fierce debate but there are concessions for anglers aged 12-16, the registered disabled and senior citizens. The licence is valid for two rods

when fishing for coarse fish or eels.

The coarse fishing season runs from June 16 to March 14 although many enclosed stillwaters have traditionally offered all-year-round sport, but only where local byelaws permit the relax-

The rod licence helps pay for fisheries work carried out by the National Rivers Authority.

ation. These laws are now under review.

The principle reasons for maintenance of the Close Season are protection for spawning fish and other wildlife through the Spring. But the need for this protection has long been the source of dispute and fish frequently spawn in the opening months of the season.

The Close Season will probably always stay in force on rivers but stillwaters are sure to remain a bone of contention whatever the NRA decrees.

Boats limit sport on canals in high summer but it's still possible to catch fish between the traffic.

accent is very much on accessibility for all-comers.

Choosing a venue can start within the pages of *Angler's Mail* itself and the Where to Fish feature which describes the location and potential of day ticket venues throughout the UK. The local tackle shop is also a very good source of information and many sell tickets and club books for nearby venues.

Where day tickets are sold, they might be obtainable from a bailiff on the bank, or sometimes in advance from a tackle shop, post office, or private address. Most publicity about waters, explains which procedure is required and sometimes the signboards at fishery entrances explain how and where to buy tickets.

Where season permits, or club books are needed, you may have to apply in advance, but it's not normally a particularly complicated process and generally membership details are well publicised.

Day tickets cost on average from £2 to £5. There are usually concessionary rates for half day, or evening visits, and special rates for children, the disabled and senior citizens.

Season tickets are well worth considering if you intend to fish a particular venue frequently. They can work out much cheaper in the long run, often costing between £10 and £30 for at least nine months' fishing.

Membership of large angling associations like London AA and Birmingham AA, will open up more venues than you could possibly cover in the space of a year.

Another option is to join a commercial fishery group. A good example in the South East area is Leisure Sport, who offer a tremendous choice of gravel pit fisheries for a relatively modest annual outlay.

Some specialist waters are run on a syndicate basis. This prevents too many anglers flooding onto the venue, but can be an expensive option and sometimes there's a long waiting list to join.

Different types of venues can produce different species and the fish may also have very diverse feeding habits from one water to the next. The beginner will do well to note that the skill factor also varies in catching these fish, even when the same species are present in varied types of water.

Rivers may hold species normally associated with running water, such as barbel, chub and dace. But they often also hold more widely distributed fish like roach, bream and carp. Canals are often linked to rivers and it's not unusual to find large colonies of river fish like chub and dace living in them. Just as commonly canal venues

The unmistakable perch with its sharp dorsal spines.

The changing seasons have a bearing on how fisheries perform. In the warmer summer months, higher water temperatures make the fish considerably more active. It's easier to tempt bites and to draw fish with liberal amounts of feed.

When the fish are feeding well at these times, the angler can often get away with less finesse in both his tackle and feeding technique. Fish will often take baits up in the water, or even on the surface.

Good catches are still possible in winter, but with much lower water temperatures, the fish are sometimes very lethargic and may be tightly shoaled in their cold weather quarters. Some species only feed for short periods when water temperatures rise by a degree or two.

Now the angler must be very precise and careful with his feed and scale down the tackle and bait size to gain bites in the cold water. Static, bottom presented baits may be the only way to tempt a response.

will hold good stocks of roach, gudgeon, perch, tench, bream and carp.

Common species you'd expect to find in stillwaters are roach, perch, tench, carp, bream and pike. But the boom in highly stocked commercial lake fisheries has led to the introduction of more exotic fish like koi and ghost carp, golden and blue orfe and golden tench. Even experiments involving out and out river species like barbel have had some successes in enclosed lakes.

PICKING THE FIRST ROD

Great care is required, even when selecting a basic starter kit. Cheap rods are only really designed for the holiday maker and merely scratch the sport's potential. Telescopic rods are

Carbon match rod fitted with durable lined rings.

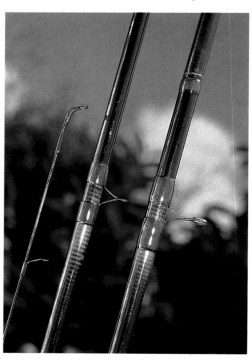

a good example. They might pack into a suitcase for a trip abroad, but they are normally on the short side and rather lacking in casting action.

The best starting point for someone wanting to coarse fish with float tackle is to choose a three-piece, carbon composite rod of at least 12 feet in length. These are often called match rods. There's plenty of good models in the £30 to £40 category and you will soon discover the extra length makes life a lot easier when casting out and retrieving the tackle.

The softer, more forgiving action of a match rod allows you to use realistic tackle on venues where the fish may be shy and require a lighter approach.

It's a good idea for younger anglers to start with a float fishing kit. The only modification here might be determined by the length of rod they can physically hold. But settle for a reasonable length, at least ten feet. It's also preferable to get a three-piece, rather than a telescopic, or two-piece model.

Cheaper kids' fishing kits, which come complete with rod, reel and some accessories, may contain a three-piece solid glass rod and these are passable. Two piece, solid rods are too short, have large eyes and are really meant for spinning. Avoid them if float fishing is the objective.

At the cheaper end of the market, rod blanks are usually made from a composite of glass and carbon. More expensive rods have a higher carbon content.

At the top end of the price range, high carbon rods are extremely light and incredibly thin. Don't let this fool you! They are surprisingly strong, have very fast actions and cost between £90 and £400.

Float rods tend to be three-piece and feature a gentle progression of between ten and 15 line guides or rings down to their tips. They're generally made in lengths between 11 and 14 feet.

Legering, or quivertip rods often start as two-piece blanks in their shorter ten feet lengths. These may look similar, or even double up as short float fishing rods. But they can be singled out by the tip ring which usually has a screw fitting. This enables a quivertip, or swingtip bite indicator to be fitted.

Other quivertip rods have a much thinner tip section, which is spliced-in, with tiny line guides – fitted quite close together. These models often feature brightly painted tips, because this is the part of the rod which shows up bites.

More expensive legering, or feeder rods may be three-piece and can go up to 13 feet in length for long range fishing. These normally have several inter-changeable quivertips, which plug into the blank proper. Multi-tip rods start at around £50 and go up to about £150. They are very versatile. The tips in most makes also fit other multi-tip rods, so a single design's capabilities can be further enhanced.

Browsing over the rod racks in a tackle shop you will notice slight gaps where the sections come together on some assembled rods. This will be seen on spigot joint models and isn't a fault!

The lower section is spigotted and fits inside the next section up. The slight gap is to allow for wear and tear and stops the sections from working loose under the stress of casting.

The overfit joint system is also common. Here the upper section of rod fits snugly over the very gradual taper of the next section down. There is no spigot and this tends to make for slightly softer actioned blanks. Sometimes with this type of rod the tip section slots over the middle piece in the same fashion. But there are also designs where the tip piece can actually push into the next section down.

Basic Actions

Match, or float fishing rods have two main actions. Tip action means the blank is stiffish,

but has a fine, softer tip. This type of model is often favoured for river fishing where top and bottom attached floats, like sticks, balsas and Avons are used.

In order to get such a forgiving tip – which allows the use of fine lines – a short length of finer solid carbon is often spliced into the tip section of the blank. The strike is often to the side,

Above: **Feeder rod featuring inter-changeable quivertips which are stored inside the handle when not plugged into position.**

Left: **Overfit and spigot joints.**

Tip Action – usually spliced tip – is favoured for stick and balsa fishing on rivers.
Through Action – usually hollow tip – is ideal for long range work with wagglers.

or slightly upwards with tip actioned rods. Their fast actions are designed to lift line cleanly off the surface.

Through actioned rods rarely have a splice, unless they are very soft and short like some specialist canal models. They generally have hollow tips and bend gradually throughout their length when put under pressure.

These designs are used for long range fishing with waggler, or bottom-end attached floats. Less effort is required to set the hook. Often, the strike is low and less hurried, leaning the rod into a taking fish.

RINGS AND HANDLES

A factor which helps to determine rod price is the type of line guide, or ring the manufacturer whips to the blank.

Cheap rods often have chrome guides. They will stand up to a fair bit of use, but will eventually need replacing. Ceramic lined guides have a much greater life span and they cause far less friction on the line as it travels through them. These should last several years.

There are also very streamlined, one-legged, models which suit ultra thin, carbon float rods. They won't detract from the rod's action in any way at all.

Silicone carbide guides are the most expensive and hard wearing. They are only to be found on top of the range specimen, match and feeder rod designs. These may up the price of the rod dramatically, but it should be remembered that they will probably never need replacing.

Most rod handles are still covered in cork, but you will also find some companies experimenting with synthetic rubber handles, or a combination of both materials. Rubber, or Duplon handles have received a mixed reception. This material is now mainly to be found on split handled specimen rods and as an end grip on certain top range match rods.

Standard reel fittings consist of two collars which lock the reel onto the handle. It's best to check these provide adequate security. Some cheaper rods have alloy fittings which tend to work loose while fishing. Plastic and graphite fittings are better formed and generally help the reel to sit more snugly and comfortably on the rod handle.

Some top flight float rods now have screw-in reel fittings, where the upper part of the handle tightens down onto the foot of the reel. These are very secure.

Most split handled specimen rods also have screw fittings to keep the reel from working loose during long casts.

REEL CHOICES

FIXED SPOOL Three types of reel are commonly used in coarse fishing. The most popular is the fixed spool. This design has an open face, exposing the line spool. It is probably the best, least complicated reel for a beginner.

Once the bail arm is opened, line flows out unhindered on the cast. Greater distances are achieved and there are rarely any problems with the line bedding in on the spool.

The only drawback with open-faced models occurs when fishing into a facing wind. The line does have a tendency to billow back and tangle around the bail arm mechanism.

TEST CURVES

Test curve readings are rarely applied to match style rods - their fine tips would have pretty minimal readings anyway.

They are really only relevant for rods which are used to cast heavier weights over greater distances. Some specialist feeder rods do now give a casting weight guide.

But test curves are more in the domain of specimen rods, where carp anglers particularly, think nothing of punching out a bait 100 yards.

The test curve of a blank is gauged by pulling the tip of the rod down into a 45 degree angle with a spring balance. Typical specimen rods will give readings of 1 lb to 3 lb.

The test curve is used as a rough guide to judge the casting weights the rods will comfortably handle. The common equation here is to relate poundage of test curve into casting ounces.

Therefore a 2 lb test rod should be comfortable casting around two ounces.

The system is showing signs of being outdated by modern specimen rods, which can be pushed a lot further than their test curve readings might suggest.

There's some very good, budget priced rods for the budding specimen hunter. Carbon composite, 11 foot models can be purchased for between £35 and £50.

Slimmer full carbon blanks from 11 to 13 feet - the extra length is desirable for long range casting - cost between £70 and £300.

KEY PERFORMANCE FEATURES

A: The open-faced fixed spool – first choice for any newcomer.

B: Wide line roller which rotates smoothly is vital.

C: Stern drag with variable settings is adjusted to release line if the pressure exceeds the breaking strain. The anti-reverse switch is turned on to prevent the reel backwinding.

Some fixed spool models have automatic bail arms. They work on a trip mechanism, so if you flick any part of the bail with your index finger as you cast, it will open in one movement and release line. These reels are popular with competition anglers where speed is so vital.

Most fixed spool reels have manual bails. This isn't a handicap as it doesn't take long to get used to opening the bail with your free hand, before casting. Then the index, or second finger of the rod hand is used to trap line against the spool as the rod is positioned. The line is released and allowed to flow out freely as the rod is brought forward to cast the tackle.

Some fixed spool designs have front drags, or clutches, but on the majority they're mounted at the rear. One slight advantage of the rear drag is that it doesn't get in the way if you need to make any adjustments while playing a fish.

The function of a drag is to regulate how line is released from the reel when the bail arm is closed. Some anglers set the drag lightly, as an added insurance if they strike a bit hard. This should prevent the hook length from breaking and also guards against line breakages when playing a good fish, should it bolt off unexpectedly.

Some experienced anglers prefer to tighten the drag right down, relying solely on backwinding the reel if a big fish runs hard with the tackle,

but it's safer to slowly work up to this stage.

Another important feature to look for on this particular reel design is the line roller. This is located to one side of the bail arm and on a good reel will rotate as line is retrieved. It protects the line from excessive wear as you wind in heavy tackle, or a fish, and it will also cut down on line twist and generally gives your reel line a longer life span.

Many reels now have ball bearing actions. One ball bearing is usually good enough to make a reel very smooth in its handling. Top models may have two, or three and this does make a noticeable difference, producing even greater

The classic Mitchell Match set the standard for automatic reels. The bail is simply depressed slightly to flick open.

13

Front drag fixed spool.

Shallow match spool and deeper model for heavier lines.

Bottom right: **Closed face reel - copes well in a facing wind.**

smoothness, which in turn helps to eliminate problems when bringing in fish and tackle.

Most reels have two options for engaging the bail arm. The first and most often used is automatic. Simply turn the handle and the bail springs back into place and you can start start retrieving line.

The alternative is manual. The bail is folded back into position with your free hand and clicks into place. This is preferable when trotting your tackle on running water.

If you strike and connect with a fish while the bail is open, you will have already trapped the line against its spool with one of your rod hand fingers. Now your free hand can close the bail onto the line. This prevents any slack line, or jolting movements, which might result in the hook losing its hold.

Any attempt to transfer a taut line from its trapped position by winding the bail arm shut, causes all sorts of problems.

When viewing reels you will notice some have shallow and others deep spools. Many models in fact come with two, or three spools and these may vary in depth.

Shallow spools are for lighter, float fishing reel lines in the 2 lb to 3 lb breaking strain category. Deep spools take thicker, stronger monofilaments and are either for legering, or heavier duty work.

It's also worthwhile remembering that wider designs of line spools tend to store the line better. It won't twist-up so easily and certainly shouldn't tend to bed-in, which can cause casting difficulties.

CLOSED FACE Closed face reels, as the name suggests, have a housing over the line spool. There's also no bail arm. Instead, the line is released by pushing a button, or skirting at the front of the reel.

These models are very popular on running water. This is because the line can be very tightly controlled as it is fed out. This helps when trying to slow float tackle down, against the flow, which is often a vital way of enticing bites on hard fished waters.

The closed face has a pick-up pin hidden inside. This will retract as the front button is pushed to release line. The pin will then re-engage as the handle is turned, so once a fish is on, the line can be easily wound off your fingers – if a fish has been hooked while trotting the tackle.

Closed face reels are mainly used for short range fishing, but most match anglers also carry them as a back-up for awkward conditions, where a facing wind might cause problems with fixed spool designs.

These models will cope with longer casts, such as when fishing waggler tackle, but often a slightly bigger float with a heavier loading is required to get the required distance. The enclosed line is restricted slightly when casting with these reels.

CENTREPIN Centrepins are not recommended for beginners. These are specialist reels, and take some getting used to, mainly because they are so free running and need operating in a very controlled manner.

Although centrepins can be used in diverse ways, they have gained a reputation as excellent trotting reels. This is due to the way the reel will rotate on its own – if the tackle is balanced correctly – when fishing flowing water. This method relies on top and bottom attached floats. By gently prodding the drum of the pin, as the tackle is laid onto the water, the drum will carry on rotating and feeding line. This results in a unique form of tackle presentation, keeping the float leaning back as it trots.

In plain English, it causes a very slight slowing down of the tackle and this technique is particularly favoured by anglers after river roach – a species renowned as fickle feeders.

The other main role for centrepins is for fishing close-in when after another river species, barbel. This type of reel can be used when laying on with float tackle, or when fishing a light link leger. Barbel tend to bolt when they pick up a bait and sometimes conventional reels can't cope with this initial surge.

But the centrepin has no restrictions on the line and responds well to these sudden demands. Some models do have drag settings, but these are very light and will still release line fast enough to compensate for an unexpectedly sharp pull. In

Specialist centrepin built by Dave Swallow of Ringwood has milled edge on the drum for improved grip.

fact, the clicking sound the drag makes is often used by barbel specialists as a bite indicator.

HOW THE POLE SCORES

While rod and line fishing is an essential part of learning the art of watercraft, there is another equally effective way of catching fish and that is with the pole.

Earlier this century, the roach pole as it was known, was something of a specialist item, limited to just a very small band of canal anglers. In those days poles were heavy, being made from bamboo, or other hollow woods. But because they were longer than most rods, advantages were exploited in catching shy biting fish like canal roach.

A shorter line between the pole tip and float

REEL POSITION TILTS BALANCE

It is very important to position a reel correctly on a rod. Many beginners fix the reel too far down the handle, making the rod feel top heavy.

In 99 per cent of cases, it's best to fit the reel very close to the top of the rod handle. This achieves a balanced position and the rod won't feel over-weighty if you are holding it for long periods.

It also means you can support the butt of the handle under your elbow when playing a good fish, so the increased weight puts less of a strain on your arm.

Check that the reel fittings fit flush to the corks and offer a secure hold for the reel without any suggestion of slackness or wobble.

Fit the reel in this position and you'll achieve a better balance.

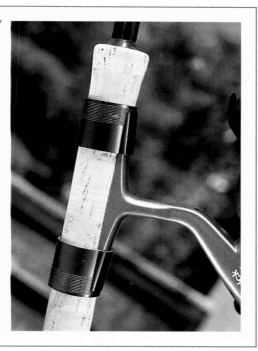

The great benefit of a pole is its ability to present ultra fine tackle with absolute precision.

results in more bites being hit. That's especially true with baits like hempseed, which bring lots of very fast bites.

The roach pole re-emerged as a good catching method with the advent of fibre glass models, but these were still relatively heavy and cumbersome. Pole fishing only really began to be taken seriously with the emergence of carbon fibre models.

The method also soon lost the 'roach' tag, because the new breed of extra long and extremely light poles suddenly opened new doors, as a very potent way of catching most species on most types of venues.

Today's poles are very sophisticated. Top of the range models extend as long as 15-16 metres. Most ten-metre models are also very manageable in one hand. Space age technology has advanced incredibly the strength, lightness and stiffness factors in carbon poles.

The main disadvantage with pole fishing used to be the lack of give, if a big fish was hooked. Anglers had to rely on the finer tip section to absorb punishment on the end tackle. The tip was often referred to as a flick tip and these are still used for some types of pole fishing, particularly when after small fish.

Often, this wasn't enough to stop good sized fish and pole anglers resorted to ringing up poles, even fitting them with small reels.

The main advancement in pole fishing, has been seen in the internal shock absorbing systems now being used. Much of the development in this department originated in this country, even though it was the Continentals who actu-

ally started the pole revival several years back.

Specially treated pole elastics come in numerous grades, specifically designed for different species and sizes of fish.

There's also special PTFE bushes which are fitted at the forward end of hollow top sections of the pole – through which the elastic emerges. This self lubricating material keeps everything smooth running.

But the main secret of pole fishing undoubtedly lies in superior presentation of tackle and hook baits. Often, when the running line angler is struggling to present his tackle in an acceptable manner, the pole man is capitalising. Much smaller and delicate floats can be fished than with running line rigs.

This translates into better, more hittable bites. The tackle can be manipulated to encourage bites when the fish aren't really in a feeding mood. It's possible to edge the hook bait along the bottom, to lift it invitingly, sometimes to virtually coax it into the fish's mouth!

The pole will also hold a hook bait dead still when the water is racing through – a feat near impossible with rod and reel tackle. Long poles can also be used to lower baits into areas not very accessible to rod and reel.

An experienced pole man will not be afraid to drop stepped-up tackle into a tiny opening in thick weedy areas, or guide his float right up against the opposite bank cover on canals, or small rivers. The long pole will often extract particularly good fish from such areas, simply because the pole tip is directly overhead and it can be used to steer the fish from snags. There is noticeably less control with the shorter rods.

The distance between the pole tip and float is also minimal compared to running line, so even shy, half hearted bites are hittable.

BUYING POINTERS

When shopping for important items of tackle, make sure that the product feels right. Don't be swayed by sales talk. If an item seems comfortable in your hands, remember it will be you who will be using the rod, reel, or pole at the end of the day!

Tackle choice is difficult for a beginner, so it's better to try and lead the retailer into showing you several items in a particular category. Then you can choose, rather than being directed to one product.

It's uncanny how a rod, reel, or pole which feels right the first time you pick it up, turns out to be exactly that when you get it on the bank.

There are many other pointers here which will eventually become second nature as experience grows.

When picking up a rod in a tackle shop, ask the tackle dealer if he would mind pulling the tip down. This indicates the rod's action and what it will handle. (It is better to let the retailer do this anyway because accidents do happen and it's more likely to be at the tip end of a rod, rather than the handle!)

If you're also purchasing a reel, don't be afraid to ask if you can fit one to the rod you like. It needs to balance and you won't know this until you try.

When holding a fully assembled rod you also want to try jiggling it about a bit. This trick soon exposes any loose joints. Normally you will hear them knocking, you may even feel this transmit up the blank. Don't be afraid to request another rod from the stockroom, if there are any doubts.

When selecting a reel, make sure it sits securely on the rod of your choice. If it's loose, ask the tackle dealer if he can change the reel grips on the rod. Plastic ones are superior to alloy and might only add about £1 or so to the bill!

Also, make sure you can reach the front edge of the line spool on a reel with the fingers of your rod hand. This is very important, so you can feed out line, or cast properly.

Look for free running reels, not stiff actioned ones. If the bail arm engages jerkily, look to another model.

Check before you commit yourself to see if a particular model is supplied with spare spools. If it doesn't, make sure that the extra spools are easy to obtain.

Pole choice is the most difficult of all. You can ask to be shown the pole outside the shop if it isn't big enough for the pole to be fully erected. Remember most long poles feel good at 8-10 metres, but some suddenly turn very sloppy in action as 11, or 12 metre sections are added. Insist on seeing the whole pole erected!

Also make sure the sections fit properly and will come apart with ease. You don't want to spend the next six months constantly rubbing male sections down with wet and dry to get a good fit!

A very good tip when a pole is fully set up is to ask someone to hold it, while you take a look back down its length from the tip end. It's amazing how this will highlight any badly sagging sections. A good actioned pole will have a very gradual curve. Steer clear of models with butt section sag. This tends to transmit down the whole length, when you strike and generally adds up to a sloppy action.

Another important question needs asking here – is the pole supplied with any spare tip sections? These will inevitably be required, so you can carry several grades of elastic shock absorber, ready set-up. Ask about the availability of spare sections, just in case you need any more, or suffer an accidental breakage. Most tackle shops offer a good after sales service.

A ROD FOR EVERY JOB

Venue choice and the angler's objectives generally influence tackle selection. So an angler who intends to exclusively fish big rivers may be happy to go equipped with a tip actioned float rod and maybe a medium to long range feeder rod-as a back-up. But this gear wouldn't suit a canal, or lake venue. A softer, through-actioned float rod would be more suitable here and for legering, or feeder fishing, softer quivertips are required to spot what are often more leisurely and less positive stillwater bites.

The angler concentrating on canal fisheries might well select a pole as his first line of attack while those with big fish in mind will want stiffer actioned specimen rods.

All this needs to be borne in mind when visiting a tackle shop. State your objectives as precisely as possible and the tackle dealer should be able to pinpoint your exact needs.

ACCESSORIES

There are hundreds of accessories in coarse fishing from bread punches to waders. Here is a small selection of the more important items which will almost certainly become part of your kit.

BAIT WAITER

The idea of the waiter is to keep the bait conveniently close to hand. Regular feeding is made a lot easier if you don't have to stretch for hookbaits and groundbait.

The most common type is made from moulded plastic with recesses to take standard bait boxes. There's a centrally fixed screw with a standard thread which fits most bank sticks. It's a good idea to use an adjustable stick to position the waiter at the right height, for both sitting and standing.

Table top waiters are popular with competition anglers and the most versatile are fitted with four adjustable legs making them suitable for hard banks like canal towpaths. This particular design holds up to six square bait boxes.

The most basic waiter is a simple aluminium tray with a bank stick screw fitting.

CARRYALL

Most standard carryalls feature a side pocket with drainage holes for the keepnet and landing net. The main compartment is for bait boxes and there's usually enough room left for a flask.

Deluxe carryalls may have extra end pockets for accessories like catapults and bags of groundbait. These usually have a zip-up top flap, so the contents are kept dry.

The better carryalls are fitted with a shoulder strap, as well as the usual carrying handles – useful for long hikes to distant swims.

BANK STICKS

Most anglers carry a selection of bank sticks in various lengths and thicknesses – larger diameter ones are usually more robust.

The most versatile bank sticks are telescopic, either those with a locking nut, or perhaps a thumbscrew, so they can be fixed at exactly the correct height for whatever accessory they are supporting.

All bank sticks have a uniform thread, so they will accept just about any rod rest head, keepnet, angle lock, target board, pole roller, or bait waiter.

Bank sticks are usually made from a lightweight alloy, but practically all of the more expensive and durable designs are made of stainless steel. Most bank sticks have pointed ends, but you can get some flanged types. It is worth remembering, however, that the flanged ones won't swivel round in soft ground.

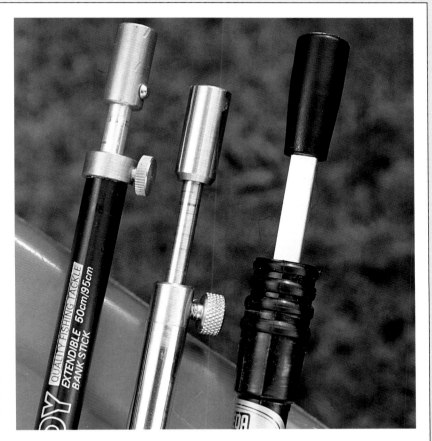

KEEPNET

Basic keepnet shapes are round and square. Round nets are generally cheaper and surprisingly often have a longer life-span. Square nets store neatly in carryalls and offer the fish more room if you tend to visit venues with very shallow margins.

The main drawback with square designs is that the corners tend to wear out quite quickly. But you can purchase special clip-on edge protectors which will prolong the life of the net by preventing the corners from rubbing against rough bottoms through wave action.

It's best to buy a large net if only to be fair on the fish you intend to keep in it. Longer nets are handy anyway when fishing from awkward high banks, or in shallow margins so you can stake the end sections out into deeper water.

Net materials vary in mesh sizes and some are fitted with a sacking type base which provides a dark sanctuary for the catch. Knotless keepnets which are soft to the touch have become universally used following bye-law changes which have created minimum standards for the whole country.

Mono mesh, which is quick drying and odourless, has also become popular and is equally kind on the catch.

Always stake keepnets out and, if possible try to position them in a shady area. You shouldn't aim to retain fish unless you really have to and then don't keep them in nets for over-long periods.

FLOAT TUBES

While it is possible to store many floats in tackle boxes, some have awkward shapes, or are too long. It's possible to buy round or square float tubes. Some also have the handy facility of extending for protecting those really long wagglers. If you haven't enough room to keep a tube in your tackle box or carryall, it's often possible to slip one in a side pocket of a rod holdall. Some anglers use float tubes to store spare quiver and swingtips.

ROD HOLDALLS

The best holdalls feature a padded shoulder strap, plenty of room inside the main compartment for protective rod tubes and a couple of side compartments for umbrella and bank sticks.

Some holdalls open from the top and a zip runs at least a third of the way down their side for easy access. There are also roll-up versions which open out completely.

In the tackle shop you'll see some designs which accept up to ten tubes, standard models take about five or six rods, but there are specialist, longer holdalls which are used by carp anglers in particular. These have side reel pockets so two piece specimen rods can be strapped inside with the tackle made up.

Check the strength of the stitching because the holdall is almost certainly going to be subjected to a great deal of wear and tear. Drain holes in the base and umbrella compartment are also desirable.

The average holdall should last for many seasons so make sure your choice of model meets all of your requirements.

ELECTRONIC BITE INDICATOR

Electronic bite indicators with audible alarms and visual LED displays are chiefly used used by carp and other specialist anglers, especially when fishing with more than one rod.

The top-of-the-range indicators usually have volume and tone controls and a latching light which comes on for several seconds, directing you to the right rod.

CONTINENTAL TACKLE BOXES

Expensive continental tackle boxes are constructed with lift-up trays, or pull-out drawers, which usually comprise the top section of the box.

The lower section holds larger items such as reels and on many models you'll also discover built-in adjustable legs. The box invariably has a cushioned seat and the leg facility helps you to achieve a comfortable sitting position, even on fairly awkward banks, which is vital when pole fishing.

Systems like the Conti-Box pictured have many optional extras and will almost build into a complete fishing station. It's possible to purchase different size drawer and tray units, to customise the box for your own requirements.

Side drawers allow easy access to small items like hooks, line and shot without having to move from your fishing position.

The base unit holds a surprising amount of gear.

LEGERING REST

For quivertipping work it's advisable to use a wide front rod rest head, with several channels where the rod can be positioned. The Drennan Quiver Rest is adjustable and low slung for easy location. It allows the rod to be critically positioned to gain the optimum setting for the very sensitive quivertip.

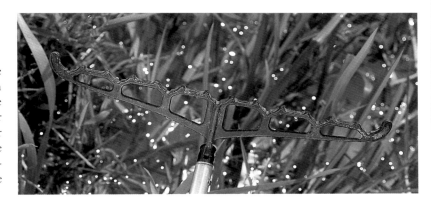

FRONT AND REAR ROD REST HEADS

Rod rest heads for float fishing need a wide gape, so the rod can be positioned easily. The front rests should have a groove to prevent the reel line being trapped under the rod, and the back rests must be reasonably deep and stay upright under the weight of the rod.

Some rests are fixed in one position, while others are adjustable with a ratchet, or locking nut system. This facility is very handy on front rests, which are often set at an angle on a long bank stick to position the rod out over the water.

UMBRELLA

The main sizes are 45 and 50 inch. A 45 inch umbrella could be classed as standard size and there's certainly enough room underneath to keep angler and gear dry. The 50 inch models offer more room when the brolly is used to support a bivvy for longer sessions.

Most up-market umbrellas incorporate a tilt device and this is very useful when there's a side wind, combined with rain.

LANDING NET

Round, or pan landing net heads are the most universal. The best types have fine mesh bottoms and larger mesh sides. This prevents them from getting too waterlogged and heavy to lift on a long handle. Rigid frames are preferred to triangular nets with a flimsy front cord.

Triangular shaped nets are favoured by many big fish anglers. These offer a wider gape at the leading edge but, all things considered, I believe that the circular frames tend to be more efficient.

It is possible to use cheaper, alloy handles on smaller nets. But the best handles are of the two or three-piece telescopic glass fibre, or carbon types. Some of these can reach up to ten feet in length, fully extended, thereby reaching over nearside weed. Long, one-piece handles up to six feet in length are popular with specimen anglers.

Waders

It's a good idea to always keep a pair of waders in the car. They might not be needed on some venues, but will make life a lot easier when banks have been eroded by boat traffic, or where you need to stand out some way in shallow water, so you can cast freely without snagging dense bankside vegetation.

Most waders withstand at least two or three seasons of hard use but leaving the tops permanently rolled down could cause premature cracking of the rubber in time.

Suspend them by the belt straps in the garage when not required – and take great care in the vicinty of barbed wire! That's ruined many a fishing trip and brand new waders.

Wader repair kits are obtainable through tackle shops and adequately deal with small rips.

Never leave waders in the boot of the car between trips – perspiration quickly affects the linings!

Trolley Platform

There are some very good angling trollies, which will take tackle box, carryall and sometimes the rod holdall as well.

Other trollies convert into platforms and the Boss Tackle Developments design is a classic example. This model even has pneumatic tyres, to make it much easier to pull large loads over the roughest of terrains.

In its platform mode, this design has six adjustable legs, making it very stable. But it is the greater mobility over uneven terrain that is its greatest strength when compared to those makes fitted with solid, nylon wheels.

There are many venues where it's not possible to get a comfortable sitting position. A fishing platform solves this and also often allows you to gain vital extra yards, by setting up your stall well out in shallow margins.

DISGORGERS

These are essential if a fish swallows the hook. Providing you locate the disgorger's groove on a taut line, and then run it into the fish's mouth, it's a simple task to gently nudge, or turn the hook free.

Micro disgorgers are designed for small hooks and won't damage fine lines. Standard sizes remove spade end hooks from size 14s to 20s. Larger models are suited to most larger spade end hooks and they also work on medium to small sized eyed hooks.

With larger mouthed fish, it's sometimes more practical to remove the hook with surgical forceps.

Brightly coloured disgorgers which float are probably the best buy, as these tend to disappear from the tackle box with frustrating regularity.

Alternatively, use a lanyard attachment to suspend the disgorger from around your neck or keep it propped in the bait box.

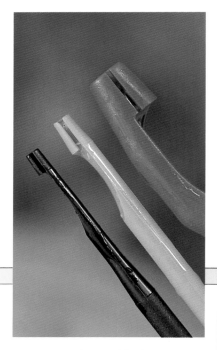

SCALES

Clock face scales are easy to read and usually incorporate an adjuster for zeroing in the weigh bag. Lightweight, compact sets can be stored away in a tackle box just in case you want to check-out the weight of an exceptional fish, or catch. There's also very expensive and highly accurate match fishing scales which weigh down to grams and can cost several hundred pounds.

Spring balances are even more compact and surprisingly accurate. These are not sophisticated enough for serious competitions, but are fine for personal use. Tubular versions like the Salter are available in several weight bands.

SHOT PLIERS

Non-toxic shot is rather too hard to bite onto the line. A pair of shot pliers allow you to position the shot perfectly, apply just the right amount of pressure and fix the weights exactly where you want them.

Shot pliers can also be used to move stubborn weights which might otherwise damage fine lines. Loosen the shot by applying pressure against the split. This should open the shot's grip enough to be able to slide it to a new position.

OTHER GEAR

CHAIRS

While most coarse anglers choose to sit on solid tackle boxes, some prefer the comfort of lightweight chairs.

The Shakespeare design folds away neatly and has a carrying strap. Fox designs have adjustable legs for use on uneven banks and are low slung, making them comfortable for extended stays at the waterside.

These are by far the most versatile and feature disks on the feet to stop the chair sinking into soft mud.

GROUNDBAIT MIXING BOWL

Although you'll see square mixing bowls in the tackle shop, round models are more practical for achieving really consistent ground-bait mixes. By adding water gradually and stirring vigorously, the water is worked into the whole mix. With square designs it's possible to miss groundbait which collects in the corners. Clean out the bowl after the session to avoid the build-up of stale fragments.

TARGET BOARD

In summer and autumn, bites are mostly easy to spot when quiver or swingtipping. But this changes in winter when the fish are more lethargic and may only move the 'tip a fraction of an inch. By positioning a target board, as a backdrop behind the bite indicator, these very small indications are magnified.

A target board could make all the difference on really dour days.

ALL ABOUT BAITS

Good, fresh bait catches the most fish. Watch any expert angler setting up by the waterside and you'll see different baits, such as casters, maggots and hemp, all carefully segregated in their own bait boxes. If the weather's hot, and the angler has travelled some distance to the venue, he may even have transported the bait in a cool box.

It is worth seeking out local tackle shops which have a reputation for selling quality bait. Those shops which are popular with matchmen will usually stock the biggest and freshest maggots and casters.

Buy your maggots neat and check that the bran, maize meal, or sawdust is added after they have been measured out into your bait boxes. Beware of tackle dealers who only dabble in fishing gear. They may not have good refrigeration facilities on the premises and offer you a pint containing old, small maggots and dirty sawdust. You'll end up paying the same price for a poor product and much less of it!

Good bait draws more fish into your swim. It also behaves in the correct manner to catch fish. Old casters and sweaty maggots often float, which are no good if they drift out of the swim. Fresh bait also hooks well. It is softer skinned and more attractive to the fish.

TIPS ON STORAGE AND PREPARATION

Bait quickly deteriorates if it's not looked after correctly. Maggots, casters and cooked hempseed should be stored in a fridge, particularly if they're collected well in advance of an trip.

Clearly, it's not always practical to keep livebaits in the kitchen. Keen anglers solve the problem by purchasing a cheap, second-hand fridge for use in the garage.

If you don't have this facility, there's still a lot you can do to maintain bait in a reasonable state. In hot weather, place your casters and cooked hemp in a cool box, along with a couple of ice packs. You'll need to replace the ice packs every 12 hours.

Out of a fridge, maggots are best stored in lots of sawdust, or bran. It is important to give them plenty of air to keep them cool. This is best achieved by laying them out in large, shallow trays. Position them in a shady, dry place, such as a shed, or garage floor.

Casters are purchased in plastic bags, normally in either pint, or half pint measures. If they're to be retained for any length of time, casters require air to keep them alive and prevent scorching of their skins against the bag. They will use up what little oxygen is inside, so it's best to open bagged casters after eight to 12 hours and to breathe them for five minutes. Also shake them in the bag, so those pressed up against the sides get moved.

You'll need to reseal casters to retard their development because if they are allowed to darken too much they become floaters. But when sealing a bag of casters, it's prudent to leave a little air inside.

Maggots stored in a fridge should be kept in open topped, deep sided containers. Sawdust and bran are the best storage mediums. Maize flour helps keep maggots soft, but don't put too much of this on the bait while it's stored, because it cakes-up and may make the maggots damp. Maize is, in fact, best added to maggots just before you go fishing. It revives and softens flagging bait, absorbs any excess moisture and makes the bait easier to riddle and feed.

Most anglers carry a small maggot riddle in their kit and shake off any storage media on the

Hemp and casters – a winning combination.

Right: **Sometimes a specific colour of maggot like bronze works better.**

bank, before starting fishing. Neat bait is easier to feed and you don't get a face full of sawdust every time you throw, or catapult some maggots into the swim.

Hempseed is a very good attractor and holds fish well. It can work on its own, but is also very potent when used with maggots and casters.

It is easy to boil your own hemp in an old saucepan. Remember hemp swells to almost double its original volume, so you need to carefully gauge how much you think you will need. Pour the dry seeds into the saucepan and add approximately the same amount of water. Bring this to the boil and then let the bait simmer, until most of the seeds slightly split open and are showing small, white shoots.

When the bait reaches this stage you will need to wash it off with cold water –this is best done through a strainer –in order to stop it from overcooking. Cooked hemp can be stored in the freezer compartment of a fridge. It's not a bad idea to prepare and bag up a large quantity all at once, so you can take a pint or so as it is required.

If the hemp is still frozen solid by the time you reach the venue, it will thaw out in just a few minutes if you drop a bag of it in your keepnet and suspend it in the water, while you tackle up. If you are short of time and facilities, cooked hemp is available in most good tackle shops.

COLOUR AND SEASONAL FACTORS

Many pleasure anglers are happy to go fishing with a pint of maggots and perhaps a small bag of groundbait. This simple approach catches fish, but often a little research before an outing can make you better prepared for the particular way a venue is fishing.

The types of baits which anglers regularly feed

REVIVING STALE BAIT

In an ideal world it would be nice to take perfect bait on every trip, but things go wrong! The tackle shop might have the odd late delivery, or coldroom problems in really hot, humid weather. Large volumes of maggots are very hard to keep. They give off a great deal of ammonia, which is a constant worry to the tackle dealer. The ammonia eats through pipework, causing a big coldroom to lose gas and unexpectedly heat up. So very occasionally you are bound to get some slightly below par bait, no matter how good your supplier.

There may also be the odd occasion when maggots sweat-up on the way home from the bait shop, or you simply forget to transfer them to the fridge. Whatever the reason for livebait getting out of sorts, it will result in some shrinkage and give off a rather nasty odour.

Warm, active bait deteriorates further if you take no action. It's best to quickly riddle it, which is the fastest way of cooling it down and this process also removes smelly sawdust. Add clean dust, or bran which will clean and cool the maggots further.

Poor bait can also be revitalised by adding some concentrated flavouring. There are specially formulated maggot flavourings you can buy in the tackle shop, and liquid flavours used by carp anglers on boilie baits are also suitable. Sweet and savory smelling baits will enhance your chances of catching. A good flavouring will also help to draw fish to maggot baits in coloured water more quickly.

Add some flavouring to revitalise stale bait.

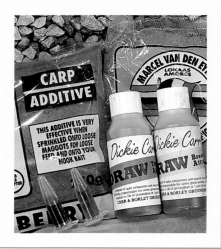

into different venues strongly influence what the fish will accept. In many cases, they will become preoccupied with a particular type of bait and you could be wasting your time by trying to wean them onto something else. There will, of course, be occasions when a different approach works wonders but in general it's advisable to follow form.

There are few venues where you won't get bites on maggots. This is, after all, the best selling bait up and down the country. But you'll find a particular colour works better on some waters, bearing in mind commercial maggots are widely available in white, bronze, red, yellow, fluorescent pink and sometimes even an exotic green!

The fish might prefer a specific colour because it is used most frequently by anglers or closely resembles their natural food. In either case, if you have done your homework, you are likely to experience more action if you have the right shade of maggots.

In similar fashion, a water may respond better to casters than maggots. This is often the case when after bigger fish. They might have grown wary of maggots, or the casters could mimic a natural food on which the fish like to forage.

Another point worth remembering with an inert bait like the caster, is that it won't attract smaller fish as readily as a lively maggot. Putting a caster on the hook might take you longer to get a bite, but it also gives bigger, slightly less active fish a chance to find it.

Bait requirements change with the seasons. Some are more associated with summer fishing. A classic example is sweetcorn which is productive for species like tench, bream and carp, from June right through to September. But once the first signs of night frost appear, it rapidly loses its effectiveness.

Although hemp attracts fish and holds them in a swim for most of the year, as a hookbait it only fishes consistently in the warmer months. This applies to most seed baits.

Other baits have good winter reputations. When the water is really chilled and goes very clear, it can be a devil of a job to buy a bite with maggots, and yet a small piece of worm, jigged along the bottom, will entice an immediate response.

Small pellets of bread, known as punched bread, fished with a cloudy groundbait will also bring a lack-lustre swim to life.

Matchmen often turn to baits like bloodworm and jokers in winter. These are the bottom dwelling larvae of the midge and represent the

Above: **Punched bread – capable of bringing a swim to life when fished with cloudy groundbait.**

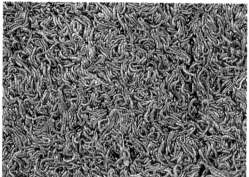

Left: **Bloodworm – wriggle enticingly in cold water.**

staple diet of several species, notably bream and carp. The bright red, and lively worm baits still wriggle enticingly in very cold water Fish might turn up their noses at conventional, lifeless baits, but bloodworm and joker have an almost magical way of exciting them into feeding. It's possible the angler relying on maggots might not get a bite when there's ice in the margins of stillwaters while those using bloodworm are invariably kept very busy.

HOW MUCH BAIT TO TAKE?

The best policy is to try and take a selection of baits with you on every trip. Obviously, if you've discovered a bait with good form for the water in question, this will be the No.1 line of attack and form the bulk of what you take. But if you also carry smaller quantities of other baits, you have other options if bites dry up at some stage.

It's also a good idea to feed different baits in different parts of the swim. That allows you to rest an area, and this is a ploy which very often brings the first line back to life again, later on in the session.

The Role of Groundbait

Groundbait has to be tied in closely with feed baits and, of course, hookbaits. The type of groundbait you use is also dictated by venue characteristics and the target species.

There are many different types of groundbaits, but selection is made easier, if you bear in mind the most important reasons for using it. These are:

■. To attract fish.
■ To act as a carrier to get other feed baits into the swim.
■ To hold fish in the vicinity of the hookbait.

Groundbaits can be mixed in differing ways, regulated by the amounts of water you add. That way it's possible to achieve different consistencies. You can also purchase different consistencies. Some are soft, fine and cloudy. There's also very heavy, binding mixes...and quite a few in-between! It's also perfectly viable to blend several mixes together, in your search for a special consistency.

Cloudy groundbaits are normally used in stillwaters. Regular feeding of them tends to spur fish into activity on hard waters. This type of mix also pulls fish up, off the bottom.

There's lots of medium consistency groundbaits. Most Continental brands will form a cloud if mixed very dry or wet, but mix them somewhere in-between and small balls of feed begin to disperse as they near the bottom. This type of groundbait is the most popular, because it's ideal for feeding squatts, bloodworm, jokers and casters.

Heavy, binding groundbaits are used to stiffen softer mixes. On their own they make a good carrier for getting loose baits to the bottom in flowing water. They will form larger balls, which break down slowly after they reach the bottom of a swim, releasing particles of other baits which have been mixed in.

Small amounts of some heavier consistency groundbait are also used to pack the particle baits into open-end swimfeeders.

It is possible to form plugs of groundbait at each end of the feeder trapping the particles inside.

Taking the right quantity of bait is often determined by the type of venue and the species you are after. Normally, you'll need more bait on a river, or when seeking big fish like barbel. Generally, on flowing water you'll need to feed not only more heavily but also more regularly, to draw and hold the fish otherwise they'll drift away in the current.

Lake fishing is often more leisurely, unless you know very big catches of bream, tench, or carp are on the cards. For a normal lake session, you might get away with half the quantity of bait considered essential for a river.

Canal requirements are usually for very small amounts of more varied baits.

Excluding groundbait, a realistic bait menu for a river session could be two pints of hemp, four pints of bronze maggots and a pint of casters. The hemp would be loose fed on the float line, along with maggots, or casters. If this didn't work, there would still be enough maggots to consider a change to the swimfeeder – a method which can use up several pints of maggots over a few hours' fishing.

On a lake outing an angler might take one pint of hemp, two pints of casters, one pint of red maggots, half a pint of red and fluorescent coloured pinkies and perhaps a small pot of red worms.

There's much less quantity here, but still plenty of options. Casters and hemp could be fed on a running float line and red maggots can work well on the hook with this combination. If the swim didn't respond, the pole could be tried with the red maggots, or if the fishing was really hard, the smaller pinkies might come into play. A third option might be to try the open-end feeder with a mixture of hemp, caster and pinkies as feed. In this case, the casters and pinkies are candidates as hookers with worm and red maggots possibly worth trying.

Canal fishing might demand a pint of white squatts, half pint measures of casters, hemp and mixed pinkies, a small pot of worms and maybe just a handful of some larger maggots to try on the hook.

There are countless pole methods that could be coupled with this small but varied amount of bait. The waggler, or even a light leger rig might also be used at some stage.

All these examples are by no means hard and fast ones. They demonstrate how bait quantities and types should tie in with the type of venue and relevant methods. There are also plenty of good back-up baits, which you won't necessarily need to obtain from the tackle shop. Many anglers get in the habit of slipping a few slices of fresh white bread into their tackle boxes. This provides some useful bait options on many types of venue.

A tin of luncheon meat might sit in your tackle box for several outings, but sooner or later it could catch you a big chub, carp or barbel.

Sweetcorn is another bait that can swing things your way – especially when small fish are mopping up maggots rather too avidly.

CHIEF HOOKBAITS AND THEIR USES

MAGGOTS Standard big maggots in their natural form are an off-white colour. They're sold in various dyed shades of bronze, red, fluorescent and yellow.

White maggots are pretty universal in their attracting qualities and catch most freshwater fish. Bronzed are next in popularity and make particularly good river baits for species like chub, roach and barbel.

Red is a colour which has great appeal to lake species like tench, bream and carp. Red maggots also score well in highly coloured water and are a good all-round bait for perch.

Fluorescent dyed maggots usually turn out as very bright, mixed shades of oranges, pinks and reds. These are good change baits and their high visibility is an advantage when legering, or float-fishing off the bottom.

Yellow maggots are also a good change bait. They retain high visibility when fished in really deep water and have a reputation as superb roach and dace baits.

Maggots are best hooked through the small flap of skin at the tail or blunt end. This procedure won't burst them and makes them still wriggle enticingly.

Pinkies are about one-third of the size of big maggots. They have been given their name because of their pink tinge in their natural form. They can be purchased dyed bronze, red and fluorescent pink.

This small maggot is very effective on harder canal fisheries, both as feed and mounted on tiny fine wire hooks. Pinkies are often fed in groundbait mixes, especially in the open-end feeder. Red and fluorescent types are good for skimmer bream and perch. White and bronzed ones are popular for roach, skimmers, dace and gudgeon.

Squatts were originally only used in groundbait, as a holding feed, by bream anglers. These tiny maggots are only half the size of a pinkie and the advantage of feeding them in groundbait is that they remain static when immersed in water. Fish easily pick them off the bottom, but won't tend to be over-fed by them.

Over recent years the squatt has also evolved into a top match fishing bait on canal venues. It can still be fed in groundbait as previously, but other very successful pole and waggler techniques involve cupping and catapulting this bait

out neat for small and medium sized fish.

Maggots eventually turn into chrysalids or casters and if you catch these at an early stage of development they make a superb big fish bait. In their very early stages, they are white, then they turn pale orange. Left open to the air, casters keep on darkening, progressing to a lovely bronze colour and later to a reddish, dark brown. Finally, they turn almost black.

From their white form to their early brown state, casters sink in water. The lighter they are, the quicker they sink. The darker they become the slower their fall rate. Normally, a bag of casters contains a mixture of colours and their differing fall rates in water often prove very attractive to fish.

Most anglers prefer casters when they are orange, or bronze. Canal anglers might let their bait progress to slightly darker stages for harder venues, but this must be carefully regulated, because if they mature too much they'll float!

Floaters only have minimal applications. They can be useful as feed on some well stocked carp lakes, when the angler wants to get the fish boiling on the surface. A floater used as hookbait sometimes fools very wary fish, as it disguises the weight of the hook.

It takes several pints of maggots to get a few good pints of casters, so most anglers purchase them from the tackle shop. These normally have to be ordered a few days in advance as this is a very popular bait.

Casters have a big fish reputation for most species and are equally effective on lakes, rivers and canals. They are excellent to use as feed because they lay lightly on the bottom and won't bury into silt, weed and gravel like maggots.

Casters can be lightly hooked like a maggot, but their other advantage is you can completely bury a hook inside them, which is a great way of enticing big fish in clear water.

WORMS Several types of earthworms are widely used in angling. The largest are lobworms which have excellent fish drawing qualities, especially if chopped up and introduced into the swim neat, or in groundbait. These are also used whole, or in sections, on large hooks for big fish like chub, carp and barbel.

Brandlings are the most common worm you'll find on sale in tackle shops. This is because they're relatively easy to produce. Brandlings are an effective bait for many species, particularly bream, perch, chub and roach.

Redworms are harder to source, but if you can

Maggot

Lightly-hooked maggots (through blunt end) will wriggle enticingly.

Caster

Caster (hook buried)

Hook casters in similar fashion to maggots when fish are feeding freely.
Bury the hook inside to fool wary big fish.

31

Whole lobworms are great attractors for many species including greedy bream.

Worm

Hook small worms through the head segment for best presentation.

obtain a supply, they make superb bream, perch, chub and roach baits.

All worm types, including the common earthworm, can be chopped up and used in groundbait. Another more recent winning method, particularly when the going is hard, has been developed by pole anglers. They fit a special cup on the end of their poles and carefully tip neat chopped worms over the float line. This often brings a quick response from perch and also works for skimmer bream, tench and carp.

Bloodworms and their smaller, livelier cousins, jokers, are collected from the bed of streams and lakes. This is hard work, particularly in winter, so these baits are expensive. They are also very effective when sport nosedives in cold weather. Competition anglers are the most likely to consider these expensive baits viable. They also tend to pull lots of smaller fish, useful to the match angler, but not perhaps everyone's idea of what fishing should be about.

SEEDS Hempseed has an attractive smell when freshly cooked. It also produces an oily residue, which roach in particular seem to find very attractive. As a feed, hemp is a good attractor in most venues and for a cross section of species.

As a hookbait, hemp mainly scores in the summer and autumn months. It performs best

in clear water for roach, but will also tempt chub, hybrids and dace. This is a specialist bait, which requires very regular feeding in small amounts. It produces lightning fast bites, mostly on-the-drop, and tackle must be spot-on.

Tares are cooked in a similar fashion to hemp but are a much larger, more filling seed. They're softer and can be used as a hookbait with hemp. Tares often produce more positive bites and apart from catching 'hemp' fish like roach and chub, also give better chances of connecting with other species including carp, barbel and bream.

Sweetcorn can be fished over hemp. But it's also a bait with good drawing powers in its own right. This is mainly a summer bait, associated with fish like tench, bream and carp. It attracts big fish, so sturdy tackle is in order.

BREAD, MEATS AND CHEESES Bread is an amazingly versatile bait. It works in flake, crust and paste forms. It can also be punched out into compressed pellets on a flat board, so it stays more firmly embedded on smaller hooks.

Fish with a preference for bread baits are tench, bream, carp, roach, chub and barbel. It's a cheap, worthwhile option on many venues.

Luncheon and sausage meats are renowned big fish baits. They can be fished with other baits and feed, but also suit the roving approach and will often bring savage takes almost immediately, if dropped into fishy looking swims with cover. These baits are excellent for chub, barbel and carp.

River anglers have recently been experimenting with raw steak and minced beef and taking big catches of chub. This method originated on the River Trent, but is spreading fast and gains a response on float and feeder methods. Strips of steak are used on the hook, while mince is mixed with groundbait as an attractor.

Most cheeses can be formed into a paste, if need be, kneading them into a bread base. The stronger smelling ones are favourite for chub and barbel, if large pieces are shaped around big hooks. Smaller pellets of cheese paste will take roach and bream.

Hemp (bend pushed in to split)

Tare (lightly hooked)

Sweetcorn (through middle)

Flake (on shank)

Punch (through middle)

Meat (use a boilie stop)

BOILIES Ready-made boilies have advanced over the years from frozen baits into more convenient shelf-life packs. They're now bagged and sealed in a phenomenally wide range of colours and flavours, and in four diameters: micro, small, medium and large. Neutral boilies which need dousing in the flavour of your choice are also obtainable.

These little balls of high protein are sold with savory, seafood and fruit based labellings. There are many exotic recipes and if these don't take your fancy, it's possible to buy basic ingredients and produce your own concoctions.

It's difficult to make boilies work on waters where they've never been used, but where they are regularly introduced, the fish are soon weaned over to them. In fact, on many carp lakes the fish are preoccupied on these rich baits and the name of the game is finding out which type and colour are most in-vogue.

This information is normally gleaned from the local tackle shop, or the bailiff. It's also a good idea to pick slightly different, but related recipes, if the water is heavily fished.

Boilies are primarily directed at carp, but bream and tench also become dependent on them where lots are fed.

The beauty of these baits is that they're usually immune to the attentions of small fish and single out the specimens instead.

GROUNDBAIT TACTICS

On some occasions, loose feeding alone provides a good day's fishing. But there are many other times when groundbait brings far better results. Sometimes a delicate balance of the two methods is needed.

It's very difficult to explain how these decisions are made because even the most experienced anglers get it wrong! Mainly, it's a case of feeling your way. When there are other anglers about, it's wise to loose feed carefully at the start and check to see if those using groundbait are getting results.

The response you get from loose feed, often directs you towards using groundbait anyway. Sometimes you get the feeling loose feed is bringing too slow a response, or failing to hold fish. But it's certainly a better idea to start any session carefully and gently build up your feeding regime. That's definitely preferable to throwing mounds of stuff at the fish. Once feed

Hair-rigged boilie pivoted from mid-shank with a short length of silicone.

is deposited in the swim you can't get it back!

If you do decide to kick off a session with groundbait, it should be done carefully. It can always be stepped-up later. Try a couple of experimental balls of groundbait and if they bring no results, little harm will be done. You can then revert to loose feed.

Sometimes you might find the fish in a strange mood as they respond initially to loose feed and then fade away. You try groundbait and the same thing happens. In this instance, it's sometimes productive to rotate both methods, feeding groundbait to get the fish into catching range, then reverting to loose feed to hold them...for as long as the bites last. Often this process needs repeating again and again. Groundbait will normally work particularly well when there are many fish about, or on vast waters where a positive approach is necessary to gain a response. There are also methods, like bread punch which rely on groundbait's attracting qualities.

Fish are inquisitive creatures and the splash of large balls of groundbait sometimes lures them in to have a look. There's many a time when match anglers try stirring a shoal into action by bombarding an unproductive swim with several large balls of feed!

As you become more experienced you will undoubtedly reach the stage where you have several groundbaiting techniques up your sleeve. As long as you use these tactically, rather than habit-

ACCESSORIES

A maggot riddle is a worthwhile investment. Apart from running bait through it to remove unwanted skins and other debris, it is also used to produce your own casters – if you want to save bait which is turning.

Groundbait should also be sieved through a maggot riddle, both in dry and mixed form, to ensure it has a better consistency.

There are also smaller meshed pinkie and squatt riddles for running small maggot baits and for the important job of cleaning off sawdust and sand.

In the tackle shop you'll see a good selection of round, square and sometimes even partitioned bait boxes. Some are now even escape proof!

Make sure you buy a bait box for maggots that's plenty big enough. This bait needs air otherwise it will sweat-up. Square boxes store particularly well in carryalls.

Some shops sell shallow hooker boxes for small baits like bloodworm. These are insulated to keep the contents cool in summer and prevent freez-

Square bait boxes store neatly in carryalls.

ing in winter. They usually have a flip-top which avoids wind drying the bait out. Most have a screw fitting at the base which allows the box to be positioned nicely to hand on a bank stick.

If you intend to use bread, a punch board gives a firm base to compress the bread, so it stays on the hook better.

Most of the commercially manufactured boards have an outside lip and double up as open topped hooker boxes.

A selection of plastic bags are always handy for storing a variety of baits. Casters store well in these, as do hemp, tares and dry groundbait. Some anglers carry a couple of extra bags in their kit and may save unused groundbait at the end of a session. This will last several days in a fridge if it's sealed properly.

ually, groundbait will often make a big difference to your catches.

MIXES

The most basic groundbaits are brown and white bread crumbs, sold in varying grades from fine to coarse. There's also a special type of coarser, punch crumb. This is white, but is freeze dried, so it won't bind together like normal white feed.

Brown crumb produces a good cloud mix while white in its natural form is a good binder. Punch crumb fragments on hitting the water to give a very attractive trail of mixed size particles as they descend to the bottom.

White is mixed with brown crumb to achieve different consistencies. A minority of anglers swear by pure bread feeds and they do work well on numerous venues.

But many anglers find bread feed on its own too bland for their requirements. Apart from offering many different consistencies, Conti-

nental groundbait mixes also give amazing colour and flavour options. You can still bulk these out with basic bread feeds, but the resultant mix has a far more potent aroma.

Many rich ingredients go into Continental feeds. Some are obvious like crushed hempseed, maize, biscuit and powdered sweetcorn. These additives are thought not only to hold the fish for longer but also to attract certain species, more than others.

In this area, Continental groundbait specialists such as the Belgians, Dutch and French are arguably more advanced than ourselves. They are very keen on specialised recipes, aimed at particular types of fish and venues. In fact, many ingredients which go into their most popular groundbaits are kept secret.

That is why much of the Continental groundbaits that you'll see on the shelves in tackle shops are clearly labelled for specific venues and species.

It's certainly worth experimenting with them,

perhaps together with bread feeds, because they do achieve consistent results.

Because Continental mixes are more expensive than plain bread feeds, it's a good idea to bulk them out with crumb, particularly when a fair amount of groundbait is required. This makes them go further and also achieves a slightly more manageable consistency when the feed is wetted.

In winter, when less groundbait tends to be used, it's much better to introduce Continental feeds neat, as it really utilises their superior drawing powers.

Always mix water, in small amounts, to your groundbait, not the other way around. By adding water gradually and stirring vigorously with your hands, you'll get a nice, evenly dampened, fine consistency. Try pouring dry groundbait into water and it goes very lumpy! It's also hard to regulate the correct amount of moisture this way.

Most anglers wet their groundbait just sufficiently to get a dry, fluffy mix, then leave it for five minutes. This allows it to absorb the moisture properly, then the process is repeated two or three times, until the mix feels and looks right.

Neat Continental mixes are sometimes harder to work because they may be less absorbent. Give these their first application of water the night before you go fishing, so they have plenty of time to fully absorb and expand. Then, any finishing touches can be applied on the bank.

Probably the best mixing bowls for groundbaits are the round collapsible type. These store neatly and help achieve more even mixes. Square bowls are passable, but it's difficult to get at the dry groundbait which collects in the corners.

Collapsible, round
groundbait bowl –
makes for a good mix.

FIRING AND FIXINGS

A: Three essential catapult designs – Image canal caster, Canal King mini model and a groundbait cradle.

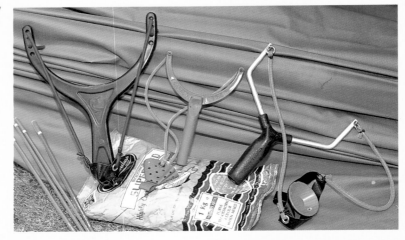

B: Great ingenuity has been shown in fixing catapult elastics to the frames including the use of a split ring and electrical tie.

C: Threaded latex fixing developed by Image.

D: Plug and push-fit attachment.

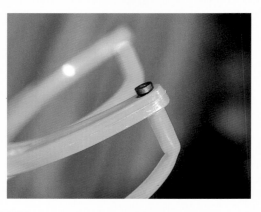

E: Everybody has their favourite way of firing the catapult and Dave Coster achieves greater accuracy by tilting his grip to one side. In wind, it's best to fire upside down and low to the water. When using a pole, grip it between your legs and fire the catapult over the top for close grouping of the bait.

CATAPULTS, CUPS AND DROPPERS

Loose feed and groundbait have limited scope if fed by hand, but there are some excellent purpose designed catapults for both methods. Loose feed catapults tend to group the bait better and certainly give far greater distance than is possible by throwing it in. Groundbait catapults extend your feeding range up to 80–90 metres and they are very accurate.

The pole cup is a useful device on hard canal venues. This gadget clips on the tip section of the pole and is manoeuvred out precisely over your fishing area. Small quantities of neat baits, or groundbait are then tipped into the swim inch perfectly. This is better than risking the odd, misplaced helping of feed, which might ruin your swim completely.

Bait dropper in action

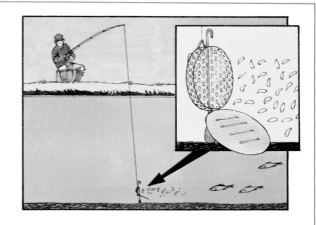

Bait droppers are fixed to the hook and lowered, or cast into the swim with your tackle or a spare rod rigged up for the purpose. They have quick release mechanisms which open a side, or base flap as they hit the bottom. This results in loose feed like maggots, or casters being deposited in a very tight area. Bait droppers work well in getting feed

down in flowing water, or through nuisance small fish.

Throwing sticks are another way of loose feeding in a reasonably tight circle, slightly beyond arm range, with maggots, casters and hemp. There's also specialised boilie throwing sticks, which will put these baits out quite accurately up to 70 metres.

Above: **Pole cup tips bait exactly where you need it.**

Right: **Boilie throwing stick.**

Below: **ZLT mini and Thamesly droppers.**

TERMINAL TACKLE BASICS

Right: **Spade and eyed hooks.**

HOOK CHOICES

There are countless hook designs in every conceivable shape and colour. Each pattern might have several uses and as many as a dozen sizes. Some series run in even numbers – 16, 18 and 20 are popular sizes – while certain specialised match hooks graduate in odd sizes, such as 17, 19 and 21. High numbers are designated to small hooks, while smaller numbers signify larger hook sizes. The largest freshwater hook is a size 2 and they go as tiny as size 28s or even minute 30s for match fishing purposes. Many are chemically sharpened, which in plain terms means their points are finished by etching them in acid. This process produces more precise, longer and sharper points.

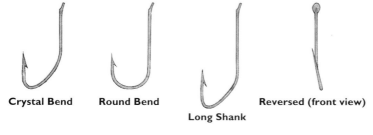

Crystal Bend   **Round Bend**

Long Shank

Reversed (front view)

Some hooks have large barbs, but modern patterns are more conservation minded and possess micro, or whisker barbs. There are also barbless patterns which are easiest to remove.

Anglers tend to classify hooks into two categories – eyed and spade-end. Eyed hooks are formed with a small ring at the top of their shanks through which the line is threaded, making them the easiest to tie. Spade-ends have a flattened flange at the top of the shank which the knot butts against. Sophisticated knots are essential here and they may not be within everyone's grasp.

If you can master the art of tying spade-end hooks, it is well worth the effort. These patterns are more streamlined and less obtrusive, particularly in smaller sizes. There's also a far greater choice of designs available to the angler who can master tying a good spade-end knot.

But don't despair if you are all-thumbs at

knots because there are ready-tied spades in a variety of patterns and nylon strengths. Manufacturers are now producing the right kind of relationship between breaking strains, hook designs and sizes. Some products are nearly as good as top anglers might achieve, but shop carefully, because there are also a minority of inferior, poorly tied items.

Right: **Correctly tied spade with the line coming from the inside of the shank.**

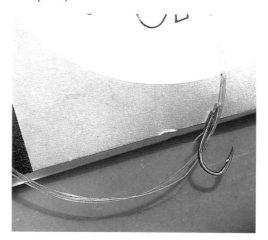

Colours, Shapes and Wire Gauges

The majority of hooks are finished in bronze, gilt or silver colours. But colour coatings, which give red, green and blue finishes have become increasingly popular. Therefore it is now possible to select a hook pattern to tie in with most bait colours.

For example, pale silver hooks are popular with white baits like bread punch and squatts. Bronze hooks obviously suit bronzed maggots.

Red hooks are identical in hue to bloodworms and are hardly noticeable when attached to red maggots. Gilt, or gold coloured hooks match sweetcorn and yellow maggots. Dark blue hooks make a good choice for casters and hemp.

Hook shapes, or patterns are also selected to help present certain baits better. Crystal bend hooks are widely considered superior for maggots, mainly because these lively baits can't wriggle free from the steep bend which precedes the upward turn to the point.

Round bend patterns tend to have slightly wider gapes and are very good for seed and bread baits.

Reversed, or offset hooks have points which slightly lean to one side, rather than pointing directly upwards. These offer increased hooking potential on feeder and leger tackle.

Long shanked designs make hooking small baits like bloodworm a much easier task. Sometimes, short shanked patterns produce more bites from wary canal fish.

Design considerations like these often boil down to personal preference –but the question of wire gauge or thickness is crucial. Fine wire hooks are light and less likely to cause a fish to reject a hookbait. They also help achieve balanced tackle when fishing with fine diameter lines on harder venues.

Obviously, there are limits to the size of fish you can realistically aim for with some light hooks, although expert anglers land some surprisingly big fish on them. If this sounds confusing, the trick is to use as light a hook as you feel safe with.

Medium wire hooks are probably most popular and prove adequate for a lot of general fishing situations.

Forged hooks are very strong, but their extra weight and bulkier appearance might result in fewer bites –unless they're disguised by using a lighter, or buoyant hookbait.

On certain venues like fast flowing rivers, a heavy hook has a negligible effect. Feeder fishing demands this type of hook anyway, especially at long range, where a savage take from a chub, or barbel would straighten out a fine wire design very easily.

In the interests of preserving fish stocks, some fisheries insist on anglers using barbless, or micro barbed hooks which are easier to extract.

Barbless hooks offer advantages. They need less power to drive them home and they are the easiest hook to remove from fish. They are popular for short pole fishing, stick float and light waggler work.

A small barb is preferred when fishing at distance with baits like maggots, because it helps stop them wriggling off the hook. The barb will also ensure baits stay on when legering and helps to keep a good hook-hold on fish when unshipping sections of longer poles.

How to Weigh Up Nylon Diameters

The numerous brands of nylon line broadly fall into two main groups – reel and hooklength monofilaments. But it's not quite that simple, because some reel, or standard diameter lines, also double as good hooklengths.

There are major differences between standard monos and the so called low diameter lines which offer a much higher breaking strain for the same, given diameter. This combination of low diameter and high strength allows anglers to experiment with much finer hooklengths than with standard monos.

Standard lines have thicker diameters in relation to their breaking strains. Their strength is also often under-stated, so there is a safety element here. They will do more than their labelling suggests. Standard line is also more robust, again due to its thicker diameter.

Low diameter, high tech. lines have been a revelation over recent years. They offer greatly reduced diameters if you equate them against the same breaking strains in standard lines. This gives the angler a much better chance of fooling wary fish. Lighter lines make hookbaits perform more naturally. They are less visible and certainly much more supple when a fish draws the bait inside its mouth. All in all, this adds up to more bites.

KNOT TYERS AND STORAGE SYSTEMS

If you experience difficulties tying spade-end hooks, there are some good hook tyers on the market. It may take a little practice to perfect techniques, but these devices are relatively easy to use and form secure knots.

It is possible to tie hooks on the bank, but make a habit of doing it at home, the night before a session, and it will save valuable fishing time. Fragile hooklengths should be stored carefully, to avoid damage and tangles.

There are several hooklength retaining devices including colour coded plastic spools and fluted plastic boards around which hooks and nylon are wound. Wallets with pouches or plastic, see-through sleeves are another option.

The small, plastic winders used by

Right: **Trace board with pins stores hook lengths neatly.**

Below: **It's possible to store running line rigs on pole winders.**

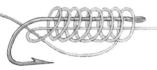

Reversed spade-end knot

pole anglers to store complete rigs are also useful for hooklengths. Some anglers make up complete running line waggler and stick float rigs and keep these on larger pole winders.

Small chemically sharpened hooks rarely need any attention on the bank. If they blunt it's probably quicker to tie on a new one. Larger hooks lose their points more easily when legering over rough ground. Therefore, it's sensible for you to carry a small hook sharpening stone for these occasions. It will only take a couple of seconds to hone the hook point back into good shape.

The down side of this new technology, lies in the safety factor being lost on low diameter lines. Their breaking strains are spot-on and there's no buffer against mistakes like over zealous striking or attempted bullying of fish into the landing net before they are ready. Being a lot thinner, they are also far more prone to tangles and spinning-up on the retrieve. In addition, low diameter lines are less hard wearing.

All this leads us to the conclusion that the standard monofilaments are still best for use on the reel. They absorb an incredible amount of wear and tear – which they need to do as they are repeatedly cast and retrieved.

PICK A LINE FOR THE JOB

Some standard lines are more hard wearing than others. Some are more supple or sink well. Others have built in floatability. All these factors suit particular methods such as the waggler, stick float and leger.

For instance, sometimes it's essential to keep the waggler still and if the surface is drifting badly, you will need to cut a sinking line under the water.

Floating lines are essential for top and bottom attached floats like sticks to work the swim properly. A buoyant line mends more easily, without pulling the float off course. It also lifts from the surface swiftly as you strike.

Sinking lines are obviously preferred for legering.

It's advisable to opt for standard lines as hooklengths when a rugged bottom or strenuous long range work, imposes extra stresses on the terminal tackle. These lines are also best when big catches and hefty fish are expected.

Low diameter lines come into their own for hooklengths when seeking small fish or when the fishing is hard. They are also used extensively on the pole as main line and hooklengths, because their thinness greatly improves tackle presentation. These lines don't suffer so much wear on pole tackle, because most anglers use elastic shock absorbers.

It's best to gain some experience before trying low diameter lines as hooklengths on running line rigs. They need special knots and careful treatment when retrieving them and unhooking fish. They also weaken after several good fish have been landed and, as a result, may need changing regularly.

Many anglers now refer to their lines by diameter, rather than breaking strains. Although most spools of line will have both diameter and breaking strain details printed on them, it's a good idea to think this way, because low diameter is a more important factor in fooling the fish.

AVOID UV RAYS

Line should always be stored away from sunlight. Ultra violet light causes monofilaments to deteriorate if they're exposed for long periods.

FILLING THE SPOOL

Before winding new line on the reel, it must be firmly attached to the spool. To the inexperi-

Specialist reel lines. The floating Daiwa brand is suitable for stick floats and the Toray suits wagglers.

Standard workhorse lines – reliable when the terminal tackle is subjected to extra stresses from big fish or snags.

Low diameter lines provide superior presentation.

enced this can be a more difficult task than it appears. You will need to use a slip knot, or arbour knot as it is sometimes known, so the line is pulled tight and grips the reel spool.

And it's critical to wind new line on the reel correctly to avoid it twisting-up badly.

Sliding Arbor knot (three turns are adequate).

ALWAYS USE A LIGHTER HOOKLENGTH

Whichever lines you choose, use a hook length with a lighter breaking strain than the main line.

That way, if you're accidentally broken by a good fish, it will not be left trailing yards of tackle.

If your tackle becomes snagged on the bottom or bankside vegetation, a lighter hooklength will break first, again reducing the risk of losing a long length of nylon which could prove lethal to water birds and other creatures.

If at all possible, you should retrieve a lost hooklength from weeds or bankside bushes. It must be cut up into smaller lengths and then taken home and dropped in the dustbin.

Hooklengths rarely need to be longer than 30 inches and in many cases can be made much shorter.

The loop to loop system is the most effective way of joining a lighter breaking strain hooklength to the reel line and it is particularly recommended for low diameter monos. A small loop is formed at the end of the reel line and another at the end of the hooklength. The hook is threaded through the reel line loop and then brought back through its own loop. Finally, gently pull and the two loops will interlock.

Strangulation knots like the tucked Half Blood must be avoided at all costs with low diameter hooklengths because it severely reduces the breaking strain of the rig and its ability to absorb sudden lunges from the fish. The Grinner knot is recommended if you intend using an eyed hook.

Water and blood knots are better suited to joining standard lines. They also significantly weaken the breaking strain of lower diameter lines.

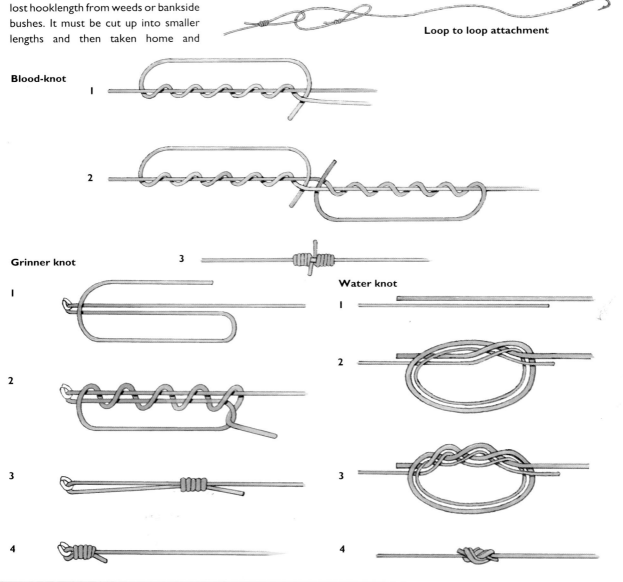

Loop to loop attachment

Blood-knot

Grinner knot

Water knot

After attaching the line to the spool, mount the reel on a rod and wind the line in through the fingers of the hand supporting the rod. To do this, your rod hand will have to be positioned slightly forward of the reel.

It's possible to regulate how the line goes on the reel in this way, always keeping it slightly tensioned, so it doesn't lie loosely and hinder its flow during casting. Most importantly, you can feel the line as it runs through your fingers. If it's tending to twist, it is leaving the line spool in the wrong direction and the spool will need to be turned over.

Once the line comes off the spool correctly, you will notice the difference. It runs smoothly through your fingers and stays straight.

If you experience problems, ask someone to hold the line spool for you. Get them facing you, so the line is loaded flush to the face of the reel spool for ease of flow. It's best to load reel spools level with the rim. Less line than this will restrict casting distances by creating excessive friction as the line pulls over the spool rim. Over-loaded spools spill too much line off and cause tangles.

SPLIT SHOT

Split shot are non-toxic in sizes larger than No. 8s (0.06 grams). Lead shot are still popular in legal size 8s and smaller as it's considered they present no threat to wildlife.

Leading non-toxic brands include Anchor Double Cut and Thamesly Sure Shot which were among the first companies to develop successful alternatives to lead weights.

Double Cut are less harsh than most alloy shot because of their unique design. They have a normal, 'forward' split which is closed on the line, but also a back cut, which makes the shot more pliable and certainly less severe when applied to finer lines.

These shot are excellent when used as lockers around bottom-end floats. Anchor market two extra and very useful sizes, SAs and ABs. They are also good when formed into strings of bulk shot and as individual droppers.

Thamesly Sure Shot have a black finish and tend to grip the line more firmly than Double Cut which is an advantage on heavier wagglers rigs. Larger Sure Shot can be formed into link legers, and medium sized ones stay firm when strung out, or if they are bulked on fast water float rigs.

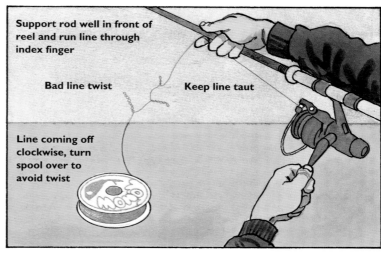

Support rod well in front of reel and run line through index finger

Bad line twist   Keep line taut

Line coming off clockwise, turn spool over to avoid twist

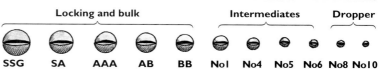

Locking and bulk					Intermediates				Dropper	
SSG	SA	AAA	AB	BB	No1	No4	No5	No6	No8	No10

Top: **Loading the reel** If the line is twisting as shown turn the spool over

Above: **Split shot sizes**

Left: **Double Cut shot are kinder on fine lines.**

HOW TO USE DIFFERENT SIZES

Big shot, (SSG, SA, AAA, AB, BB and No.1) are often used to lock waggler style floats on the line. These also form the bulk of the casting weight to

Sure Shot offer benefits on heavier waggler rigs.

STYL WEIGHTS

Styl weights are now available both in lead and non-toxic alloy. They were originally designed for pole anglers, but as running line rigs have become lighter, their use has spread further afield.

Styls are tiny elongated, celery shaped weights, with a groove running down one side. These are very soft, so they won't damage fine hooklengths. Pole anglers use larger Styls spread, or bulked, as their main weighting and

smaller Styls as droppers. They also combine very small dropper Styls with other weights like olivettes and shot.

Because they are soft and sink slowly, Styls are sometimes used as droppers on waggler rigs, for mid-depth and on-the-drop fishing.

Olivettes are used as a bulk weight to speed the bait down to the bottom layers. They're trapped in position with a slender peg or micro shot.

Styls and olivettes.

---

get the rig out. Larger shot are often called locking shot. They're also grouped to form lower down bulk loadings, when using bigger top and bottom attached floats on powerful rivers.

Medium sized shot, (No. 4, 5 and 6) are usually strung out at equal distances between the float and hooklength, or grouped in a bulk just above the hooklength when fishing top and bottom river floats like sticks, Avons and balsas. They're also utilised as smaller bulks, or as dropper shot down the line on waggler rigs.

Number 8s, or dust shot as they are commonly called, are used for fine tuning rigs. Many anglers taper their shot down in size towards the hook, so the last shot, or tell-tale as it is nicknamed, is a No. 8. This is a vital shot, because it pulls the float tip down to its final setting. This shot won't register on the float if a fish has taken the bait as it settles, and the angler knows to strike.

It's normally very important to keep shot small as they near the hook and not to place them too close. The fish will soon become suspicious if

Micro shot for fine tuning.

the last shot is pulling the hookbait down too fast and if it's too heavy, it will cause the tackle to constantly snag on bottom debris. Number 8s are also very good strung out on light stick float rigs, either individually, or in sets of twos and threes.

Shot smaller than 8s are called micro shot. Sizes available are 9, 10, 11, 12, 13 and 14.

There's a call for shots between 9 and 12 as fine tuners, or very small dropper shot on some running line rigs. But micro shot are chiefly popular with pole anglers. They give lots of options in the way small pole floats are weighted.

THE PRIME ROLES FOR A FLOAT

Floats play two important roles. They are bite indicators which is why they've got highly visible, brightly coloured tips. They are also used to present the hookbait in a certain manner at particular depths.

A float only indicates bites clearly and performs sensitively if it is shotted correctly. It's vital to spend some time getting this right, because once a float has been rigged up, you will be using it for long periods. You want it to work for you, not against you.

Many beginners make the mistake of leaving too much float showing above the surface. This causes an imbalance in the tackle and often makes it drift uncontrollably. Worse yet, a biting fish has more float to pull under and might reject the hookbait because of this extra resistance.

Most floats have a fluorescent tip colour and a

band of white underneath. Shotted correctly, the tip colour alone should be left showing, the white band should be submerged. When a float is dotted down this way, lift bites signal clearly because you will see the band of white rising out of the water.

Similarly, on-the-drop bites also show up well, because the white band won't settle properly and this signals to you that something is going on.

THE MAIN FAMILIES

There's an amazing variety of floats to choose from. Some have specific jobs, others can be classed as all-rounders.

The first important step is to know the difference between river and stillwater float designs. Some cross boundaries here, but there are many types which should be kept to specific usage.

The main families of floats which are fixed to the line top and bottom, such as sticks, Avons, balsas and chubbers, have no valid applications away from running water. These are out and out river floats. In fact, these designs rely on flowing water to work properly. It's important to keep a tight line to them, so the hookbait is trotted on a straight path, or slowed by differing degrees.

If you tighten up the line to these floats they won't go under. A bottom-ender would, so there is nowhere near the same control with other floats on flowing water.

Floats attached to the line by the bottom ring only, known as bottom-enders, or more commonly wagglers, are more versatile in their applications. These are the family of floats to choose when fishing stillwaters, but some designs are also highly effective on rivers.

Wagglers come in straight, stepped, insert, loaded and bodied forms. There are also specialist canal wagglers which are small, streamlined and have very fine tips.

The types of wagglers which most commonly double-up for river fishing are the bodied,

straight and insert models. These are very effective on flowing water, at distances beyond those which top and bottom fixed floats are capable of fishing. They may also be used closer in, when awkward weather conditions are spoiling good presentation with top and bottom fixed floats.

As previously mentioned, wagglers won't achieve the same degree of control on rivers, as you can get with out-and-out river floats. But they're effective when the fish are up in the water, or want a trotted bait. Straight wagglers can also be used to drag a bait over-depth. This is the nearest they'll get you to top and bottom float presentation, but clearly it will never be quite as good.

Because our climate is so prone to sudden changes, a fair selection of floats is a good idea. Very often one float of a particular design is not sufficient to cover all eventualities. Floats are usually available in sets of at least four sizes. It's a good idea to buy both lighter and slightly heavier floats, to back-up the particular size you think you'll need. That allows you to step your tackle up or down, should the need arise. You may end up switching to lighter tackle if the fish are shy, or you can add more weight to your rig if a bigger, more stable float is required to combat deteriorating conditions.

STICKS Fishing the stick float is a very prolific way of catching river species like roach, dace, chub and perch. This slim float design is attached to the line with two, or possibly three float bands if you want to prevent slippage in faster water. This method relies on regular feeding, aiming to run the tackle through in unison with the free offerings.

There are different types of sticks. Some have domed tops which work better in faster rivers, others have more pointed tips, which are more sensitive and suit slower flow rates, or fishing up in the water.

Base materials are very important. Light cane will only slowly cock this float –which is ideal

---

MATERIALS

The materials that go into making floats are very diverse.

They include plastics, wire, glass, quills, reed, different grades of balsa and harder woods. All dramatically affect the way a float performs. Largely it's down to personal preference, regarding the types of materials you lean towards. Some anglers are traditionalists and tend to shun high tech materials like plastic. Instead, they favour natural floats made from quills, reeds and balsa.

That's not to say there's anything wrong with more modern floats. In fact, they often out-perform their rivals. But it's your choice.

Cane, wire, glass and alloy stemmed stick floats, all have their special roles and you will need to be aware of these subtle differences, if you want consistent results.

Popular sticks (from left): mini Gardener, Allerton with shoulder for faster water and Middy. A domed top to the float allows it to be dotted right down for dragging through the swim while a pointed top is more sensitive for holding back. The stepped design is more visible at range.

Far right: Topper, wire stem and traditional Avons. The balsa bodied Topper is a fine long distance performer while the wire stem works well in turbulent water.

Right: Balsas are the next step up from the stick.

when fish are taking baits on-the-drop. Heavier canes like lignum give the stick greater casting distance and stabilise it in gusty conditions.

Glass, medium density cane and plastic stemmed sticks tend to be very versatile and take fish at all depths, providing the lower shot are jiggled around to suit. Wire stem versions are certainly the most stable in strong winds and boily surface water.

The top body segment in all stick floats is made from balsa. It's normal to begin a session with the stick, using strung-out No. 4, 6, or 8 shot. These can be regrouped into a bulk, with just a few, or several droppers, if the fish are responding best near the bottom.

BALSAS These are a natural progression up from the stick float, when faster, or deeper water requires more shot to be used. Although similar in shape to sticks, balsa runs right through from tip to base eye. Some balsas are slightly fatter than sticks. The same strung-out, or bulked shotting is utilised with this design, the latter being more popular.

AVONS The traditional Avon has a balsa body fitted to a crow quill stem and tip. There are also versions with cane, balsa and peacock tips. Stems are also made from tapered cane, plastic and straight fibre glass.

Avons are used with large strings of No. 1, or BB bulk shot, which gives them far greater casting range than sticks and balsas and excellent stability. They are one of the best floats to use in very deep river swims.

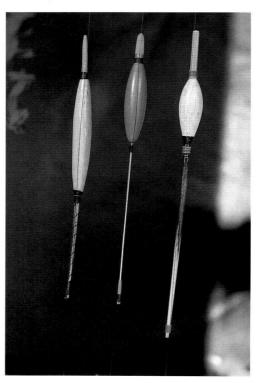

CHUBBERS These fat, cigar-shaped floats are made from all-balsa, or clear plastic. Their job is to present big baits like bread, meat, lobworms and sweetcorn at long range. They are used with a main bulk, some two to three feet from the

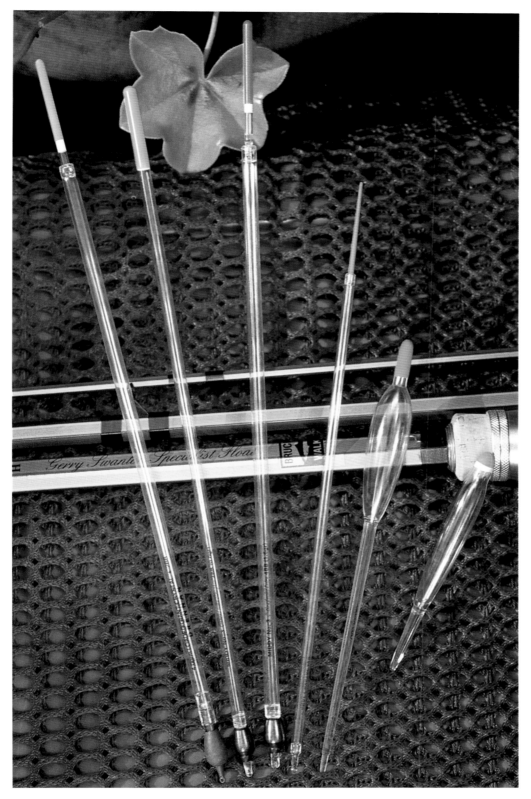

Collection of clear
floats including loaded
insert and straight
wagglers and a fine
tipped Canal Crystal.
The top and bottom
attached floats on the
extreme right are
Avon and Loafer
models.

hook and one quite large dropper shot, about a foot from the hook.

Chubbers cast well and are often used to fish alongside far bank features on small to medium sized rivers. In turbulent water they're also used to present maggot and caster baits. They are good for species like chub, barbel, dace, grayling and big roach.

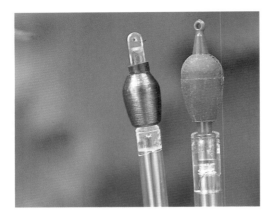

Right: **Middy C-Thru (left) and Drennan Crystal inter-changeable weighting systems for wagglers.**

Below: **Loaded, bodied wagglers also function as sliders.**

STRAIGHT WAGGLERS This is the most basic form of waggler. Having a thickish tip, it can be used to fish well over-depth in drifting stillwaters and quite fast flowing rivers. Straights are normally made from peacock quill. Most of the shot capacity goes into locking the float, but in deeper water, more weight can be placed down the line, as long as it doesn't exceed one third of the float's overall capacity. Good for most species.

INSERT WAGGLERS These have a finer tip for greater sensitivity. A good all-round float. They are often used at distance on lakes, or for fishing the far bank on wider canals. Also a good trotting, or up in the water design on slow to medium paced rivers.

Inserts are made from peacock quill, sarkandas reed, balsa, or plastic. Most shot goes around the float, with usually just two or three small droppers spread down the rig. They're good for most species.

LOADED CLEAR WAGGLERS Several companies now produce loaded, clear plastic wagglers. These are available in straight, or insert form. The latter have inter-changable tips which can be an advantage when you are in changing light conditions.

Each design has several float sizes and different weight loadings to match. The loadings can be switched from lighter floats to heavier capacity ones. This can be very handy when slightly larger locking shot, or more dropper shot are required.

Clear loaded wagglers are popular when fishing up in the water, or at range in shallow water. They are less visible in the water and are therefore less likely to spook the fish.

BODIED WAGGLERS An extension of the straight, or insert waggler principle, with a balsa body so more weight can be added for greater casting distances. A very stable float when you find conditions are swamping conventional wagglers closer in.

Some bodied wagglers are made of clear plastic. There are also some specialist jumbo sized ones which are quite often loaded for long range carp fishing.

QUILLS Cut lengths of peacock quill and smaller porcupine quill floats still have a place in angling. These designs are best for close-in fishing, such as laying-on in the margins, or close to weed beds, for tench and bream.

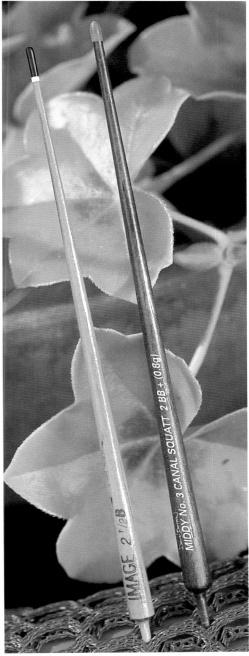

they slide up to and which is usually fixed at full depth. It's best to use bulk shotting with these floats and just one large dropper shot.

CANAL WAGGLERS These miniature wagglers are often shaped entirely from balsa and taper down to very fine, sensitive sight tips. There are squatt and caster versions, the latter have slightly thicker tips for larger baits.

Canal wagglers are also made out of peacock, reed and clear plastic. Generally, these floats are short, so they don't cause a lot of disturbance as they land in shallow water. They are often used bottom-end style on the pole, when drift is a problem, or to-hand style when the water is particularly clear, to keep the pole tip from spooking the fish.

The majority of shotting goes around the float when canal wagglers are used on running line. Smaller shot are used to lock these floats and a bulk used down the rig, when they are used on the pole in deeper water.

ODDBALLS There are quite a few other types of floats including thick, bulbous tipped wagglers. These are called windbeaters. They look strange but in rough water perform rather well, as they don't get swamped by the waves.

Another strange looking float is the Trent trotter, a cut-down bodied waggler. It is excellent when fast river shallows are thwarting your best attempts with conventional stick and waggler floats.

Don't be afraid to make, or experiment with floats which lie outside recognised categories...

Left: **Miniature canal wagglers. There are squatt and caster versions.**

Below: **Quill, Trent trotter and windbeater sight bob.**

SLIDERS Top and bottom sliders are mainly intended for fishing deep stillwaters close in. They also work on slow to medium paced rivers. This design is normally all-balsa, with side and base eyes.

Bottom-end sliders are more commonly used on deep stillwaters and slow paced rivers. They are basically bodied wagglers, with a small loading in the base, to help cock them quickly (so the line can run through them smoothly). They also have a very small base eye, or swivel.

Both types of slider rely on a stop knot, which

PLUMBING UP

Once you have rigged up a float, making sure it's dotted-down correctly so not too much tip is showing, it is time to plumb the swim.

Many anglers hurry this procedure, or approach it in a slap-dash fashion, which is a shame, because it's inevitable they won't be able to take full advantage of their swim.

The most common types of plummets are clip-on and cork based. These will serve you well in finding the correct depth with top and bottom fixed floats. But they're a little heavy and make it difficult to cast waggler rigs. A smaller pole plummet may be better here, or some anglers pinch a large split shot on the bend of the hook.

You may have a good idea which part of the swim you intend to fish, but when plumbing-up, it's a good idea to try and build up a mental picture of the bottom terrain over the swim as a whole.

This way you won't miss hidden features like shelves and depressions, which might hold a good head of fish,

Above: **Traditional cork, Image brass and clip-on plummets.**

Right: **Plumbing the swim**

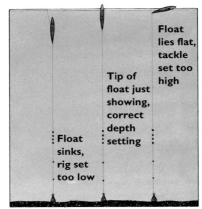

maybe just a few feet away from where you first intended to try. Extensive plumbing will also reveal any underwater weed beds and it's crucial you know where these are, so you can steer big fish around them.

It's normal practice to begin a session with your hookbait presented just on, or just off the bottom. To find the exact depth you need to make a rough guess to begin with and try an experimental cast. If the float sinks out of sight you will know the rig isn't set deep enough. Retrieve the tackle and slide the float up the line by a foot or so. Keep

doing this until the float bobs up, remembering to leave the reel line slack or you'll get a false reading.

If you have set your float too high, it will lie flat on the surface, or stand too proud. This is because dropper shot are lying on the bottom. In this instance you will have to keep sliding the float down the line, until only the very tip shows.

Once you are happy that the plummet is resting on the bottom and just the float tip is showing, you have the rig set at the correct depth and can start fishing with confidence.

BOMBS AND FEEDERS

Arlesey bombs vary in size for a given weight depending on the density of non-toxic material.

The float won't always bring you the best results. Sometimes the fish require a static bait and this isn't always possible to achieve with float tackle.

Also, the fish could be beyond the range of your float rigs, or maybe the conditions make it too difficult to present a float properly. That's the moment to consider using either the leger or swimfeeder.

Arlesey bombs are the most popular and streamlined leger weights. They are suitable for both light legering and long range specimen fishing. They begin at 1/8oz and are now made from non-toxic alloys up to an ounce. Larger versions are still made from lead.

Bream anglers particularly favour this type of weight, because it casts accurately and doesn't make a lot of disturbance over shallow water.

Light leger rigs are normally fished within range of loose feed. They work well in their own right, but this is also a good option to try after a swim has been 'fished out' with float tackle. It's surprising how a static bait can bring new life to a swim after it has apparently dried up.

Heavier leger rigs are extensively used by carp anglers. It's possible to loose feed boilies over great distances, into open water, or towards fishy looking features such as distant islands. It's a very productive method.

Another popular long range legering method, is to fish over a bed of groundbait laced with attractive feed like casters, hemp and squatts. Balls of groundbait can be fed accurately up to 70 yards by catapult and it's a very good method for catching bream, tench and smaller carp.

TYPES OF FEEDER

Straight leger tackle won't always bring the best response. Flow rates might make it difficult to get loose feed in the right place, or the fish may want more regular, smaller amounts of feed. In these cases, the swimfeeder is a potentially productive method.

Open-end feeders are designed to take groundbait in varying consistences to suit the type of water being fished. Groundbait can be used neat, if you feel the fish don't want a lot of feed, or when simple baits like bread are used and you don't want to confuse the fish with lots of other offerings.

But one of the most telling open-end feeder tactics, on both rivers and stillwaters, is to use minimal groundbait. In this case it's simply a holding medium, so the feeder can be packed out with tasty tempters like casters, hemp, squatts, pinkies, chopped worm, sweetcorn...the list is almost endless.

The feeder is often positioned quite close to the hookbait. This guarantees free offerings are deposited around it on every cast.

There are several open-end designs to choose from. Some have heavy weights for distance, or fast water work. Others are lighter and designed to lift up quickly off the bottom on the retrieve to stop them snagging in weedy or rocks.

Most open-enders are constructed with perspex bodies, but there are also cage designs, made from wire, or plastic mesh. These are useful in gaining improved cloud effects from wetter, or very dry groundbait mixes.

Blockend feeders come into play when you suspect groundbait won't have any beneficial effects. These tend to work best on rivers, but will still have the odd good day on stillwaters. They are primarily designed for use with neat maggots, but also work well, packed with casters and hemp.

Large maggot feeders are productive on rivers holding a big head of chub and barbel. To draw and keep these hungry fish interested, it's possible to get through nearly a gallon of maggots in a

Above: **Open-ended feeders made from perspex with side weights.**

Left: **Cage feeders produce improved cloud effects.**

Below: **Thamesley and Storey blockends. They're mainly used with neat maggots.**

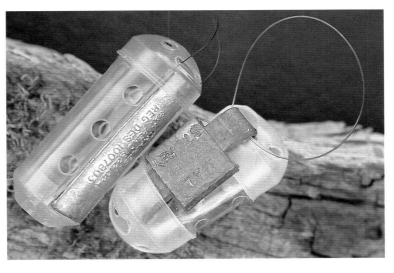

Versatile blockends with inter-changeable weights.

Springtip shows up very delicate touches.

bream, roach and hybrids, you've probably got the choice right.

On a river venue, the open-end feeder can bring a fast response, then fade rapidly. It could be there's no bream around and if you have caught odd small chub, this will tell you it's time to switch to the blockend design.

Some blockend feeders have inter-changeable weights. This is a good feature, so if flow rates pick up, or a longer cast is required, you can alter the rig very quickly.

Another point to watch, is the size of the holes in the body of feeders. This isn't crucial with open-enders, but a blockend with too small exit holes, won't release the feed fast enough in many situations. It's possible to purchase a small plastic tool which will enlarge feeder holes.

When casting long range, the reverse may apply. Lively maggots soon wriggle out of a feeder, even while you're getting positioned correctly to launch it out. In this case, you may need to cover the lower exit holes with some waterproof electrical tape, or fill them with special feeder plugs.

long session. But don't worry, there will be just as many days when a smaller feeder scores well!

On hard winter days it's often better to go easy with the feed. A small link feeder, fished at long range to far bank cover, often produces big catches of chub. Closer in, the method also tempts big roach and perch.

Selecting the correct type of feeder comes with experience. But if you're unsure, start on the open-ender, if only because it's more economical. If this method brings you fish like

BITE INDICATORS

Quiver, spring and swingtips are the main bite indicators used when legering, or feeder fishing. The quivertips are the most popular and easy devices to use, and these can be screwed into a threaded top eye. However, many specialist leger and feeder rods now come with several plug-in versions.

Quivertips are graded by test curves. They go down to very sensitive 0.50 oz and 0.75 oz models for spotting delicate stillwater bites. The 1 oz to 2 oz tips are used at long range in stillwaters, or on medium paced rivers while 3 oz to 4 oz tips are for fast flow rates.

Springtips usually have dual settings. In one mode they work like a conventional quivertip, but they have the added facility of a special housing, which when unlocked, brings a much more sensitive spring into play. The tip shows up very delicate touches when used on the spring and is worth trying on difficult stillwaters and slow flowing rivers.

The swingtip offers less resistance than the other two major forms of bite indication. This makes it popular for breaming methods on stillwaters. In order to combat surface drift, weights can be added to the end of swingtips, which normally hang loose on a length of silicone tubing. There's also specially stiffened, moulded rubber housings, which can be fitted to some swingtips. Apart from making them more effective in drift, this also makes it possible to use them on medium paced rivers.

For stillwaters, an electronic bite indicator which registers any slight movement on the line, takes some of the strain out of keeping your eyes glued to a quivertip. Some indicators rely on a basic antenna connected to contacts and against which the line tightens to complete the circuit and sound the alarm. With more sophisticated models, the line rests on a revolving wheel and any movement cuts through an internal photo electric cell to register a bleep and activate light emitting diodes.

Electronic indicators are essential for long sessions on the bank – chiefly for specimen sized fish. They're almost always set up with a monkey climber which comprises an indicator clipped on the line and suspended on a vertical steel needle for stability in wind. A popular alternative to monkey climbers are Swingers which fit on the front bank stick below the electronic indicator and hang from the line by way of a metal arm and line clip. A movable weight permits variation of the resistance to defeat surface drift or wind and the Swinger falls free once a run pulls line from the clip.

Left: Swingtip - effective for bream on stillwaters.

Below: Swinger indicators with electronic bite alarms and stable rod pod – a favourite set-up for carp.

BASIC TACKLE SET-UPS

Opposite: **The bodied waggler has done its job and another bream hits the net.**

FLOAT RIGS

There are numerous ways of shotting up a float but newcomers should first gain confidence with the basic, well tried set-ups. Simple shotting arrangements are less prone to tangles. More complicated ones may sometimes catch you more fish, but not if your tackle is out of the water, more than it is in! Well balanced rigs are absolutely essential if you are going to master casting techniques and general handling of the tackle.

STICKS

There are two basic shotting-up systems for stick floats. Many anglers start the session with strung shotting. This involves evenly spacing small, or medium sized shot between the float and hook. Most stick designs are marked with their capacities – classic examples are four No.4 and six No.6.

This doesn't mean you must slavishly follow these formats because floats are rarely marked to their exact capacities. Often, with a four No.4 model, the manufacturer will have left room to add a couple of No.8 shot to dot it down cor-

Bulk and strung stick

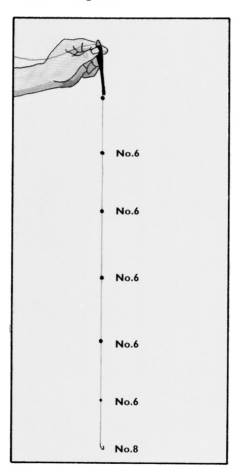

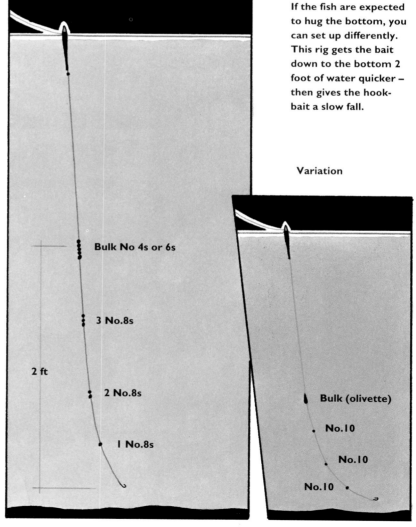

If the fish are expected to hug the bottom, you can set up differently. This rig gets the bait down to the bottom 2 foot of water quicker – then gives the hook-bait a slow fall.

Variation

rectly. This is useful because one of these No.8s can be fixed under the float to act as a marker while the other serves as a dropper shot, nearest the hook.

In a swim approximately four feet deep, a stick float carrying four spread out No.4 shot and a No.8 dropper will perform quite well. But in deeper water, say eight feet, the spacings between this minimal amount of shot will be too great and the rig won't cast very smoothly.

In this case it would be more practical to reduce the gaps by switching to No. 6 shot. This gives eight smaller shot to play around with down the line, possibly even ten if the float will also take a couple of No.8s as marker and dropper shot.

When spreading shot, try to pick a mid-range size which will give you six to ten inch gaps, evenly spaced down the rig. Fixed in this way, the set-up is more streamlined and therefore easier to cast out in a straight line. This is one of the very few instances where more shot will not cause tangles.

The other option in deeper water – if you don't want to greatly increase the amount of shot you use – is to begin spreading them with smaller gaps, from half depth downwards.

Spread shot arrangements are very versatile. They take fish both on-the-drop and from different levels, including the bottom, as the rig trots through the swim. Spread shot also offer the option of bulking them together, should the fish show a preference for more bottom presented baits.

Bulk shotted sticks get the hookbait down fast when small fish attack it before it has a chance to tempt bites from better quality samples. This kind of set-up may also perform well if the fish won't budge from the bottom, or if the swim is a bit pacey.

Usually, the bulk is fixed 2–3 feet above the hook, with between one and three smaller dropper shot spread out below.

Use small weights as bulk, if you wish to retain the option of quickly altering the rig to fish spread shot. That allows you to respond immediately by shuffling the shot if the fish start competing for feed up in the water. Or it is possible to use larger number No.1s or BBs.

When rivers are pushing hard, experienced anglers often get a sixth sense feeling that the fish won't accept baits off the bottom, so they use a more streamlined olivette as bulk.

Bulk shotted rigs are easy to cast by flicking out underarm. But don't get into the habit of

using them because of this slight advantage alone. They are not always right.

There is also a good case for using very small strung-out shot in some situations with lighter stick rigs. At first sight it may appear over-complicated to string lots of tiny No.8s down the line, but when flow rates are minimal, this trick will help to pull the rig through better than a few larger shot might achieve.

BALSAS

Balsas are a natural progression up from sticks when the water is pulling a bit hard, or is too deep for light shotting. These floats take quite a lot more weight size for size.

It is possible to string out larger shot, such as No.4s, or No. 1s with this type of float, but more

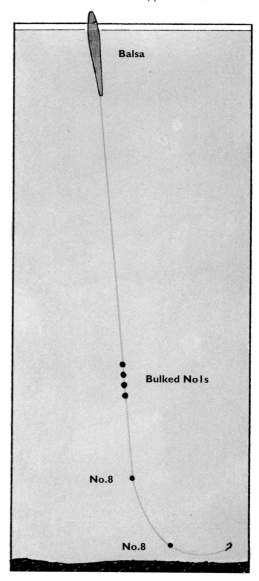

often they work best with a bulk weight. Number 1s, or BBs are favourite here, then it's a good idea to taper shot sizes towards the hook to keep the rig balanced.

After the bulk, a typical balsa rig might have a No.4 shot ten inches below, a No.6 the same distance below that and finish with a No.8 shot as the final dropper.

Always keep bulked shot below half depth and you almost certainly won't experience any tangles on the cast.

CHUBBERS

These large capacity floats are always used with a main bulk. To further simplify the rig and minimalise tangles, it's a good idea to match up a large olivette to chubbers. Once you have this

fixed on the line, just one or two dropper shot, usually No.4s or No.1s are needed to complete the set-up.

For long casts it's best to position the bulk quite close to the hook, probably about 20–30 inches away.

STRAIGHT WAGGLERS

With any bottom-end attached float, it's advisable to place at least two thirds of the weight capacity around its base. This insures it will always precede the rest of the rig in flight, gaining good distance and accuracy. If you try balancing a float's loading equally between locking shot and those spread down the line, it will almost certainly cartwheel on the cast and cause all sorts of problems.

The straight is used in medium to fast flows, where the hookbait is wanted down fast.

Chubber

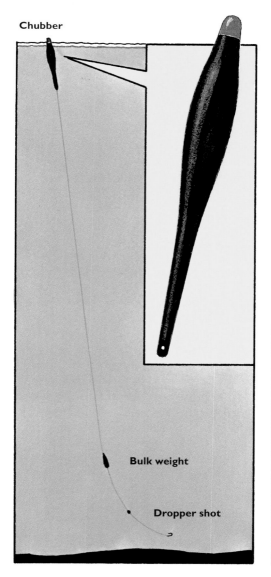

Bulk weight

Dropper shot

Straight

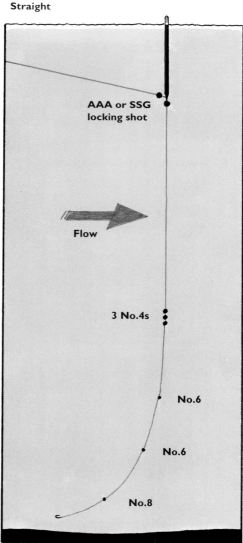

AAA or SSG locking shot

Flow

3 No.4s

No.6

No.6

No.8

Straight Peacock

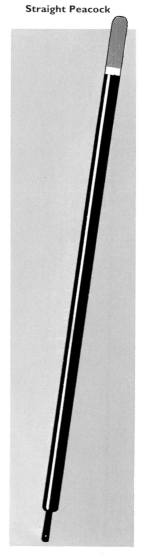

Fixing a heavier shot loading down the line instead of around the base of the float impairs accuracy and halves the casting distance.

The crucial rule which must be observed with properly loaded wagglers, is to feather the reel line with your fingers, just before the rig lands. The main shotting around the float propels it out, but you must prevent the lighter shot following behind, wrapping around the reel line above the float as it lands.

If you feather the reel line correctly, the float touches down very lightly on the surface. This is a good thing in itself, but most importantly, the end tackle will overtake the float and land in a neat straight line in front of it. You probably won't get any tangles once you've mastered this simple technique.

For flowing water, once a straight waggler has

been locked on the line with two-thirds of its capacity, the remainder of the loading can be utilised as spread, or perhaps semi-bulked smaller shot.

Shotting down the rig is, in fact, very similar to that of a stick float.

If the fish are taking up in the water, more shot can be used around the float, so only a few small shot are spread down the rig. This gives the hookbait a slow, enticing fall. Number 8s and No. 10s are the favourites for this set-up, using just two or three spread evenly from just below half depth.

On stillwaters, it's rare that a lot of shot will be needed down the rig with a straight waggler, unless small fish are a problem in the upper layers. Generally, in this situation, a straight waggler would be used to drag a bait over-depth. Three or four No.8 or 10 shot spread over the last four feet of the rig should achieve the right setting. A couple of the lower shot can actually be used to drag on the bottom where they will act as a brake.

INSERT WAGGLERS

Most of the time, very light shot are used down the rig with insert wagglers. These floats perform well when the fish are taking baits off bottom. When that happens, most of the float's loading is used to lock it on the line. Perhaps only three No.10 shot might be required to give the hookbait a slow fall.

On calm, shallow stillwaters the same format often gives options of fishing on-the-drop and on the bottom – should the hookbait get that far without a response.

If the float begins to drag out of position, you may need to alter the shotting to slightly more substantial No.8s.

Inserts can also be used with a light bulk, maybe three or four No.8s set three feet from the hook and a couple of No.10s spread out below.

These are the best floats when you're looking for spot-on accuracy, such as when casting tight to far bank cover. This is the only time with a waggler rig where the reel line isn't feathered hard. The idea is to get the float as tight in to the cover as possible.

If you feather the rig properly here, the end tackle will end up snagged in the bushes and trees. You can risk a straight cast to the desired spot, or just lightly dab the reel line at the last moment, so the lower part of the rig falls to the side of the float.

Inserts are better for more delicate on-the-drop or off-bottom bites.

Insert Peacock or Reed.

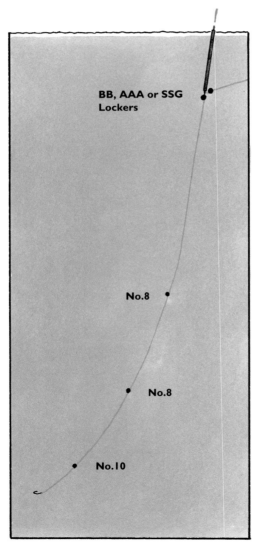

BB, AAA or SSG Lockers

No.8

No.8

No.10

Bodied Wagglers

These should be looked upon as extensions of straight and insert wagglers. The body at the base allows more casting weight to be added for greater distances. Shotting formats down the line are similar.

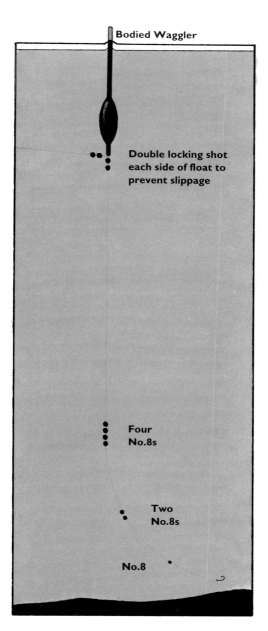

Bodied Waggler

Double locking shot each side of float to prevent slippage

Four No.8s

Two No.8s

No.8

Quills

These are best used close-in with very minimal shot. A favourite method is to anchor one large shot on the bottom with the float set over-depth by about 20 inches. The rod tip is sunk and the line is tightened up, so just the tip of the quill is left showing. A bite usually registers by the float lifting as a fish picks up the hookbait and with it the anchor shot.

Sliders

These specialist floats require some form of bulk shotting in order to pull the line through to the stop knot.

Top and bottom sliders have a main bulk set approximately 3–4 feet from the hook and one or two dropper shot spread below this. Large shot like No.1s, BBs and AAAs are used for bulk, and an olivette is also passable. Droppers are usually quite big No.4s or 1s.

The majority of bottom-end sliders are normally semi-loaded. This helps cock the float quickly so line runs smoothly through the base

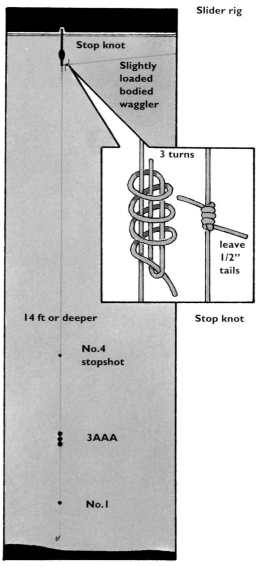

Slider rig

Stop knot

Slightly loaded bodied waggler

3 turns

leave 1/2" tails

14 ft or deeper

Stop knot

No.4 stopshot

3AAA

No.1

59

Sliding rubber float stops.

feet above the bulk. This stops the float from tangling with it and the hooklength on the cast. It's vital the distance between this upper shot is greater than the distance between the bulk weighting and the hook.

Bottom-end sliders can also be cast from a position where they are resting on the bulk shot. This gains far greater casting distance because the loaded float and bulk weight fly out together. But it's a difficult set-up to work with and tangles are always possible. The rig must be feathered before it touches down and even then in gusting winds the hooklength has an annoying tendency to wrap itself around the bulk shot.

Because sliders are deep water floats, the stop knot will often have to travel through the rod rings. This means leaving at least half-inch ends of line after the knot is formed and tightened, otherwise it will snag. It's best to use 3 lb line to form this knot, anything thinner might force its way through the slider float's eye.

If you don't fancy tying slider knots, it's possible to purchase sliding float stops made from small beads of soft rubber. These come on wire or nylon loops and are easily transferred to the reel line, before setting up the tackle. The reel line is threaded through the wire loop and brought back on itself. One of the rubber stops is then slid off the wire and onto the reel line, where it can now be further advanced up the

eye. These require smaller bulks comprising No.1s or BB shot. Droppers are No.4s or No.1s (often just one).

A good trick to prevent tangles with both types of slider is to position a No.6 shot several

FLOAT ATTACHMENTS

Top and bottom floats like sticks are fixed to the line with float rubbers. It's better to ignore the base eye on most models. Instead, you should thread three rubbers on the line and fix the stick into them so the top rubber – usually the largest – is approximately half an inch from the top of the float. The next rubber is positioned at the top of the float's stem and the final one – normally the smallest – fits at the base of the stem.

Apart from making the float more secure, fishing with three rubbers provides a spare already installed on the line should the top one split.

Wagglers are best attached to the reel line with an adaptor which pushes onto the base of the float. There are several types, including pure silicone, swivel, and wire and silicone models. They're a more versatile method than feeding the line directly through the float's base eye because it becomes possible to swap floats without breaking the rig down.

This quick-change facility is often needed, as conditions can alter and a smaller or larger float may be required in a hurry.

Silicone adaptors suit floats carrying up to 3AAA capacity. Swivel, or wire waggler links are better for larger floats, because the line won't cut through them. Some specialist canal floats have swivel adaptors designed to fit base pegs without an attachment eye.

**Waggler adaptors –
Middy River and
Drennan Silicone.**

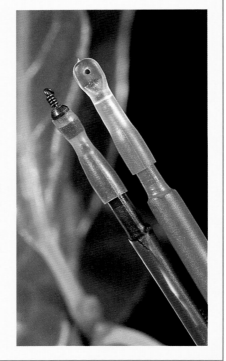

line, above the short piece which was first doubled back.

Some anglers prefer to use two of these stops together to prevent slippage.

CANAL WAGGLERS

Canal wagglers are scaled down in size, because casting distances may only be 10 to 15 metres and the venues are mainly shallow. Some canal floats are simply smaller versions of insert wagglers, made from peacock, clear plastic, or reed. But most popular nowadays are the more gradually tapering all-balsa designs.

Whichever canal waggler you select, one common characteristic lies in shotting patterns. Most shot goes around the float, with perhaps only two or three No.10 shot, or even smaller micro shot spread out as droppers. Some canal regulars use tiny No.7 or 8 Styl weights, because these give the hookbait an even slower fall rate.

Most canal wagglers take between a couple of No.1 shot and two AAA as lockers.

LEGER RIGS

Many anglers experience lots of tangles when first trying to use leger tackle and yet with a little thought, it's possible to arrive at quite basic rigs which will hardly ever give any trouble.

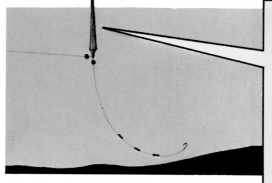

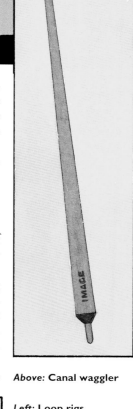

With legering we enter a world of beads, loops, swivels, booms and rig tubing. There are lots of accessories, so it's easy to see why some anglers persist in getting this quite simple method wrong.

The secret is to keep accessories to a minimum. Only use them where they are essential.

LOOP METHODS

The popular loop method is a classic example of a simple uncluttered rig which works superbly well with leger weights and feeders.

A standard loop rig is formed after threading a small snap swivel on the reel line followed by a tiny round plastic bead. The line is brought back on itself by about a foot, leaving the swivel and bead free running within the loop and it is then knotted.

At the base of the large loop, a smaller one

Above: **Canal waggler**

Left: **Loop rigs**

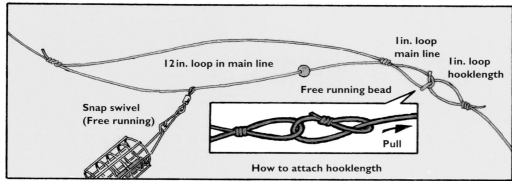

12 in. loop in main line

1 in. loop main line

1 in. loop hooklength

Free running bead

Snap swivel (Free running)

Pull

How to attach hooklength

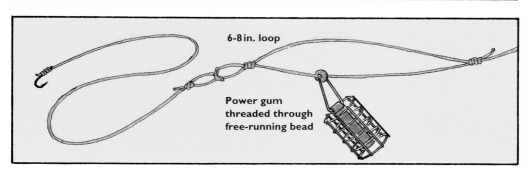

6-8 in. loop

Power gum threaded through free-running bead

inch loop is formed, to which the hooklength is eventually attached. At this stage it's easy to see why the bead is there – it stops the swivel from jamming, or over-riding the smaller loop knot.

Once a leger weight, or feeder is clipped to the snap swivel, the extra weight pushes against the smaller loop, sending it out to the side. This in turn keeps the hooklength away from the rest of the tackle on the cast. Tangles are very rare with this set-up and although the leger, or feeder is trapped, bites are still very confident.

It is possible to simplify the loop method further by specially fitting your feeders with Powergum links, which have a small bead ready installed on them. The reel line is threaded through the bead and a small loop is formed, so just the bead and feeder is running in it. A smaller loop is formed again to take the hooklength and you are left with a very good river feeder rig. Some anglers shorten the loop on which the feeder is running to just a few inches if bites are difficult to hit. This often causes the fish to dislodge the feeder and hook themselves.

FREE-RUNNING LEGER

A good basic rig to try with a bead is a free running leger. An Arlesey bomb is either threaded direct on the line, or clipped to a swivel link first. Next, a small bead is threaded on and then the end of the reel line is formed into a small loop to attach the hooklength. A small shot, or leger stop is positioned directly above this loop to hold the

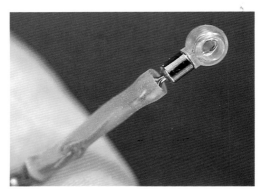

leger weight away from the hooklength.

To simplify this rig even further, a specially designed sliding bead replaces both the original one and the snap swivel and the weight is fixed direct to this.

The basic running leger used by carp anglers features a hook link formed from nylon or braid with a swivel for attachment to the main line. This swivel acts as the stop against which a rubber buffer bead rests to prevent the bomb chaffing the knot.

Shorter links of possibly six or eight inches are preferable for hard bottomed waters.

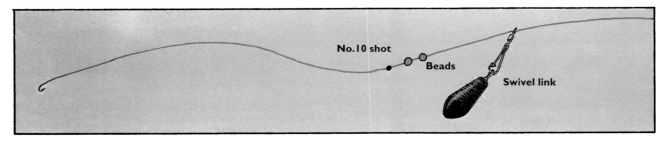

No.10 shot   Beads   Swivel link

PATERNOSTER

This is the most simple leger rig. The bomb or feeder is tied direct to the end of the reel line, then six to 12 inches back up the line a tiny loop is formed on which the hooklength is fixed.

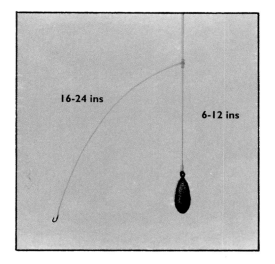

HELICOPTER RIG

When carp become suspicious of long rig tube set-ups, the helicopter or rotary rig will also prevent soft, braided hook links from tangling. Numerous systems have been developed but the basic idea remains the same. The weight is tied directly to the end of the line and a swivel bead with the hook link attached rests directly above this with beads either side for easy rotation. The beads are trapped in position with rubber float stops. Other, purpose-made systems eliminate

the float stops by simply incorporating a length of silicone tubing which fixes on the swivel eye of the bomb.

LEGER COMPONENTS

BOOMS Some anglers use short plastic tube booms to keep the hooklength away from their feeder rigs, but in reality this only works when casting over short ranges. They're sold with bead and clip ready installed and usually have a good diagram on the packaging explaining how to set them up.

RIG TUBE Soft silicone tubing is useful for partly covering swivels and nylon links on feeders. It stops the hooklength from tangling back around the feeder. Long, stiff lengths of tubing are also regularly used by specimen anglers to prevent hook links of soft, limp braid tangling around the weight and line when hurled over long distances. They often thread the line through 12 to 20 inches of fine, stiff tubing which critically must be at least a third longer in length than the hook link itself. The leger weight is then hung on a swivel bead which fits tightly on the tube.

SWIVELS Standard barrel swivels can be used on feeder links, but most feeder manufacturers now fit their products with diamond eye swivels. These have a more pointed eye, which hangs and anchors a knot better.

Swivel links, also known as American snap swivels, are popular for attaching leger weights and feeders to rigs. They offer a useful quick change facility.

Helicopter rig.

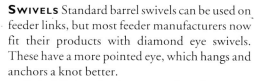

Silicone float rubbers, leger stops and swivels.

NETTING FISH

After you have mastered getting the tackle out cleanly and begin to catch better sized fish, there is a simple netting procedure to follow. As the fish nears the bank, you should position your landing net directly out in front of you and submerge the net. It is very important to bring fish in over the net, never try to chase the fish around with it.

If you try to hurry the fish in, by following it with the net, you risk spooking the fish, or bumping it off the hook.

LEGER STOPS These come in two sizes. They consist of a plastic peg, which pushes into a ring. This locks the device and is more secure than relying on a split shot. It's advisable to only use leger stops on reel lines over 3 lb, because they can pinch and damage finer monofilament.

Below: **Eyes focused on the target for the overhead cast.**

Below right: **Overhead cast.**

Bottom: **Underarm cast.**

CASTING TECHNIQUES

There are three main casting styles. The overhead is most frequently used by anglers, but bankside terrain doesn't always make this practi-cal. Therefore, underarm and sideways casts must also be mastered. The sideways action is often a better way of casting tackle underneath far bank cover.

OVERHEAD It's best to learn the basics of overhead casting from a stationary position. This technique is good for both leger and float tackle. The tackle is brought over your head and held still, with the rod pointing backwards at approximately 10 o'clock. At this stage, it's best to focus on your target, then the rod is propelled sharply forward, over your head and the tackle released at 2 o'clock.

It requires practise to get the hang of the timing involved here and it might be easier to try the technique with a small leger weight first – if only to sort out a rhythm and work out the crucial rod positioning.

As experience is gained, it's possible to bring the rod back and then forward to make the cast in one movement. If the bankside behind allows, it may also be feasible to bring the rod even lower, to gain a greater casting arc and, therefore, better distance.

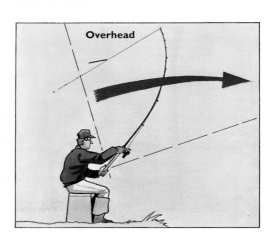

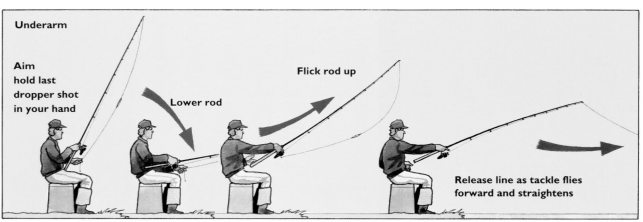

UNDERARM The underarm technique only works with bulk shotted rigs and strung stick float formats. Here, the hooklength is lightly held between the index finger and thumb of your free hand, just above the hook. The rod is brought low to the water and then flicked sharply upwards, at the same time releasing the rig from your free hand.

The weight of the shot causes the lower end of the rig to lead out in front of the float and after you have practised a little, it should go in a straight line.

SIDEWAYS Sideways casts are performed in similar fashion to the underarm. Again, you should try to hold the line with your free hand – if it's possible to sweep the rod around from that side of your body.

If the rod can only be brought around from the other side, the rig is left hanging free, with about three feet of line between its tip and the float. This manoeuvre only tends to work with shallow set floats and the rod has to be brought back and then forward in one smooth movement, to prevent the end tackle from snagging the ground.

This cast can be used to skim light waggler rigs under overhanging foliage on the far bank of small rivers and canals. It's a deadly way of catching chub and carp, species which like to hug cover very tightly.

POINTS TO REMEMBER

The most accurate cast is overhead, or very slightly to one side. This is the only way to properly launch feeder tackle, or heavier leger weights. It's also an accurate way of casting wagglers and big stick floats into open water.

Most top and bottom fixed floats can be cast underarm, but this isn't a successful method for the waggler.

The sideways cast is used with top and bottom float designs, but is normally associated with waggler tackle. Good timing, when releasing the tackle, is the only way to gain the necessary accuracy with this cast and the rod should end up pointing in the direction of the target area.

Sideways cast

Rod parallel to bank and kept low

Release last dropper shot as cast commences

Line release point

Sideways

SPECIES GUIDE

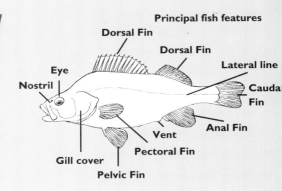

Principal fish features

Dorsal Fin

Dorsal Fin

Eye

Nostril

Lateral line

Cauda Fin

Anal Fin

Vent

Pectoral Fin

Gill cover

Pelvic Fin

Here's a checklist of the habitats, baits and British records for the most popular species in UK waters. Few anglers succeed in catching examples of every single species but in fishing you never know your luck!

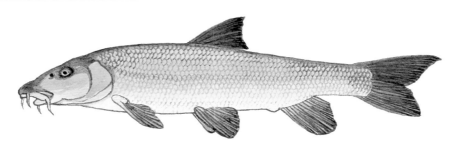

BARBEL

Barbel are a much sought after river species. On larger systems like the Severn and Trent they are prolific and relatively easy to catch while in the 1 lb to 5 lb bracket. They're primarily bottom feeders and keenly mop up small baits like maggots, hemp and casters. This makes the swimfeeder a deadly method. Big barbel are much more elusive and tend to be loners, or shoal with a handful of smaller fish.

Barbel are very powerful, streamlined fish, even a small three-pounder can prove more than a handful on standard tackle. They like fast water, especially over gravel runs and for this reason are often found in weirpools, in shallow weedy channels and swims which receive stronger flows such as on the outside of bends.

Deeper water is another place to look for this species. Barbel tend to hug any pronounced depressions in the river bed and seem to favour deep holes on the edge of faster water.

The maggot feeder is a popular method. Hemp and caster, packed into an open-end feeder, is another highly viable approach. A good bed of loose fed hemp, maggots, or casters can be put down closer in, and then fished over with a light link leger, or over-depth float rig.

Although barbel are caught on float tackle, presentation needs to be spot-on. It may involve using big floats and slowing the tackle right down so the hook bait is presented well on the bottom.

Another good way of taking them is to link leger with larger baits like luncheon meat, bread, sausage meat and sweetcorn. A roving approach pays dividends here, searching out weedy runs, letting a large bait trundle along the bottom and rest up momentarily against weed, or in slacks.

Barbel feed all year round, but best results are likely when rivers are carrying a bit of extra water, especially in late summer and autumn. In high summer when water levels may be quite low it's best to seek out more oxygenated water below weirs. In winter, deeper water usually proves more productive.

A barbel would be classed a specimen on most waters if it weighed over 9 lb.

> **BRITISH RECORD**
> 15 lb 7 oz (7.002kg).

BLEAK

These small silver fish are surface feeders. They rarely exceed two ounces and can be a nuisance on larger rivers. They will greedily boil on the surface for loose fed baits like maggots and casters and strip soft hookbaits off the hook, often without registering a positive bite, even on float tackle. Sometimes anglers have to bulk shot their float rigs in order to get through hungry shoals of bleak, just so they can

Bronze Bream

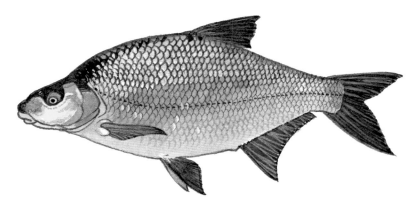

Larger common or bronze bream are thick-set fish. They are often described as slab-sided which explains the angler's affectionate nickname for them as slabs. Smaller bream up to 1 lb 8 oz tend to lie flat on the surface as they are played in towards the bank. It's often possible to skim them over the surface towards the landing net and this has led to another nickname, skimmers.

Bream are found in the majority of stillwaters and reach double-figures in large lakes, meres, pits and reservoirs. They also inhabit drains, fens and canals. Although many rivers also hold bream, they tend to be more localised.

Bream feed most avidly early, or late in the day, also at night and when the weather is humid and overcast. Generally they are bottom feeders, but they can sometimes be caught up in the water when conditions are particularly warm and bright.

Quiver and swingtipping are two of the most favoured breaming methods, combined with open-ended, groundbait feeders, or leger rigs.

Bream are shoal fish and often give away their presence by sending up strings of small bubbles, or by clouding shallow water as they graze along the bottom. Large bream also have a tendency to roll on the surface over feeding areas.

Noted bream hotspots on stillwaters are usually close to features such as gravel bars, islands, thick weed and lily beds, rush lined bays and inlets. They are often found in shallow to medium depths in summer, sometimes quite close to the bank. In winter they will move out into deeper open water.

Canal bream are often located in wide turning bays and where there are far bank features like rush beds, overhanging cover and moored boats.

River bream rarely move from noted areas. These are usually out of the main current and where the water is deeper.

This species responds well to groundbait and fair helpings of feed like casters, squatts and worms.

Bream can be fickle feeders. It's a good idea to change hookbaits regularly in the quest for bites. Red maggots, red and fluorescent coloured pinkies, casters, worms, sweetcorn and bread all have their day. This fish has a liking for cocktail baits, such as worm and caster or maggot and caster. Coloured maggot combinations, including reds, whites, yellows and bronzes are also worth trying.

Some anglers even breed their own hooker maggots for bream fishing. These are called gozzers and are larger and softer skinned than commercial shop bought bait.

A big catch of bream would normally comprise fish in the 2 lb to 5 lb category but fish up to 7 lb are not uncommon. A double-figure fish would be classed a specimen.

Silver bream are much smaller than the common variety and its distribution is limited to the south and east of England. It is easily confused with small common bream and scale counts might be necessary to differentiate the species. The British record stands at just 15 oz and reflects the uncertainty surrounding the identification of silvers.

Silver Bream

BRITISH RECORDS
bronze 16 lb 9 oz (7.512 kg)
and silver 15 oz (0.425 kg).

---

get at the bigger, bottom feeding fish.

Matchmen are probably the only anglers who might consider bleak as a serious proposition. Some top stars have become very proficient at whipping out literally hundreds of bleak on scaled down surface pole rigs and they may catch well over 1,000 during the course of a five hour competition.

Bleak are mainly found in rivers, inter-locking canals and river valley gravel pits. The best baits are maggots, pinkies, bloodworms and jokers. These are fished on the surface with a greased line, or with shallow-set pole rigs, at depths down to three feet.

Cloudy groundbait will hold them in numbers. They feed best when rivers and canals are heavily swollen by rain.

BRITISH RECORD
4 oz 4 dr (0.120 kg)

Catfish

This species has a cult following, but it's a small, dedicated band of anglers, because there aren't that many recognised catfish waters in this country.

Catfish are scavengers and are usually caught on small dead fish although a wide range of baits includ-

ing squid are used. They will feed in the day, but are more likely to pick up a bait at night.

BRITISH RECORD
49 lb 14 oz (22.623 kg).

There are signs that cats are spreading as odd ones have been accidentally caught on southern canals and rivers. On the Continent they reach massive sizes and can exceed 100 lb. A specimen British cat would weigh 20 lb but that's no easy target.

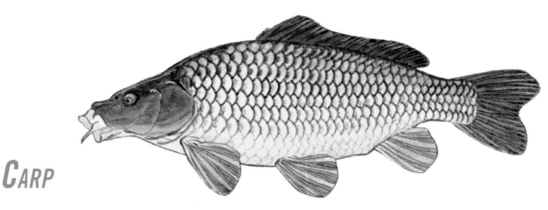

Carp

Intense cultivation of carp has resulted in several varieties but all stem from the fully scaled common or fast growing king carp. These are completely covered in regular sized scales and are frequently streamlined in shape although older specimens might grow very deep. There are two pairs of barbels on the upper lip.

line. To confuse matters still further, it's possible to catch fully scaled mirrors completely covered in large, plate-like scales.

Specimens without any visible scales whatsoever are known as nude or leather carp. You may also hear the term wild carp which in its true form is a fish that has never known any

and canals and feed in open water at all levels, including from the surface. Carp also like overgrown areas and are good at nestling into inaccessible spots. They will often be found in thick weed beds, under lilies and thick cover, even among sunken tree roots.

In the warmer months, carp are very active and feed up in the water, or

Mirror

Leather

Mirrors have an irregular scattering of large scales, notably around the wrist of the tail with odd ones dotted along the back and flanks. There are also linear mirrors with a continuous straight row of scales along the lateral

form of domestication. It is unlikely that these exist in the UK even if you hear fully scaled, torpedo-shaped fish caught from remote, ancient lakes described as wildies.

Carp are widespread in lakes, rivers

actually on the surface. They also patrol the margins and shallows, particularly over gravel bars.

They become more lethargic in winter and may only feed for short periods in deeper water on really cold

DACE

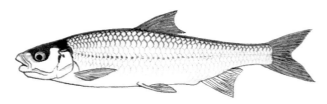

Dace are mainly river and small stream fish, but are also present in some flowing canal venues. They're very active and gather in vast shoals on clear, fast flowing shallows. They will feed at all levels, but are renowned for competing for food up in the water and on the surface.

Dace give bites like greased lightening, so it's quite an achievement to

string a catch together. They like maggots, casters, hemp and tares. Sometimes match anglers will fish

BRITISH RECORD
1 lb 4 oz 4 dr (0.574 kg).

very light rigs for dace and even resort to smaller baits like pinkies to try and put a fair catch together. These silver fish average two to eight ounces on most rivers and sometimes shoal in huge numbers on the shallows. A 1 lb plus dace is an exceptional specimen.

days. Carp are a cult fish and many specimen anglers are only interested in this species alone. They will camp out by the waterside for days, even weeks after double-figure fish.

Carp gear is very sophisticated and it's not unusual for the dedicated carp angler to fish with up to three rods resting on special pods and buzzer bars. There's an impressive choice of electronic bite indicators and other assorted gadgetry. In fact, there have been more developments in carp tackle and rigs than in any other area of the sport.

While a static approach, with legered baits is the main line of attack for many carp anglers, these fish will also take floating baits, like bread crust and Chum Mixers. A lot of serious carp men take a stalking rod out with them and leave their main fishing sta-

Crucian

tion from time to time, to wander off in search of cruising, or basking fish.

Luncheon meat, sweetcorn and bread are worth trying for carp, but boilies are now the No.1 bait for this species. These high protein offerings

can be made up to your own recipes and specifications at home, or purchased in exotic flavours, off the shelf in any tackle shop.

Boilies come in many sizes, colours and flavours. There are also countless additives and stimulators which can be applied making them even more potent. Certainly the fish seem to appreciate this new science and appear to be preoccupied with boilies on waters where they are fed in large quantities.

Carp, particularly smaller fish up to 10 lb, will feed on conventional baits like maggots, casters, sweetcorn, bread, hemp and tares. Fish in the 2 lb to 5 lb bracket are heavily stocked in many small lakes and will compete well for these types of feed on light float tackle.

Well stocked stillwaters might also hold ghost carp, which are a cross between commons and kois. These grow up to low double-figures and fight really well for their size.

While many anglers would be pleased with a double-figure com-

mon, mirror, or leather carp, 20 lb is commonly regarded as the barrier to break in specimen fishing circles.

Crucian carp are a smaller relation and rarely exceed 4 lb. These fish are fairly widespread in lakes and canals and prefer small baits like maggots, casters, bread and sweetcorn. Crucians are stocky little fish and are normally a much brighter golden colour than common carp. They are also fully scaled, but are distinguishable from other carp by the lack of barbels on their mouths and their tubby appearance.

This is in complete contrast to the chub-like profile of the grass carp which is now becoming more widespread in the UK. It grazes on all forms of aquatic vegetation and in numerous waters is used as a form of biological weed control, eliminating the need for chemical treatments. But stocking levels are crucial because it is quite capable of completely denuding a fishery of all weed. Like the crucian, it has no barbels and is fully scaled but it is impossible to confuse the two because of the grass carp's wide head and elongated body.

BRITISH CARP RECORDS
51 lb 8 oz (23.358 kg).
Crucian 5 lb 10 oz 8 dr (2.565 kg)
Grass 25 lb 4 oz (11.453 kg).

CHUB

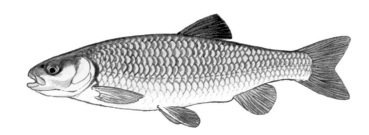

Although chub are primarily a river fish, they do thrive in some canals. Some enormous specimens are also stocked in gravel pits, but they're extremely elusive.

Rivers provide the easiest chances of catching chub. They are a species which has a definite liking for features. If there's overhanging foliage, then it's almost certain a shoal of chub will be in the vicinity – if not tucked right underneath it.

Chub also like streamy water, weir pools, weedy areas and smooth glides – especially if they end in rippling shallows. While it's possible to take good catches in open, flowing water on rivers, canal chub are often more wary and a bait has to be presented very tight to cover to entice a response.

Average sized fish run to 3 lb and often make up good catches on feeder gear. The stick float is a good method in medium flow rates, while the waggler takes over on slower rivers, or when fishing to more distant far bank cover on smaller rivers and canals.

A good quantity of maggots, or casters may be required to keep a shoal of chub interested. They also respond to hemp and tares in summer and autumn.

Larger baits work well for chub. They have a reputation as scavengers, so it's doubtful if they'll ignore anything on the recognised bait lists.

Favourite chub methods are free-lining, link legering, or trotting with large capacity floats, often called chubbers. Big baits like luncheon meat, bread and lobworms are popular. Other good chub baits are slugs, waspgrub, crayfish, small dead fish and sweetcorn. They will even take spinners meant for perch and pike.

Chub feed year round, even in very cold temperatures when other species lay low. A specimen sized chub is usually over 4 lb.

> **BRITISH RECORD**
> 8 lb 4 oz (3.743 kg).

GRAYLING

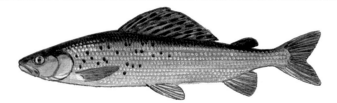

These handsome river fish are easy to recognise, due to their large, sail-like dorsal fins. They are members of the salmon family and have an adipose fin with large black spots on the flanks.

Grayling are shoal fish and prefer clean, fast flowing water and thrive in smaller salmon rivers. These fish are streamlined and even small specimens fight hard. When released, they must be held head first into the current to recover their strength otherwise they could float away belly up.

The best method is long trotting with baits like maggots using all-balsa, or Avon style floats. A 2 lb grayling is very good – over 3 lb is a specimen.

> **BRITISH RECORD**
> 4 lb 3 oz (1.899 kg)

GUDGEON

Gudgeon are bottom feeders, common in rivers, canals and some lakes. These very small fish look similar to barbel and tend to hug the margins to avoid the attention of predators.

They weigh no more than a few ounces and matchmen are the only anglers who might fish for them seriously when low weights are expected on poor canal or river venues.

Gudgeon are shoal fish, so some surprising weights of them can be achieved. A busy competitive angler might catch several hundred on a short pole rig. Canal catches can reach 10 lb over five hours. On some rivers up to 20 lb of gudgeon is possible.

Best baits are maggots, pinkies, squatts, bloodworms and jokers.

> **BRITISH RECORD**
> 5 oz (0.141 kg).

Eel

Eels are migratory fish and small ones, or bootlaces as anglers often call them, can be a nuisance on rivers. Great mystery surrounds the life cycle of the eel. They mature at varying ages, but usually after around nine years in freshwater, and then make their amazing journey downstream and across the Atlantic Ocean to the spawning grounds in the Sargasso Sea off the Bahamas. They spawn and die with each female releasing several million eggs.

Exactly how these hatch and find their way back across the Atlantic isn't fully known but many millions of elvers eventually return to our river systems and spread out into all kinds of waters.

Specimen sized fish of over 3 lb are mainly found in gravel pits and lakes where they'll often leave the bottom to feed in mid-water or even higher.

They tear at their food, are very long-lived (possibly as long as 50 years) and become considerably less active in winter.

Small eels readily snap up maggots, casters and worms. Big eels tend to become mainly worm or fish feeders and this distinction is quite marked in some waters.

> **BRITISH RECORD**
> 11 lb 2 oz (5.046 kg).

Perch

Small perch are often the first fish a novice angler catches. When they are only a few ounces in size, these fish show little caution and willingly take poorly presented hook baits.

Perch are predators and like a mobile bait. Top anglers respond to that by deliberately making their tackle behave erratically, twitching and lifting maggot and worm baits, to try and catch a bonus perch, or two.

Perch are found in most types of fishery. Up to 2 lb in size they take maggots, pinkies, casters and all types of worm., Specimen sized fish can be caught on spinners, lobworms and some small livebaits, like gudgeon and minnows.

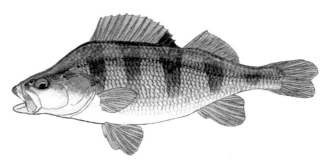

Because of their predatory instincts, these distinctive striped fish, with their prominent, spiny dorsal fins, tend to be found near features which afford cover for small fry. You can expect to find perch alongside weedbeds, margins, ledges, overhanging cover, reeds, pilings and bridges. They often give away their presence by scattering small fry.

Perch are shoal fish for most of their lives, but larger specimens over 2 lb can drift off into pairs, or become loners.

Small perch usually give a response throughout the season, larger stillwater fish become more active in autumn and winter.

> **BRITISH RECORD**
> 5 lb 9 oz (2.523 kg).

Ruffe

When fishing canals and some rivers you may catch a fish with an identical outline to the perch, but with spotted instead of striped flanks. This is the ruffe, a bottom feeding member of the perch family which only grows to around 15cm in length.

Unlike perch, the first and second dorsal fins on the ruffe are joined. They eagerly accept maggots and worms. Sometimes you'll get a response from ruffe when no other species is feeding.

> **BRITISH RECORD**
> 5 oz 4 dr (0.148 kg).

PIKE

Pike are the most impressive predators in freshwater and sit on top of the food chain. Their large, wide mouths hide rows of razor sharp teeth which are inward pointing. Prey are swallowed head first and rarely escape.

Their streamlined bodies are also geared for catching prey fish. Pike tend to lay up in ambush until potential food swims close and then accelerate into the attack at amazing speed.

They are vital in balancing stocks in most mixed fisheries and will often pick off injured, poorly or dead fish.

Pike are never far away from features like overhanging trees and bushes, weed and rush beds, underwater bars, inlets, outlets and islands.

Livebaiting is a deadly way of catching them but the method is banned on some fisheries to protect the image of the sport or as a disease deterrent to eliminate free movement of bait fish between different waters.

Dead coarse fish will catch a lot of pike, but sea fish like herrings, sprats, smelt, mackerel and sardines are usually far more productive. Pike can be caught on float tackle, or legered baits. The latter are often fished with electronic bite indicators, similar to those used by carp anglers.

Another very exciting method of taking these fish is with spinner baits, or plugs. There's a massive range of these types of lures to choose from. A double-figure pike is a good fish, a 20-pounder is an exceptional specimen.

> **BRITISH RECORD**
> 46 lb 13 oz (21.234 kg).

ROACH

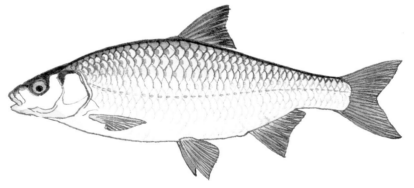

Roach are the most popular and widely distributed British coarse fish. You will have to be quick with small ones and extremely skilful to tempt older, wiser fish over the 1 lb mark.

This species takes on a slightly different appearance depending on habitat. Roach from coloured canal and lake fisheries are rather pale, with virtually a bleached look about them. But the same species from a clear, small river can positively glow with colour. There's no mistaking the bright red fins of a clean river fish.

Lake roach rarely keep to set boundaries. In the warm months they will rise up in the water to regular feed, even boil on the surface. They tend to revert to bottom feeding in winter, but clever feeding will still activate them into competing up in the water.

Canal roach are very canny. Very delicate lines, tiny hooks and small baits are required here. Squatts, hemp, punched bread, bloodworm...all have special roaching techniques built up around them.

River roach will respond to conventional maggot and caster baits, hemp, tares and wheat, but again they need to be fed and fished for with great care and more than a smidgen of skill. Big river roach also show a liking for seed baits and larger bread offerings. A 1 lb roach is a good fish while a two-pounder represents a magical milestone.

> **BRITISH RECORD**
> 4 lb 3 oz (1.899 kg).

HYBRIDS

On heavily stocked waters, species like roach and bream often spawn in the same areas. This can result in cross-fertilisation of eggs and sometimes produces hybrids.

Roach-bream hybrids tend to have the body shape of bream, but smaller, silvery scales (rather than large bronze ones,) on the upper flanks of their bodies. This usually signifies their roach ancestry.

Some hybrids are more roach shaped and lighter coloured. This can fool anglers into thinking they have caught a specimen roach! The tell tale sign, which usually gives the game away, is the anal fin, which is concave and much longer than that of a true roach.

These are very good sporting fish and can grow up to 4 lb in size on many waters. This type of hybrid can be very active and will fall to most methods.

RUDD

Surface feeding rudd are found in lakes, but also canals and rivers.

Rudd are sometimes mistaken for roach, but the bottom lip on rudd protrudes beyond the top one. Rudd's fins are also more crimson than red.

These fish are located in reedy bays and close to weed cover. They also like overhanging foliage, but will just as readily drift out into open water, particularly if a ripple is carrying insect life across a lake.

Rudd compete vigorously on the surface for maggots, casters, hemp and bread in summer. They can be caught on greased line surface rigs, or small wagglers with little shot positioned down the line. Regular loose feed and soft, cloudy groundbait is often needed to keep them interested.

They vanish after the first frosts and don't reappear until the summer. A 2 lb fish is regarded as a specimen.

> **BRITISH RECORD**
> 4 lb 8 oz (2.041 kg).

STICKLEBACKS AND MINNOWS

Stickleback   **Minnow**

Only the most desperate of match anglers might actually have a go at fishing for these tiddlers! The common three-spined stickleback is found everywhere from drainage ditches to estuary waters but is a pest because of its ability to destroy baits. They peck at maggots until you're left with an empty skin and sometimes get the bait firmly lodged down their red throats.

Minnows are a nuisance during low summer flows on rivers and sometimes it's very difficult to get through them with maggot baits.

> **BRITISH RECORD**
> minnow 13 dr (0.023 kg).

ZANDER

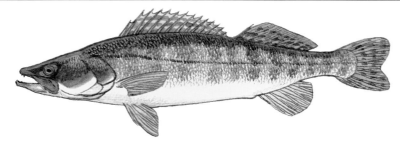

Zander, or pike-perch as they are sometimes called, were first imported in the late 19th century when they were released into ponds at Woburn Abbey in Bedfordshire. But the most significant stocking was in the Great Ouse Relief Channel – a supposedly safe base from which they have subsequently spread far and wide.

They bred very successfully in the slow, deep and coloured waters of the Channel and proved such active predators that they caused a crash in the populations of prey species. There have been similar reports from canals in the Midlands where zander were illegally stocked.

But nature now appears to have achieved a reasonable balance.

> **BRITISH RECORD**
> 18 lb 10 oz (8.448 kg).

TENCH

Odd tench to 4 lb are taken in slack bays or backwaters on major rivers. Many canals also contain prolific stocks of tench and they are sometimes recorded up to 7 lb from these venues. But really big tench are more associated with lakes and reservoirs where they can reach double-figures.

Best fishing times for tench are in the early morning and late evening. They are caught in large numbers in the summer, then tend to fade until the back-end of the season. Odd fish may be caught through the winter but they are not predictable at this time of the year.

Tench are margin feeders, but also like weedy areas and bars on the edge of deep water. They will often forage into very shallow water and backwaters in warm weather.

Although noted as bottom feeders, tench will compete up in the water with regular feeding and have also been known to take surface baits like bread crust.

On carp venues they frequently become pre-occupied with boilies. They will take maggots (reds are a favourite), worms, casters, sweetcorn, bread baits and luncheon meat.

Float fishing, legering and feeder tactics all work well on their day for this species. You will often know when a tench is rooting about on the bottom, by the clusters of small bubbles it sends fizzing to the surface. A specimen tench would be over 7 lb on most waters.

> **BRITISH RECORD**
> 14 lb 7 oz (6.548 kg).

UNHOOKING AND HANDLING CODE

Below: Repeat captures of the same fish are common and it's every angler's responsibility to handle and return his fish to the water as carefully and quickly as possible. Hold larger specimens in the wet mesh of the landing net, taking care to avoid exerting pressure on the gills. Use a suitable sized disgorger if the hook lies deeper inside the mouth.

Below: Forceps are an efficient tool for removing bigger hooks from specimen fish. Unhooking mats are essential if you intend taking up carp or pike fishing and they must be wet before use. But never lay any fish on hard ground, no matter what its size.

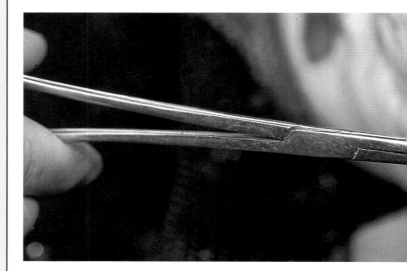

Right: Zero in a wet weigh sling on the scales before recording an exceptional fish. You can also use a strong plastic bag for the smaller specimens. But suspend the fish over a grassy bank or water in case of mishap. The same applies when photographing a fish – it should be held low to the ground over an unhooking mat or grass at the water's edge.

● Barbel frequently fight to the point of exhaustion. Return them in that condition and they could float away belly-up. They must be held head-first into the flow until they recover. Alternatively, stake them out in the stream using a special tube made of soft material.

Right below: Ideally, fish should be returned to the water immediately with the minimal amount of handling. That's the basic code. But if you must use a keepnet, stake it out in deep water, giving the fish maximum free-dom inside. At the end of the session, do not withdraw the net completely from the water and carry it up the bank. That could result in fish losing scales as they tumble down the whole length of the net and thrash about in the base. Far better to release them in the water as demonstrated here. Lift the end of the net and guide the fish through the mouth.

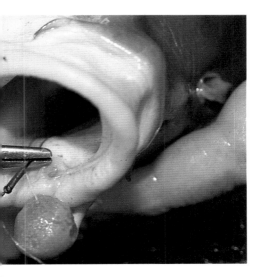

RIVER FISHING

The golden rule when fishing flowing water is to feed the swim very regularly. It's essential because river fish soon drift away unless you're in a swim where the shoals are held captive by a pronounced feature.

As with any venue, features are an important guide in locating river fish. Productive areas usually include stretches of bank with overhanging foliage, slacks, lock cuttings, reed beds, weirs, islands and bends. The confluence with a tributary is also worthy of investigation.

But on running water it's possible to draw fish wherever you are fishing by clever feeding. Many river species are nomadic and they soon locate

your feed – as long as it's fed regularly in the right quantity to make the fish compete for it.

More subtle features like clear runs between weed beds may have to be pinpointed with the aid of a good pair of Polaroid sunglasses. These eradicate reflective glare and make it a lot easier to see beneath the surface.

Regular feeding draws fish out from the weed. It may take some time, but it's often possible to keep on building this type of swim until a really good catch accumulates.

Steady runs above broken, shallow water might also hold many fish. Some of your feed

will filter down into the rapids and draw others up. It's also well worth remembering that fish like variations in flow, so look carefully at swims with a crease line, where faster water abuts a steady run.

Water at the tail-end of weir run-offs is always well oxygenated and usually holds plenty of fish. And big shoals frequently hide up right beneath moored boats, particularly when the craft are tied up on the quieter, far bank.

Don't get downhearted if the only vacant swims on a river venue are straight and feature-less. Sport may not be instantaneous but a

A successful strike at long range – but with regular feeding it's possible to draw the shoal upriver.

patient, well thought out approach often results in some really good catches by the end of the day.

Shallows are often ignored but these, too, might hold substantial shoals. The fishing can be surprisingly easy once you've sorted out a suitable rig. These pacey swims usually produce more positive bites.

TWO LINES OF ATTACK

Feature swims like islands and overhanging cover often have fish laying tight to them, but it's not wise to dive straight into these areas with your tackle. One false move, such as a bad cast, or a lost fish could ruin your chances for the rest of the day.

There are two good ways of working at these types of swim. A proven match technique is to feed the feature regularly for an hour or so and in the meantime fish another part of the swim. The idea is to get the fish taking baits confidently, so when you do go out with your tackle, competing fish will be less prone to spook when you catch one or two of them.

It doesn't matter if you spend this initial period whipping out some small fish on the pole, or on a close-in running line rig. The trick is to keep yourself occupied, while still remembering to regularly feed the area which will eventually become your main line of attack.

The second method entails trying to feed fish just a little bit away from the feature, in the hope that you can take odd ones at the edge of the shoal. If this works you may be able to stall fishing tight to the feature until much later in the session. This may well be the best route to choose

SEASONAL FACTORS

Fish are more active in summer and autumn when they often show a preference for shallow, streamy water. But following the first night frosts, rivers begin to change and so do the feeding habits of the fish. They become more lethargic and are less inclined to chase after baits with the same enthusiasm they showed in the warmer weather.

Large shoals may move into deeper, less pacey water, in preparation for the winter floods. These fish will require a totally different approach.

In warmer weather, a swim develops in many ways depending on how the fish react to your feeding. You'll obviously get through a lot more bait chasing a shoal around the swim, particularly if the fish move up in the water. You may also have to feed lots anyway, in order to get through the small fish which intercept a great deal of bait before it has a chance to reach the bottom.

In winter this isn't such a problem and you may be able to feed much less, in the knowledge that it's reaching bottom. That is not to say regular feeding has to be ignored. It's probably even more important, because you are going to have to work even harder in coaxing lethargic fish into showing interest.

During the early months of the season, baits fished up in the water and trotted at the pace of the current will take good catches. But as feed requirements drop, techniques must often change too. You will have to learn to slow the tackle down to coax bites when the going is hard. Stick float rigs may have to be edged through the swim at half pace, leger tackle and the feeder become more important methods because static baits might possibly pull more bites.

Some feature pegs remain good all-year round, but others are seasonal, so you will have to try to learn to read the river. This also means that certain swims

which appeared virtually devoid of fish earlier in the year, might be well worth investigating later in the season.

Extra water in the river totally changes its character yet again. Slacker water which teemed with minnows and small fry in the summer, often holds big fish now. They may also only be a few feet out from the bank. When the river's up and coloured like this, it's even possible to catch fish in the slacks provided by drainage ditches and cattle drinks. It's not unusual for the fish to forage up onto areas which were dry land before the river rose.

Apart from varying bait requirements with the changing seasons, tackle

if feeder tackle is the only way to reach the fish.

It is very tempting to go for a couple of good fish quickly, but if you fish tight to features at the start of a session, this is all you are likely to take! The two methods described are more reliable for doubling, or even trebling the catch potentials.

FEEDING TRICKS

With less obvious features you will have to use your imagination a little more. The fish could be shoaled anywhere on a long run between weed, or along a slow sweeping bend in the river. But instead of feeding solely where your float is going in, begin the session by putting some feed right down the swim and then at five yard intervals back to where you are positioned. That way, some of the free offerings are bound to be found

quicker. Only do this once, then revert to feeding regularly at the head of the swim. It's a good opening gambit because the fish will move up to you a lot faster than they would with just the one feed area.

In seemingly featureless swims, try a couple of exploratory casts before starting to feed. As you search the run with your tackle you may discover underwater weedbeds, or a very pronounced inside ledge. This helps to decide the most suitable line of attack.

Similarly, there may be areas of the swim where it's too snaggy to run your tackle through at full depth. It's better to discover where these are before loose feeding the fish into areas where you can't catch them.

There's also little tricks you can employ on totally featureless parts of the river. In order to

Left: **Summer fishing generally produces more bites simply because the fish are more active.**

Right: **Hampshire Avon specialist Bob James draws a chub over the net after a spirited fight in the shallows.**

modifications should also be considered carefully. When the fish are feeding well in summer and autumn, you might get away with a double hookbait, impaled on a size 16 hook tied to 1.7 lb line. The same end tackle on a cold, clear river might not catch you anything! You may have to scale down to a single maggot bait, fished on a 20 hook and 1 lb bottom to tempt a response.

But remember, with the fish being more lethargic, you will have a much better chance of landing bigger samples on fragile tackle. You still have to take care to balance the rig, but if you take it easy you may well be surprised by what you can land.

get the best from these spots, the fish will probably have to be drawn a fair distance. On faster flowing waters, some bait will naturally filter downstream and pull fish up over long periods of continuous feeding. But on medium and slow paced waters this won't be the case. Baits like maggots and casters will sink to the bottom only a few yards downstream of where they have been fed and are likely to stay there.

Another match fishing technique is to feed big maggots at the head of these swims, but also to feed smaller maggots like pinkies at the tail-end of the trot. These take twice as long to settle and will eventually pull bonus fish onto your main line where the big maggots are being fed.

If a river swim is wide enough, it might pay to vary your attack between, say, a stick float line and a further waggler swim. If one method dries up, you have somewhere to go with the other and can rest the first part of the swim, which may come back strongly – if you keep a little feed going in while it's rested.

It's Critical To Permutate Baits

For the first few weeks of a new season, rivers respond well to a bait like maggots, fed quite heavily. You may need quite a few pints to draw fish and feed off small fry and surface feeders like hungry bleak and small dace. If the water receives heavy angling pressure, the fish population soon wises up to this approach and a change bait like casters, or even hempseed might bring better results.

When fish are taking maggots avidly, bottom rigs will probably catch early in the day, then you

will have to change to strung shotting, or even a light, long pole rig. The waggler is also very effective in this instance.

The best way to catch competing fish up in the water is to feed first, then drop the tackle in over the top. This gets the hookbait falling in unison with the free offerings and brings more positive bites. By feeding every cast in this way, a lot of bait will obviously get used up.

Casters are more effective for bigger fish and when these are catching well you probably won't need so many. Caster tends to be a better bottom bait on rivers. Some of the feed will still be lost to small fish, of course, but in summer this bait works particularly well with hempseed and holds fish in the swim.

If you can catch good fish tripping the bottom with caster, you might find it's better to feed these less regularly, say every three or four casts. More casters will avoid the smaller fish this way and you can still continue feeding hemp, in-between times.

If there are a lot of roach and dace around, it's always worth trying hemp on the hook. This has a tendency to work better later in a session and you can stop feeding casters altogether if the seed brings regular bites. If you can't connect with the hemp bites, a tare should produce more hittable responses, even if these haven't been fed. The other advantage of using this slightly larger hookbait is that it doesn't come off the hook as easily as hemp, so you can strike several times without having to re-bait.

Hemp works better as a feed with maggots later in the year. It's still a good holding bait and won't fill the fish up too quickly. In a typical winter swim, it's often possible to build a good weight by feeding a dozen grains of hemp and just three or four maggots every cast.

Loose feeding is likely to out-score groundbait at river venues on nine out of ten outings. But it's worth carrying some groundbait for these odd occasions. A heavy groundbait is useful in deeper swims, for getting a mixture of hemp and casters down quickly, especially if you are fishing the pole. After a while, the fish get used to a small ball of feed going in regularly. If this seems to unsettle them, another trick is to feed several large balls to get a fair bit of bait down, then to top up very occasionally during periods when bites have tailed off.

Softer groundbait also revives shallower swims, when fishing for species like dace, roach and chub. Fish are inquisitive creatures and cloud groundbait simulates the bottom being

Try hemp on the hook when there's a lot of roach in the swim.

stirred up. They associate this happening with food, so the odd ball of groundbait can work wonders for a flagging swim.

Blockend feeders can be fished with neat maggots, or on really long sessions it's possible to make this expensive bait go much further by half filling the feeder with hemp first, before adding the maggots.

As mentioned earlier, when casting a long way, you'll also save on wastage by covering the lower exit holes on feeders with waterproof, electrical tape. This stops bait wriggling out while you line up the rig and while it's airborne.

Groundbait feeders are more economical. A pint of casters, a pint of hemp and a smattering of pinkies and squatts go a long way in half a kilo of groundbait. It's best to introduce several baits like this because, apart from letting you experiment with hookbaits, a good mixture of offerings pulls a wide variety of species into the swim.

CALCULATING THE BAIT MENU

There's a big difference in bait requirements if you intend to follow a roving approach instead of staying put in the same swim. Some anglers like to travel light and drop big hookbaits like luncheon meat, or bread, into likely looking spots, giving each swim just a couple of casts, before moving on. This approach does bring results by the law of averages, simply because the chances are the bait is going to be dropped right on the nose of a good fish.

Half a loaf of fresh bread and a tin of luncheon meat may be sufficient for a day's fishing this way.

The stationary approach favoured by most river anglers will invariably require more specialist bait menus. And these will vary with the changing seasons:

MAGGOTS In the warmer months, it may be necessary to spray the swim with several pints of maggots, to work your way through small fish, or draw big fish away from cover. A stick float session would need at least two pints, a waggler approach 4-6 pints and possibly up to a gallon if big feeders are being used for species like chub and barbel.

In winter, it's possible to halve these quantities, perhaps supplementing loose fed maggots with more hemp.

Barbel like this seven-pounder captured by TV wildlife cameraman Hugh Miles demand a lot of bait to get them preoccupied and overcome their natural caution.

CASTERS Two pints of casters should be adequate for a long summer stick float session. Between three and four pints could be used on a waggler line, but this is halved if you intend to feed hemp as well. Two pints of this bait will satisfy most groundbait feeder requirements. In winter, a pint of casters goes a long way. There's rarely a need for more than two pints, even if you intend switching between the float and a groundbait feeder.

HEMP Still a relatively cheap feed bait and it's a good idea to always have a little more than you think you will need, just in case a good day depletes other bait stocks rather too quickly. Hemp teams well with both maggots and casters. Two pints is normally sufficient for most methods, unless the target species is barbel, where it can be very effective to feed 4-6 pints of the seeds to form a good carpet on the bottom.

TARES A handful of tares is all you will need for hookbaits when fishing with hemp. There are odd occasions when a pint of these larger seeds will pay dividends when chub are the target on long range waggler tackle. You don't need to feed a lot of tares, but they do out-distance hempseed by some 15-20 metres, if the fish won't move in.

Everything tastes good to a chub including stewing steak.

BREAD A good winter bait on rivers. Flake and crust work well on a straight leger, or in combination with crumb feed in an open-end feeder. Half of an uncut loaf should be enough for a session, with perhaps the other half of the loaf being liquidised for feed. This can be bound together with a couple of pints of breadcrumb groundbait. Punched bread is also good for big roach and chub on float gear. Take several thick slices of white bread for the hook, together with 3–4 pints of liquidised bread, or punch crumb as groundbait.

WORMS A pot of redworms is a useful standby bait when rivers are carrying extra water. On a link leger, or laid-on over-depth, this bait pulls bonus chub, perch and big roach. It's a good option to try when fishing the open-end feeder. Lobworms are worth experimenting with when roving the banks for chub and barbel or legering in known big fish areas.

PINKIES When the river is out of form, a pint of pinkies helps pull fish, if fed down the swim. They are also a good scratching bait in winter. A few fed into open-end feeder mixes can also be worthwhile. Pinkies are sometimes used in flood conditions to take big bleak catches by fishing up in the water in slacks.

RIG STRATEGIES

Where possible, keep float rigs versatile. This allows you to modify the tackle quickly if the fish follow expected feeding trends and move up in the water, as good feeding technique begins to take effect.

More small shot positioned down the rig, instead of far fewer larger ones, opens up greater possibilities here. It's well worth the time and trouble to group several No.8 shot as a bulk on waggler tackle for instance, if you know that later in the session it will only take a few seconds to spread them out, to form a better on-the-drop rig.

The same thinking applies to top and bottom attached floats, bulks can be split up more effectively if they're formed with smaller shot.

If you start fishing a stick with strung shot, and the float set at depth, there are several different ways this rig can be developed, to suit the changing demands of the swim. You can deepen off the tackle and hold it back slightly, to try and gain extra bites. If the float begins to ride up as you tighten the line to it, try adding an extra shot, something like a No.8, below the float. This will dot it back down as you trot the tackle downstream on a tight line and keep the float leaning backwards.

If this rig still seems to be moving through the swim too quickly, group the smaller strung shot together, so that they form a bulk, a couple of feet away from the hook. This normally stabilises a rig better when trying to slow it against the flow.

Similar shot movements are beneficial with waggler tackle. You start a waggler session with a bulk of No.8 shot set three feet from the hook and a couple of No.10 dropper shot spread below this. Initially, this helps get the bait through the small fish which are always active as you begin a feeding campaign.

But later, as the swim develops, there's quite a good chance that some of the bigger fish will scare off the small fry, so you will be able to spread the bulk well out, to catch competing fish up in the water. If you find that there are too many shot down the line for this, a few can be pushed right up under the float's locking shot.

Waggler bulks of small shot can also be spread down the lower half of the rig, at shorter intervals, to act as a brake if you wish to try dragging the tackle over-depth.

It's not possible to be so versatile with specialised float designs like chubbers. But bulk weights on Avons and balsas can be spread out slightly in deeper water. This helps pull these floats through better, if there's an undertow.

Occasionally, downstream wind makes it tricky fishing a top and bottom attached float. If the line bows out, to the side of the float, pulling it off course, a back shot solves the problem. First, try a No.10, positioned two feet above the float. If this doesn't work, use a No.8 which should definitely provide enough weight to keep the line properly mended behind the float.

Waggler tackle can also be back shotted, providing you are using a floating line.

As you progress in fishing, you will get to know the type of swims which need a dual approach. A top and bottom fixed float may be discarded for a waggler rig, fished over the same line, if fish move up.

Once you are proficient with bigger stick float rigs, you might want to experiment trying one over a redundant waggler line, if it is within casting range. It's surprising the difference a slower bait presentation makes in these cases.

Very shallow river swims are normally best approached with waggler tackle. There's a special, short bodied waggler called a Trent Trotter which works well down to minimal depths of just six inches.

When using feeder tackle on flowing water, always try and point the rod downstream in its rests.

Balance just enough weight on the feeder to hold bottom and feed a little line out when the rod is set in this way, bites will then be more positive. This is called fishing the bow, simply because the force of the current puts a bow in the line.

A taking fish will upset this delicate balance and normally result in the quivertip dropping back as the feeder moves. The pressure of the current on the line is normally enough to set the hook, otherwise you gently lean the rod into the fish. This is a far more productive method than tight lining to the feeder.

SQUATTS Only take a pint of these on river venues if you know the open-end feeder offers chances of finding skimmers and bream.

MEATS, PASTES AND CHEESES These are only normally used on the hook. A small tin of luncheon meat, or a ball of bread or cheese paste about the size of an orange, is usually sufficient for a river trip.

Chub anglers have recently discovered stewing steak and minced beef are effective big river baits. About 4 oz of steak suffices as hookbait and a pound of mince is separated and bulked out with several pints of breadcrumb. This method is worth trying on float, or feeder tackle.

GROUNDBAIT It's not a bad idea to carry a bag of heavy consistency, Continental groundbait for deeper river swims or for use with the open-end feeder. Crushed hemp is a good binder and attracting agent if you know the open-end feeder succeeds with chub on the water in question. A few pints of breadcrumb are useful for bread sessions in winter.

PIT AND LAKE FISHING

GRAVEL PITS

Some of these waters display the clarity of tap water, while others which contain dense stocks of bream and carp are an impenetrable soup of disturbed bottom sediment. Clear, shallow water usually encourages heavy weed growth. Species like tench, perch, roach, pike and carp will always be close to well weeded areas.

Many gravel pits are dotted with tree covered islands. Large shoals of carp and bream congregate alongside these features.

Gravel extraction leaves troughs and ridges. In summer and autumn, many fish will be found feeding on the shallow, gravel bars, or patrolling the shelves running into deeper water.

Unlike many stillwaters, the deepest water on a lot of gravel pits is often around the margins where channels have been formed for barges to haul the gravel away. These gulleys can accumu-

late a lot of natural food and they will nearly always hold a large head of fish like roach, perch, tench and skimmers.

Weather conditions influence the movement of gravel pit shoals. Many anglers make the mistake of heading for sheltered areas, when the banks facing into the wind have coloured water close in, caused by the wave action. This disturbs a lot of natural food and is normally a signal that big bream, tench and carp catches are a distinct possibility.

In very clear pits, a fish holding feature greatly enhances your chances. The type of swims worth investigating might have one, or more features such as tree or weed cover, islands, rush lined bays, visible gravel bars and dark water gulleys.

On an open swim with no such pointers, it's a fair bet the best chances of catching any fish will be long range leger, feeder, or waggler tactics.

LAKES

Large lily beds are a welcome feature on clear water lakes as they provide abundant food and shelter beneath the canopy. Many of the characteristics which make for special swims on pits also apply. Deeper water close in is worth investigating, but on bright days long range tactics are important.

Coloured lakes are normally quite shallow and very productive during the warmer months. It's not so vital to seek out feature pegs for a big

There's a gully running close to the bank and that's where Dave Coster hooked this sizeable bream.

catch on these waters, although good features will still hold fish.

Small, day ticket lakes with artificially high stock densities have become much more widespread. It's possible to achieve good catches from most swims in the inevitably coloured water. An attacking feeding policy may prove more important than swim selection.

TACTICS FOR A BIG CATCH

As with river fisheries, it's not always a good idea to be too quick off the mark in trying to exploit a feature. Many stillwaters respond quite well to close-in tactics at the start of a session, particu-

larly at first light. Fish tend to feed in the margins at night and some linger on into the first hours of daylight.

If the swim has a distant feature it's a good idea to feed this up for an hour or so, while first trying to take some fish from a nearer line. When starting close-in, more time needs to be spent plumbing the depth than you might allot to a river swim. Bottom terrain is an important pointer on stillwaters as to where most fish will be caught. Lake fish have more time to inspect a bait and tend to feed more confidently on ledges, or close to weed cover.

Drawing fish with feed is a slower process when there is no flow. Instead, the bait must be

HOW SPORT FLUCTUATES

Pits and lakes are normally most prolific during the warmer months. Sport slows dramatically in really cold weather unless you are after pike, which become very active in clear, cold water. Many stillwaters pick up at the back-end of the season, as temperatures rise with

the March winds and fish shoal up, in preparation for spawning.

In summer, pit and lake fish may vacate deep water and actively search for food in the shallows and at medium depths. Many species are also prone to feeding up in the water as they compete for feed.

A fair amount of feed is needed at these periods and there are also some

seasonal baits well worth considering.

It's unwise to totally ignore stillwaters in winter. The fish must still feed, but need much less, as they are less active. They tend to switch on for shorter periods, usually when daytime temperatures reach their peak, or during the last hour of daylight. Certainly little bait is required in cold weather.

It's possible to use heavier tackle in

presented in areas where the fish patrol, or live, or feel safe.

Once you have gained a good mental picture of the swim at close range, by spending several minutes with a plummet, you may begin fishing near a weed bed, or just over a nearside ledge. It can pay to simply loose feed maggots, or casters. Fish are often resident by such features and this tactic won't scare them.

Groundbait is much more important in still-waters to get a swim going. But it should never be introduced blindly, because it will still spook fish if it's thrown directly over them.

Initial loose feeding might take a couple of quick fish, then bites cease. Now is the time to kick-start the swim with some groundbait. A couple of balls of fine cloud mix is one option. This will leave a fine carpet of particles on the bottom. A regular ball every five minutes or so will probably activate small fish into feeding up in the water. This approach is developed gradually with loose feed, into attracting larger fish later on in the day. Or you may wish to adopt a big fish approach from the off, by using a slightly heavier groundbait mix, putting in several balls, well laced with hemp and casters.

Groundbait attracts fish on its own, but a lot of the time it works better in unison with loose feed, or as a carrier for loose feed. On hard fished waters, the more cautious larger fish are likely to

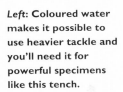

Right: **This mirror carp fell to a grain of sweetcorn fished just off the bottom.**

Left: **Coloured water makes it possible to use heavier tackle and you'll need it for powerful specimens like this tench.**

warmer, coloured water and may be essential if good fish like tench and carp are active. It's not unusual to use 1.5 lb to 2.5 lb hooklengths on the waggler and feeder during the warmer months. But as with river fishing, colder, clearer water often warrants lighter gear and lighter gauge hooks to tempt bites.

In summer, larger hooks are disguised by bigger baits. Double helpings of maggots and casters sort out bigger fish from the fry.

Sweetcorn is effective for tench,

bream and carp. Fruit flavoured boilies are also very good. Seed baits like hemp and tares are worth trying, particularly if you are having small fish trouble.

Smaller offerings go hand in hand with smaller hooks in winter. This applies if you are looking for a catch of fish, rather than odd bigger fish.

Big baits like boilies are still worth persevering with for species like carp on specimen gear. Sweetcorn tends to lose its effectiveness but bread baits are always possible winners.

Bottom baits are much the best in winter, although a surface bait might tempt the odd good fish on some of the milder days. Fish will feed at all levels in warmer weather.

In clearer, frost affected water, cloudy groundbait and small pieces of punched bread might spark a response. Baits like squatts, bloodworm and pinkies activate smaller fish and possibly provoke later interest from larger species. It's more a waiting game with bigger baits.

lay just off a groundbaited area, so spray some loose feed just beyond the main line of attack.

It may be possible to keep an inside line producing bites for a fair time, or at least until the sun gets up. But unless you are fishing a particularly well stocked water, once this area fades, it normally stays dead until the evening.

This is why it's such a good idea to prebait a more distant swim for later in the session. If it's a feature you've been feeding, approach this in the same way as on a river. Take as many fish as possible by dropping your tackle short, before attempting to fish tighter in.

Open water swims are also worth prebaiting for later in the day. You might discover a ledge further out with your waggler tackle, or need to search at even greater distances with a bomb.

To do this, tie a reasonably weighty Arlesey bomb on the reel line of a quivertip rod. If you count the bomb down on each cast, until the quivertip drops back, allowing one foot per second, you'll obtain a rough idea of the depth. Working this way and by casting around the swim, any underwater ledges and shelves should soon become apparent. Feed these features with several balls of groundbait, well laced with free offerings like casters, hemp and squatts. You can leave fish to settle over this, while you start on an inside line. Later on you can try leger, or open-end feeder tackle over the prebaited area.

There's no need for top and bottom attached floats on stillwaters, except on the pole, which is discussed in Chapter 10. On running line, main lake methods are waggler, open-end feeder and bomb. The maggot feeder also has limited applications, particularly on small carp waters.

The waggler is normally fished at full depth to begin with, but in the warmer months the fish can move up in the water. When this happens, an attacking approach, feeding lots of loose feed, or groundbait, or a combination of both, can bring some big catches on more shallow set waggler rigs.

Feeding

It's difficult to predict how different venues might respond to groundbait. Sometimes quite a lot needs introducing before the swim switches on. Certainly, putting a fair amount out is a good bet on a second line of attack, if it's left to settle for a long period.

Normally when fishing within float range, just a couple of light balls of cloud gets the swim going. You could prolong things with loose feed

after that, or add groundbait occasionally to hold the fish. It's a case of feeling your way.

When after species like tench and bream, you must consider gambling on initial heavy feeding, otherwise nearby anglers might feed your fish into their swims. If you are fishing a long way from others, this may not be a worry. But certainly if you do fill in one part of the swim, it's vital to keep another area lightly fed, so your day isn't a total disaster if things go wrong.

Generally speaking, moderate groundbait and regular loose feed brings a good response on many coloured stillwaters. But on clearer venues, you may need to keep busy with cloudy groundbait to activate and draw the fish. It will probably also be necessary to fish at long range with a soft groundbait mix carrying squatts and casters. A groundbait catapult is clearly a must. A soft mix, long hooklength and open-end feeder rig are good in this situation.

When there's a lot of small carp in a water, regular soft groundbait and some floating casters, or maggots will get the fish boiling on top.

Groundbaiting may not be so effective in winter and could even be the kiss of death on some venues. It's best to be ultra careful and precise with its use in cold weather. Only try the odd ball over float gear, otherwise confine groundbait to the open-end feeder.

Loose feed is a better winter tactic, keeping very small amounts trickling in regularly, to try and stir the fish into a response. It's a good idea to rest an area which hasn't brought any bites after being fed for a long period. Often by trying something else, somewhere else in the swim and then reverting back to the first line, a sudden burst of activity will follow.

Bait Requirements

If you have bigger fish like carp in mind, then a bag of shop-bought boilies might be sufficient. Other big fish baits include sweetcorn and luncheon meat. But the chief requirements are likely to be as follows:

Maggots Several pints may be needed on a well stocked venue, where a good response might come from spraying a lot of bait over a medium range waggler rig. White, or bronze maggots are good for this approach. A smaller amount of red maggots ties in well with hemp and caster feed and for use with the open-end feeder. There's rarely need for more than a couple of pints of maggots in winter.

CASTERS For catches of small carp, or big bream, consider taking 3–4 pints of casters. Normal needs for a floatfishing session would be 1–2 pints and 2–3 pints for an open-end feeder approach.

HEMP A couple of pints of hemp is usually quite suffcient in summer, whereas a pint will meet most of your floatfishing requirements later in the season.

PINKIES A pint of mixed coloured pinkies is always a good standby bait, whether fishing float, or feeder gear. Notoriously fickle feeders like bream and skimmers often snap up a couple of red, or fluorescent pinkies, presented on a small hook.

SQUATTS Two pints of squatts may be needed for a long breaming session on the open-end feeder. These small feed maggots are good for

Above: Pinkies on a small hook frequently prove the downfall of fickle feeding bream.

Below: Small commons are sometimes confused with crucians, but crucians have no barbels.

holding fish, when fishing at distance. They can also be introduced into groundbait mixes aimed at tench and carp.

A few squatts introduced regularly in cloudy groundbait livens up cold lake swims. It's also worth trying them as loose feed when fishing close in. Their slow fall rate will stir big roach, perch and skimmers into action when the going is slow.

WORMS Lobworms and reds can be chopped into groundbait mixes at all times of the year when fishing for bream, tench and carp. A red worm tipped with a caster, maggot, or pinkie makes a superb bream bait. Worms also bring a response from big perch in clear, cold water. When used on the hook, induce some movement into them, by twitching float, or leger gear.

BREAD A good carp bait used in crust, flake, or paste form. It will also catch bream, tench, rudd and roach. Punched bread fished on smaller hooks is a good winter option.

BOILIES A standard bag of shop bought boilies goes a long way. There may be a need for greater quantities on larger venues. Fruit flavours tend to be successful in summer while savoury recipes pull more runs in winter.

MEAT Luncheon meat is a good carp bait, particularly on waters which haven't seen many boilies. Smaller cubes also take carp and tench, fished over groundbaited areas, or over a carpet of hemp.

GROUNDBAIT Plain bread crumb is fine with bread baits, or the open-end feeder. There are also many effective Continental lake mixes. Some cloud well, others fizz for ages on the bottom and even send floating particles to the surface. There are also some special recipes geared towards particular species like tench, bream and carp...and they do work!

In summer you may need a couple of kilo bags of Continental mixes and these can be further bulked out with three or four pints of plain brown crumb. A couple of pounds of groundbait in total should cover most winter trips.

RIGS

With no flow complications, stillwater float rigs often have lighter shotting down the line. In shallow and medium depths a lightly shotted waggler covers most possibilities both on-the-drop and on the bottom.

The only time to consider using a bulk, or larger dropper shot than No.8s is when small fish are a problem, or when drift pulls the float out of position.

Generally, even long range, bodied wagglers may only have two or three No.8s or No.10s spread out down the line.

Dropper shot are stepped up in numbers for deeper water so that it doesn't take ages for the rig to settle.

There are occasions when a larger dropper shot like a No.6, 4, or even 1 are positioned on the bottom, when laying-on for fish like tench at close range. This tactic produces lift bites, which are easy to hit.

Most insert wagglers are shotted down with spread No.8s, or 10s. As with all floats in the waggler family, the majority of shot still goes into locking the float.

There are times when fishing for small carp and rudd where no dropper shot are required. In this instance, a three or four foot tail is used below the float with a buoyant hookbait like dark casters, or floating maggots. But remember, the float needs to be feathered down in order to keep the terminal tackle landing in front of it.

In deep stillwaters, a bottom-end slider comes into the reckoning. At close range, use a stop shot several feet above the bulk, to help prevent tangles. For long range requirements, it's better to cast with a loaded slider resting on the lower bulk shot. This gains much greater distance, but again it's absolutely vital to feather the tackle down to avoid tangles.

Open-end feeder rigs should be fished on the loop method, described for river fishing in Chapter 5. In weedy waters the feeder may perform better set up paternoster style. Either system can be applied to leger tackle for distance fishing. A free running leger rig only tends to be effective at close range.

Long range legering, or feeder fishing may dictate the use of a shock leader to absorb the stresses of casting. This is a length of stronger line which is attached to the reel line, so at least three turns are on the spool when the leader is fixed to the end tackle, ready to cast. If you are feeder fishing with 3 lb or 4 lb line, use a 6 lb shock leader.

The quivertip is a very efficient bite indicator for long range legering. There's also a place for swingtips, which can be handy when fishing from heavily overgrown banks. It may not be

NIGHT LIGHTS

Starlites are a low cost way of illuminating the float at night. They're activated by breaking an internal seal which allows two chemicals to mix and produce the luminosity.

The glow lasts for approximately four hours and, depending on size, they're clearly visible within moderate range from the bank.

Various diameters of Starlite and their corresponding plastic tube holders are manufactured.

There are also floats with internal chambers in which the Starlite fits. That eliminates the need for the tubing.

The Starlite can also be used to illuminate the tip of a leger rod. If you tape one end of the tube holder to the opposite side of the tip to the rings, you'll have no problems with line fouling the Starlite.

Isotopes cost considerably more but last for years. They are normally fitted within the chambers of Swinger or monkey climber indicators.

Good organisation is essential for night fishing with everything laid neatly to hand. Never use powerful torches – a subdued penlight should be sufficient for re-tying rigs.

Remember that sound travels a long way in the dead of the night and it's imperative that you avoid upsetting your neighbouring anglers by clattering around the swim.

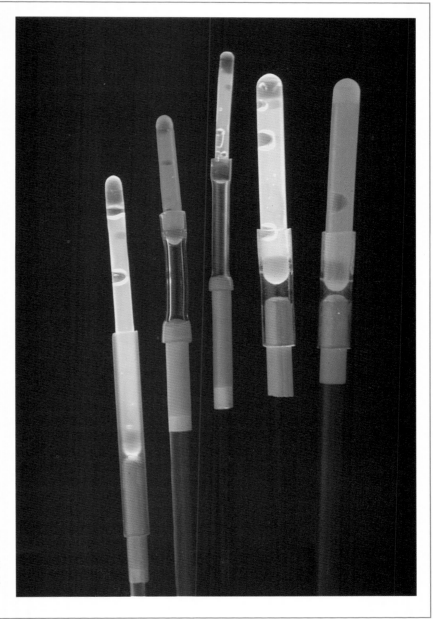

possible to position a quivertip correctly to one side in these spots, whereas the swingtip can be pointed directly out at the end rig.

Canal wagglers can also have a role on lakes and pits when fishing shallow water. These designs don't cause unnecessary disturbance as they land and are particularly effective in canal-like backwaters.

Insert wagglers fulfil the majority of stillwater float requirements, but straights are good in bad drift, when you want to anchor your hookbait hard on the bottom.

Remember here to sink your reel line. This can be done by over-casting, sinking the rod tip and winding several turns of line onto the reel quickly. Another option is to try flicking the line under, which should leave the float where it lands. This is done by flicking the rod top in the opposite direction to which the line is bowing in the drift.

Wagglers with long antennae are useful when trying to hit fickle bream and tench bites at close to medium range. These floats also ride rough water quite well.

In really choppy conditions, the bulbous sight tip on a windbeater float design is much more visible and helps stop the float continually dragging under.

CANAL FISHING

The massive network of canals offer enormous opportunities. Even grim looking industrialised pounds sometimes provide surprisingly good sport. Heavy boat traffic and busy towing paths pose problems in summer which means most canals come into their own in autumn and winter when specialist bait may be needed for consistent results.

Canals are popular with match anglers because they are generally fair venues and many swims are capable of producing winning catches. Indeed, every swim has at least some fish holding features in the shape of shelves on the near and far banks.

LOOK FOR BITES ON THE LEDGES

Noted feature pegs on canals include deeper piled banks, boat turning bays and marinas. There are also similar features to those you'd expect on some rivers, but more of them, such as locks and moored craft on the far bank. Obvious far bank features like overhanging foliage, wides, rush beds and streams running in, take on added significance. They provide havens for large shoals of fish, where they can keep away from the busy boat channel.

Many anglers avoid fishing the main channel until boat traffic dies away in the winter. But it is

possible to catch a lot of fish from this area during lulls between passing boats. The main channel tends to respond better to small, frequently fed baits, like squatts, pinkies and bloodworm. Some hard groundbait may also be required to try and hold the fish, because the bottom is so regularly disturbed.

But the most obvious lines of attack on these types of waterways are the near and far side ledges. A lot of small fish are usually caught early in a session, up and down the nearside shelf. Then normally a pattern emerges where the fish drift across the cutting.

On the far bank, very productive small fish areas are down the far shelf and further up it in featureless, shallow pegs. Larger fish normally hug thick far bank cover, or hole up where there is more depth, tight-in to far bank piling. They tend to push smaller fish away from these areas.

Small baits like squatts, pinkies, bloodworm, bread punch and hemp often score at close range and on the down side of the far shelf. They can also be used tighter across, if you think small fish are the main quarry. But caster is the No.1 bait where bigger fish are expected, followed by some bigger maggots.

Over recent seasons, chopped worm has become a potential match winning method and this is used in the boat channel, when traffic dies down later in the year.

Punched bread is a killing method on deeper, clear water canals, or where there is a lot of weed and few boats. Hemp combines well with this bait and is worth trying in its own right during warmer weather.

Because canals are popular and the water is often shallow, tackle needs to be fine and well presented for most methods. The only area where finesse may be sacrificed is the far bank. Good presentation is still essential, but many

Dave Coster reaches out with the long pole towards a boat moored on the far bank which is certain to attract bigger fish.

canals hold big fish like carp, chub and bream, so far bank caster rigs must be quite strong.

When selecting a canal swim, look for areas where the boats won't constantly disturb the quality fish. Wides, turning bays and streams running in, nearly always hold good bream, chub, carp and quality roach. Another good feature to search out is overhanging foliage which forces boats to keep away from the far side. Fish will normally hole-up underneath, or to the sides of this cover.

Permanently moored boats often hold a lot of fish. Select the derelict looking ones, or sunken craft as your first choice. Lived in, or well kept boats can also be good, but you don't know at first sight if you are going to get a lot of disturbance from people using them later in the day.

Deeper far bank swims are always a good bet and so are rush beds, which provide a haven and a lot of natural food. Deeper water areas above and below locks receive more flow and are better oxygenated. These spots are a bit too busy on hot summer days as boats queue to get through the locks, but are well worth a look later in the year.

Good nearside swims on canals are harder to define. Marginal weed growth, the inside of bends and deeper piled areas make a difference. But generally this area is pretty uniform and you will have to fish it to find out the potential.

On industrialised canal sections, buildings offer good cover and in winter may shield the water from cold winds. This draws fish from large areas...warm water outflows do likewise.

The really encouraging thing about canals is that the fish sometimes congregate in areas without any apparent holding features. This mystery element makes them all the more fascinating.

Feeding Techniques

There are several useful accessories to help keep the feed tightly located. Small pouch pole catapults prevent too much feed going in and group it better. A bait dropper deposits neat bloodworm and joker on the bottom very precisely. Most important of all is the pole pot which clips onto the top section of pole. After being filled with loose feed or groundbait, it is pushed out across the canal and the contents tipped out where needed.

Loose feed and groundbait are both important methods for this type of fishing. It's wise to confine groundbait to one area of the swim to begin with, so you have other options if it doesn't work. Often cloudy groundbait is a very potent fish puller on canals. The only line it's never used on is the far bank caster area.

Harder consistency groundbait is used to get small baits like bloodworm, jokers and squatts to the bottom when boat traffic is on the busy side.

Groundbait is essential when fishing bread punch. Fine brown crumb, white punch crumb and liquidised bread all have their day. A cloud groundbait often gets a squatt line going. Some-

---

Plan of Campaign

Fishing several lines of attack is more important on canals than any other type of fishery for several reasons. A boat may steer off coarse and ruin one part of the swim for several hours. Or you may simply fish out one area. It's rare indeed to keep fish coming from the one spot all day.

There are five major areas to consider on the average canal swim. Up and down the nearside shelf, the boat channel, down the far shelf and tight to the far bank. The characteristics of your swim may eliminate one, or two of these areas. For example, boats could cut in very close because of a bend, or obstructive far bank feature. But you still want to try and feed at least two, or three lines.

But avoid spraying bait all over the swim! Feeding should be tight and precise, so it's essential to spend a long session on the plummet to pinpoint the shelves where loose feed and groundbait needs to go.

You could find a particular method like loose feeding squatts will cover a couple of lines anyway. These small maggots tend to scatter, so if you are catapulting them across the canal, they might well feed the area up and down the far shelf. It's still possible to fish one extremity of this feed area, leaving the other section for later in the day.

You may need to feed squatts in one, or two areas, punch crumb and hemp in another and casters on a further line. Feeding three or four baits in several areas regularly isn't possible all day.

The idea is to begin this way and to rotate tackle around the swim, until a couple of good catching areas have been established. After an hour you should know which these are and can forget the non-starters, or the spots which gave you just a couple of quick bonus fish.

By trying to narrow your feeding down into two, or possibly three areas, you can afford to lose one if a large boat disturbs that part of the swim. It also helps to rest areas in shallow water every now and than. This all helps to revive the bite rate when you go back over them.

times, you can also introduce the odd harder ball of groundbait with squatts, just to try and concentrate the fish – but continue with regular loose feed. Feeding hemp over squatts may pull larger roach.

Caster is usually fed with hemp. The magic seed complements big maggots well and often works on the hook in the deeper boat channel.

Bloodworms and jokers are cupped in neat later in the year when canals go clear. Remember that groundbait could kill a swim when the weather turns cold. Jokers can also be fed in leam, a fine binding clay which won't feed the fish off.

Sometimes, almost inexplicably, a heavy handed groundbait approach brings fading canal swims back to life. But there's an element of kill or cure. Introducing several large balls of heavy consistency groundbait, liberally laced with jokers, squatts, or bloodworm, brings instantaneous results or supresses the swim for ages. When this trick works, the fish seem to home in on the disturbance. Perhaps they associate the groundbait bombardment with natural disturbances. It can certainly set them rooting about in the swim looking for food.

BAIT REQUIREMENTS

The trick on canals is to take small amounts of a large selection of baits. Squatts are the only exception – in summer you might need two or three pints if there's a chance of bream.

By feeding squatts, you can try pinkies on the hook and as these rarely need to be fed, half a pint of mixed reds, whites and fluorescent maggots will be sufficient for a session. A half-pint measure of mixed colour, big maggots gives other hookbait options and a little to feed over to the far bank if casters don't work.

Casters are fed very lightly most of the time. Half a pint is normally enough. The only time you need to take 1–2 pints is if you are after carp, chub, or bream on a very prolific boundary.

A pint of hemp will also help to cover the far bank caster line and leave enough to try a hemp attack in the boat channel.

A kilo bag of groundbait is more than enough for any method. It's very rare to need to feed more than half this amount in fact.

In winter, bread punch starts to work well. This is a very economical method. All you need is a couple of pints of crumb feed, or half a liquidised loaf and a few slices of fresh white bread.

The most expensive canal bait is bloodworm

Canal vitals – pinkies, squatts and hemp. The fine textured groundbait is a special canal formula with brown crumb added.

and jokers. But on most venues a quarter-pint of worm for the hook and one pint of jokers for feed, will catch a lot of fish. Some canal regulars take a pint of larger bloodworm if they know bigger bream are on the cards. If jokers are going to be fed over two lines, the maximum requirement is two pints...and that's on a prolific water.

The chopped worm method is worth considering in winter. You may need a pot of lobworms and a couple of containers of small reds. The worm is cupped in, usually a couple of larger lobworms and up to a dozen smaller red worms, at irregular intervals. If the going is tough, fish may keep responding with the introduction of just a couple of finely diced reds every now and then.

If you're after big fish like carp and tench, sweetcorn, luncheon meat and boilies can be effective, usually fished over to far bank cover.

RIG STRATEGIES

Running line waggler rigs are very effective on canals. These are used on soft actioned 11, or 12 foot rods, with fine lines. This is really miniature waggler fishing. Short, streamlined, all-balsa caster and squatt wagglers may only take a couple of BB locking shot and very small No. 11, 12, or 13 dropper shot. Small No. 7 and 8 Styl weights also work well.

The soft actioned rod has two purposes. It enables hooklengths as fine as 0.06mm in diameter to be used if the going is tough. Forgiving, through actioned rods also cast light gear further and more accurately.

There are several reasons why running line waggler tackle should never be ignored. The long pole can spook fish on shallow, clear canals, unlike a waggler rig – as long as you are not too heavy handed on the cast. It's also easier to feed very regularly with a light rod by positioning it between the knees after the cast, while you catapult some bait out. Clearly, it's much harder to master regular feeding with a long, heavy pole in your grasp!

Running line tackle makes it possible to cast around the swim to pick up bonus fish. It will also long trot with the current when locks are in operation.

Generally, the waggler scores towards the far bank of canals, fishing down, on, or up the far shelf. Fish can be taken off the bottom when fishing small baits like squatts, but the best approach with casters and maggots is to present the bait well over-depth.

Nearside canal lines are usually covered by the pole. Very close in this is fished to-hand style and by using heavier capacity floats, it is possible to extend this method to four or five metres when speed fishing for small fish. But conditions must be right for long lining and immediately tackle control suffers, most canal anglers switch to short lining pole methods and unship sections to bring fish in. A short length of line between the pole tip and float gives much better tackle control, particularly in windy conditions.

The long pole is also a very good canal method. There are all sorts of rig possibilities for catching fish both up in the water and on the bottom. The pole scores highly when very tight control of the bait is needed, or when some movement must be injected into the hookbait to induce bites.

The pole should be seriously considered when running line tackle pulls off position due to bad drift, or because the canal is running rather too regularly. Missed bites from small fish is another reason to reach for the long pole which is more positive on these occasions. It's also possible to bulk more weight down the rigs with this method, in order to get through small fish.

Long poles are very useful when big fish are tucked in tight to far bank features. Drop lightly shotted tackle quietly alongside the cover and a bite will often develop instantly.

Most pole rigs are used with an internal elastic shock absorber and this allows the angler to use finer diameter lines. This is a great advantage in gaining a response from shy fish. The elastic will enhance the performance of thin diameter lines, in a way that is not possible with running line tackle.

While the pole has advantages, it's best not to forget that waving a long pole about over very shallow water scares fish. The pole should always be manoeuvred carefully, trying not to splash the tip into the water. It's also a good strategy, once the tackle has been lowered into position, to move the pole tip away to the side of the float. If you can keep it to the left, or right of the feed area and quickly pull hooked fish in this direction, the swim will produce for longer periods.

Pole rigs are comprehensively covered in Chapter 10, but when thinking of using long poles on canals, it's vital to first check there are no overhead power lines in the vicinity. These are very common on canal venues and there have been some very serious burn injuries and fatalities. So, as the warning goes – look up, before tackling up.

Light feeder tackle scores on some wider canals where there is a good head of chub, big roach, bream and carp. This is usually fished to the far bank. Some canals also have streams and small rivers running into them and when these are carrying extra rain water, the feeder comes into its own.

Short quivertip rods, often referred to as wands, combine well with light leger tackle on many canals. They're used with quite fine lines in open areas, or with stepped up tackle when fishing to features. These through-actioned rods absorb a lot of punishment and some big fish have been landed on them, including carp into double-figures.

Carp are stocked in many canals and have grown to specimen proportions. Twenty-pounders are quite common and odd 30 lb fish have been reported. This makes a specialist approach with stepped-up rods and Optonics a viable prospect and carp anglers are now looking at canals more seriously.

Although there will be plenty of instances where big fish and strong tackle come into the reckoning on canal venues, generally finesse is the name of the game. Always try to use the finest lines you feel safe with. Hooks should also be fine wire where possible and it's best to keep dropper shot on the small side. It also pays to scale down the diameter of reel lines. Many busy canals have an oily surface, due to spillage from boat traffic. Finer reel lines sink beneath the surface more readily than thicker ones, when better control is wanted with waggler tackle.

Canal towpaths are not normally very wide, so it isn't recommended to spread your gear around. Mountain bikes and fragile pole sections are an explosive mix.

Keepnets need to be staked out at both ends when constant boat traffic through the locks causes the canal to flow first one way and then the other. If you leave the bottom of the net untethered, it will swing through your nearside swim and kill sport stone dead every time a lock opens, or a boat passes.

Opposite top: **Miniature waggler fishing with a soft-actioned rod is very effective on canals.**

Opposite below: **Unloaded peacock waggler with lightweight cane insert.**

Below: **Improvised leg clamp serves as a keepnet or rod rest holder for impassible towpaths.**

UNDERSTANDING POLE FISHING

When you have learnt to catch fish consistently with rod and line and realised that good tackle control is crucial, you'll experience days when it's impossible to achieve the degree of presentation you'd like. Wind, surface tow, undertow, lack of flow and extra flow all conspire at one time or another to make running line fishing difficult.

Long poles swing the balance back in your favour, when awkward conditions defeat running line tackle. The pole offers you much tighter control of the float and allows you to do things which are not always possible with a shorter rod and long length of line. Furthermore here is much less line between a pole tip and the float and this opens up enormous possibilities.

With a long pole you can even tackle swims which are hazardous to rod and reel. Think of those days when you have reluctantly walked past a noted swim because it's covered in leaves, or clogged with weed. Good areas often have a lot of bankside cover which holds the fish resident, but which also restricts what you can do with a rod. The pole is different, you can add sections and drop the tackle into a tiny opening, or lay it out just inches from overhanging cover.

The pole also scores incredibly well when the fish are only half-heartedly pecking at hookbaits. It's possible to respond immediately to minute indications on a tiny and very sensitive pole float if the pole tip is directly above. The same bites would almost certainly be missed on running line tackle and you may not even see them at all on a thicker tipped float.

THE SPEEDY WHIP

Long poles allow tighter control of the tackle. They also make a huge difference when the fish are feeding freely and big catches are on the cards. Long lining, or fishing to hand is one of the fastest ways of accumulating big weights of small to medium sized fish.

The main advantage of fishing the long pole is that it puts you right over the fish! Tackle presentation can be spot-on and this reflects in more positive bites than you might expect with a running line.

Ideally you want your rig to be slightly shorter than the pole length so that fish can be swung easily to-hand.

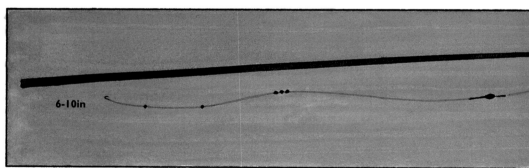

6-10in

When fully extended, all long poles will sag slightly. It's better to have a gradual even curve like this . . .

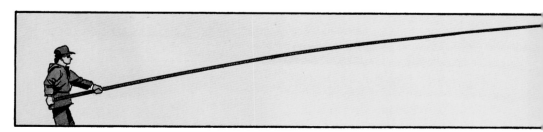

There's not a lot that can go wrong swinging the tackle out underarm, particularly if you use a bulk weight like a streamlined olivette some 14 to 24 inches above the hook. Tangles are scarce and you are getting the bait down to the fish fast.

This also applies to shorter poles, or whips as they are called. These range from just a couple of metres, up to seven metres in length.

Whips may be all telescopic for lightness, or part telescopic, so you can unship a bottom section, or two. They are primarily used for small fish. It's great fun whipping out a lot of gudgeon, small roach, perch, or bleak when nothing else is feeding. Experienced match anglers are very proficient at the method and sometimes amass surprisingly big weights.

CHOOSING THE RIGHT POLE

Budget priced poles may be made from glass fibre, or a composite mixture of glass and carbon. If you think back to when you were first choosing a rod, the same principles apply. Cheaper products are heavier and more bulky, but if you are unsure about the method, they'll at least provide an insight into what it's about and help you assess whether it's worth investing in a really top class model.

The mid-price range lies somewhere between £200 and £700 and it's possible to obtain some very good, long poles going up to 12.5 metres within this banding.

Top designs from 12.5 metres and anything up to 16 metres can cost into four-figures – so

Fishing tight against far bank cover.

while matchmen might be able to justify this level of extravagance, it's not essential for the average angler.

Overall, the more expensive poles offer superior rigidity, a slimmer diameter and are significantly lighter. Under competitive conditions, it's vitally important to gain those extra metres, because the fish tend to be pushed further out by heavy angling pressure. Pleasure anglers rarely have to fish to such extremes, because there is generally less bankside disturbance and the fish are not as well educated, if you steer clear of regular match lengths.

Having said that, it's still wise to purchase the longest pole you can afford. This isn't the contradiction it seems, because longer poles do offer more options. You may not need to fish the pole fully extended that often, but a spare couple of butt sections positioned ready on the bank can come in very useful. If a really good fish runs away from you. The quick witted angler can add a section and perhaps keep in touch with the fish.

A longer pole also comes in useful for chasing good fish across to the far bank of small rivers and canals. The better samples often lay under far bank cover and you can have a go for them.

There's more of a case for spending more on a longer pole if you know the venues you are going to fish require it.

Really you only need top-of-the-range extra-long poles if you intend competing in matches and at top level.

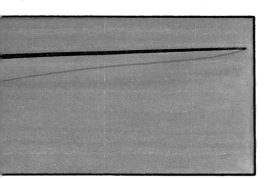

In this situation bank-side disturbance and people watching can push the fish well out.

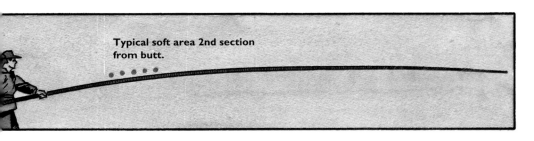

Typical soft area 2nd section from butt.

. . . than a pronounced sag at the butt end. If I tried to set the hook with this model, the bend on the lower section would transmit down the pole's length and bounce the tip all over the place.

ROLLERS AND RESTS

There are several useful devices which protect the pole from damage when fishing over rough terrain and also aid smoother handling.

The first priority is to obtain a good pole roller. This is positioned several yards behind your fishing position, so you can run several sections of pole over it, to reach the point where you want to break the pole down.

Apart from lifting the lower sections off the ground and keeping them clean, the roller also reduces strain on the middle sections and eases the pole back smoothly. This is vital if you have a fish on, because any jerky movements might pull the hook out.

A roller is not quite as essential if you are only fishing the pole at short to medium lengths. But if you drop the butt section its base will get damaged over hard ground. As a precaution, fit a protective base plug, or pole joint protector which will cushion any accidental impact, or even allow the base of the pole to be run along the ground if it's not too bumpy.

Right: **Wide gape pole roller.**

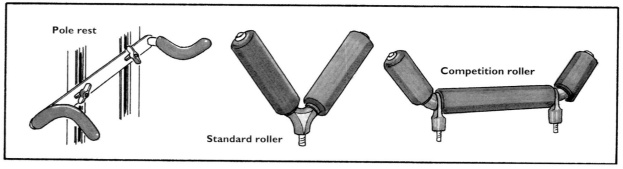

Pole rest

Standard roller

Competition roller

You may also find the fish tend to move just beyond your initial feeding range, after you've caught a lot. The last hour of a session can be really productive if you add an extra pole section.

But the most important factor behind getting the longest pole you can afford, is that it will often be better at shorter lengths, than shorter models when fully extended. An 11-metre pole will probably fish well up to ten metres, then become a little sloppy when fully extended.

If you want a good 11-metre pole, you are likely to find a 12, or 12.5-metre model much better when reduced to around the 11-metre mark, by leaving the butt section off.

Another important consideration when choosing a pole is to think about spare parts. Check with the tackle dealer about availability. You don't want to wait months if you need to replace a section, or want extra top sections.

Some mid-priced and most top of the range long poles come with an extra three or four section top kit as a spare. You can also fit different strength shock absorbers as back-up, should you need to change to lighter, or heavier tackle. Most experienced pole anglers end up with several top section kits, fitted with a diverse range of internal elastic systems to cover every eventuality.

HANDLING TECHNIQUES

When you first begin fishing with a long pole, you may find it's difficult to feed groundbait. A very helpful aid here is a pole rest. If you have a solid tackle box, there are special pole rest runners which bolt on the side. These allow a rest to be slotted in and angled at exactly the right position to keep the pole tip just above the surface after the butt section is located. There are also special rests which fix on external adjustable leg kits like the Octoplus system.

The secret of good pole handling is to keep everything smooth and unhurried, both as you manoeuvre the pole into position and bring it back, hopefully with a fish on. By trying to be too fast when fishing a short line, you risk cartwheeling the tackle into impossible tangles around the pole tip.

When a fish is hooked it should be brought up in the water, or steered to the left, or right of the shoal, before attempting to bring the pole

back. This prevents other fish from being frightened away from the feed area.

If you are confident that you can bring the pole in smoothly, it's possible to keep the pole tip above water. But if you can't at first stop the pole tip from bumping up and down as you retrieve it, try submerging the top two feet of pole in the water and this will help to cushion any bumpy movements.

It's easy to keep the float under tight control in calm conditions, but in gusting side winds the pole tip bounces about alarmingly, pulling the float off course. If this is happening you may have to slightly lengthen the amount of line between the pole tip and float. If things are really bad, you can also try steadying the pole by holding the butt between your legs and sit on the last foot of the butt, (still supporting the pole with your hands.)

Another good rough weather trick is to submerge the last couple of feet of the pole tip. This loses you a split second on the strike, but keeps plenty of bites coming by keeping the float still.

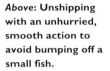

Above: **Unshipping with an unhurried, smooth action to avoid bumping off a small fish.**

Left: **Lightweight poles are no problem to hold for long periods using this relaxed grip.**

Most anglers hold poles up to 10 metres long with one hand, locking the pole under their elbow and supporting it on one knee. If wind, or a longer pole is making this a strain, try sitting

Feeding with the pole gripped between the legs.

WATCH FOR WORN JOINTS

Most poles have put-over joints. These are easier to unship and locate together, because the lower section fits inside the one above. These joints have slow tapers and come apart smoothly, so little can go wrong.

But watch for signs of wear on the sections you unship most often. When short lining, this is normally the third or fourth section down. The part which will wear most is the male half of the joint. If you can see the base cloth on which the carbon is layered showing through, the joint needs building up.

For bad examples of wear, brush on some carbon build-up liquid then rub it down so the joint stays smooth. For minimal signs of wear, or as preventative action, finer carbon sprays are certainly better. Most big tackle shops will advise on how to use these and may even undertake the work if you are unsure of what to do.

The other type of take-apart pole has put-in joints. Here the upper sections fit into the ones below. This type of joint is a little less smooth to unship when the pole is new, as it's more parallel and may require a little rubbing down with some fine wet and dry paper to begin with. Carbon sprays also help to keep these joints smooth running.

Telescopic poles sometimes need a

Where the upper section fits over the lower one, it's called a **put-over pole.** These models are popular with match anglers when smooth unshipping and speed are essential.

Worn male sections of joints which push in too far will need attention.

When upper sections fit inside lower ones the pole is referred to as a **put-in model.** This design can be stronger but less smooth, or more difficult to unship.

One or more coats of pole joint protector are applied, depending on the amount of wear.

little attention after a lot of use. You may see sections beginning to protrude further as they wear. If you take the pole apart from the butt and finely spray the lower ends of each section, the treatment should last for a season before the process needs to be repeated.

Grit and damp are the main enemies of the pole. Always try to clean your pole up after an outing. If sections remain wet and dirty, they will often seize-up during the next outing. It's very difficult to separate jammed sections and heavy handling can cause damage. A spot of furniture polish rubbed into male joints every now and then is a good preventative move.

Spray worn or damaged pole joints with a carbon restoring solution.

more sideways on and rest the butt section over both knees, steadying the pole with one hand in front of your knees and anchoring it with your other hand positioned slightly behind you.

Fishing to hand with short poles is a one-handed operation. The same technique with longer poles is best accomplished by supporting the butt between your legs and again sitting on the last few inches of the butt section. The pole is further supported with one, or two hands.

FLICKTIPS AND SHOCK ABSORBERS

Short poles, or whips are designed for small fish and should always be used with flick tips. These have a better action to help cast light tackle out

and act as a cushion if slightly better fish are hooked. A flick tip is also marginally more responsive on the strike and you'll hit far more bites by using one.

Flick tips are speedy when you're trying to accumulate large catches of small fish on the long pole, using small baits like squatts and bloodworm, or when trying to connect with lightning fast bites.

But it's advisable to use an elastic shock absorber for most of your longer pole fishing. You won't loose so many bonus fish and can in fact set your sights on catching some surprisingly large specimens.

The best and least tangle-prone shock absorber set-up is internal. The elastic is run

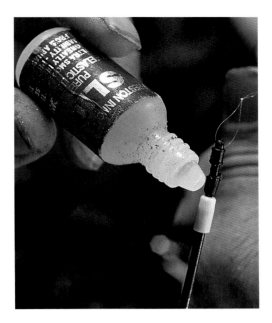

through one, two or three of the pole's tip sections. To do this, you'll need an elastic threader, PTFE bush, elastic/line adaptor, base bung and, of course, the elastic.

The hollow pole tip is cut back, to fit an inter-nal or external bush. This is vital, because being made from self-lubricating PTFE it will keep the elastic smooth running and prevent friction burn. Internal bushes may require slightly more of the pole tip to be trimmed back. They are probably better for thicker grade elastics. External bushes will save you a few inches of pole length, if you're fitting a very fine diameter shock absorber.

The next step is to decide over how many sections you want the elastic to run. There are several grades and the strength of the elastic often dictates how much you use. Fine elastics are combined with very delicate lines down to 0.055mm. They will stretch an amazing distance, even with very fine lines, so often threading them through just the tip section of pole is enough. This would entail using a very small base bung, matching one up from the wide range Stonfo produce.

Using a wire threader – Diamond Eye ones are easiest to use – the elastic is threaded through the bush end first and then pulled out of the base of the pole section where it is knotted to the hook on the base bung. The elastic should be slightly tensioned before tying the other end to a connector. This device has a protective sleeve which is threaded onto the elastic first. By removing this from the connector you will see the attachment hole which the elastic is knotted through. It is then covered by sliding the sleeve back into place.

At the other end of the connector is another sleeve which slides back to reveal a small crook. The line at the end of your pole rig is formed into a loop and pulled inside the crook and then securely locked in place by bringing the second sleeve back to its original place.

Once your elastic is installed in this manner there's one more essential task to perform on the bank. Although many pole elastics are ready lubricated, it's a good idea to smear some pole elastic lubricant over them before fishing. This guarantees many hours of smoothness and prevents water and surface debris from gumming up the works.

It is far more likely with medium elastics that you will want to fit up the top two pole sections with a longer shock absorber. Medium grades are used with slightly larger diameter hook-lengths such as 0.08 and 0.09mm mono-filament. You will, of course, be looking for better sized fish and may need to tension the elastic even more to set the hook. However, you will still need a lot of give in reserve, to stop good fish

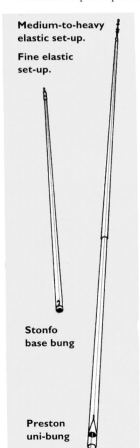

Medium-to-heavy elastic set-up.

Fine elastic set-up.

Elastic/line attachment

Stonfo base bung

Preston uni-bung

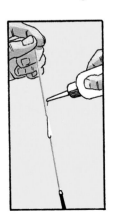

Use a lubricant on the elastic before fishing. This keeps everything smooth running.

from smashing what is still relatively light gear.

The best base bung here is a Preston Innovations cone-shaped one, which can be cut to exactly the right size to fit up inside the base of the second pole section. If you are using a pole with put-over joints you will have to locate the bung several inches inside this second section in order to slide the third section on. These bungs have a nylon, or plastic tail, so you can still remove them.

It's now normal with heavy elastics to thread up two, or even three pole sections. The latter is an open water tactic when going for big fish like carp, tench and bream. In more confined areas you may have to compromise with tensioned elastic in two sections, to have a chance of getting big fish away from snags quickly.

Plenty of pole elastic lubricant should also be smeared on two and three section set-ups. If you are catching good fish, it also doesn't hurt to re-lubricate the shock absorber two or three times during the session.

Getting the tension right in the first place is a matter of trial and error. If you are bumping fish on the strike the elastic may need tensioning more. Tensioning may have to be varied depending on how the fish are feeding on any particular day. If you don't want to cut the elastic back, it is possible to buy elastic tensioners, or some base bungs incorporate such a facility.

Below: **Basic bottom fishing format**

Below right: **Up in the water rig**

FISHING-TO-HAND

With a flick tip you can fish to hand with a bulk weight, made up of grouped shot, or an olivette,

set near to the hook. This helps swing out the tackle. But if the fish are up in the water, you can also use a strung out rig and flick it out, over-head, or from the side, utilising the pole's action.

On longer poles it's essential to use a low slung olivette to get the tackle out, but you can still put some finesse into the rig by using a long hooklength with two or three small shot spread evenly on it.

This method is best kept simplified when the fish are feeding well and one dropper shot will suffice with minimal line between the olivette and hook.

There are three main ways of taking fish on the short pole to-hand style. One is to position an olivette or bulk shot very close to the hook. This tactic normally applies to fish like gudgeon and bleak. Gudgeon are bottom feeders, so a classic rig would be a .75, or one-gram olivette set just 6–8 inches from the hook, with one No. 10 dropper shot 2–3 inches from the hook. The ideal setting here is to get the dropper shot just off bottom and the hookbait resting lightly on it. The float should have a heavy cane, or wire stem so it cocks quickly. The heavy olivette for such a short pole will also get the bait down fast. The float itself should be well dotted down. A cane, or nylon bristle is best for this.

Another good bulk rig is designed for up in the water work when after species like bleak. This entails using small streamlined balsa floats with no dropper shot, just a small bulk of No. 8, or 10 shot set 4–6 inches from the hook. These help to flick such a light rig out and allow depths of between one and four feet to be fished.

Small fish like bleak and gudgeon are nor-mally avid feeders and this is one of the few occasions where you don't have to worry about fishing a bulk very close to the hook. Speed is just as important as presentation if you are going to amass a good catch.

Species like roach, perch and skimmers will rarely be fooled by such heavy weights placed so near to the bait. You may still require a bulk for speeding the bait down to the lower depths and for swinging the tackle out, but it needs to be pushed much higher up the rig. In order to bal-ance the tackle, two or more small No. 10, 11, or 12 shot may have to be strung out evenly to the hook to give the hookbait a natural fall over the last few feet of its descent.

You can try grouping the dropper shot closer to the hook and shove the olivette down if the fish are coming thick and fast, but often they'll wise up and the bulk may have to be pushed

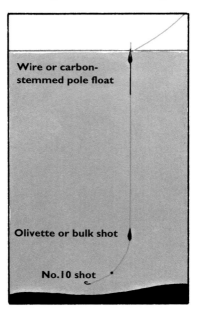

Wire or carbon-stemmed pole float

Olivette or bulk shot

No.10 shot

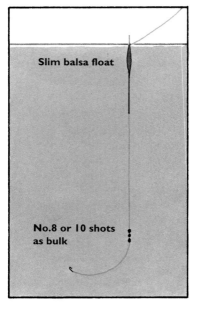

Slim balsa float

No.8 or 10 shots as bulk

three feet up the rig and the small shot below shuffled around until positive bites materialise.

The third major way of catching on the short pole, is with strung out shotting, or Styl weights. The idea is to cover the whole depth of the swim, often taking fish on-the-drop.

This is achieved by evenly stringing small shot or Styls from the float to the hook, or by starting them from mid-depth down to the hook. The latter formation may require the last few dropper weights to be spread a little further apart. This method suits fine presentation with baits like bloodworm, bread punch, pinkies and squatts. It's a good way of taking mixed catches of perch, roach, skimmers, bleak, rudd and even gudgeon once the rig has settled.

With longer lining techniques, bulk weight size is regulated by the length of pole being used, the depth of water and the prevailing conditions. Generally olivette size is determined by what you can comfortably swing out to the desired distance. Anglers visiting Ireland and Denmark may step up to really big bodied pole floats carrying as much as 8 to 14 grams for better speed, control and distance.

Regular feeding is crucial when fishing to-hand rigs. Often regular cloudy groundbait is combined with loose feed for up in the water rigs. A medium consistency groundbait may be used as a carrier to get small offerings like bloodworm, jokers and squatts down to the bottom and then break up quickly. Heavy groundbait mixes, holding a lot of feed like casters are used when after bigger fish and really big catches on the long pole to hand.

Long Pole Fishing

Most long pole fishing incoporates a short line between the pole tip and float. Several pole sections are run back behind your fishing position, so the pole can be broken down to swing the tackle in to hand. The length of line varies in relation to still and flowing water.

It's easier to connect with shy bites if the length of line is minimal, but obviously more line has to be used on flowing water, basically to

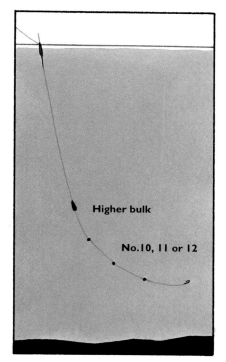

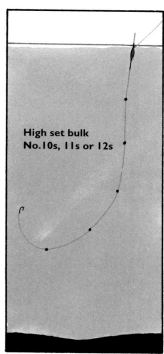

High set bulk
No.10s, 11s or 12s

Higher bulk

No.10, 11 or 12

give the tackle a reasonable run through the swim.

Long pole/short lining methods score well when the fish are less active, or when conditions make running line rigs less effective.

Apart from giving you superb tackle presentation, short lining techniques also allow the hookbait to be teased in several ways to tempt bites. The tackle can be manipulated very closely with your feeding, lifting the bait and letting it drop again each time you introduce more feed. With experience it's possible to work your tackle perfectly in unison with loose feed.

The hookbait can also be inched back against surface tow. This tactic works because often the lower levels will be going the other way. Your loose feed may appear to be travelling in the same direction as surface drift, but nine times out of ten, it will actually start to change direction as it hits the undertow.

Another very effective long pole bite inducing device, is to fish the rig set well over-depth and to twitch the bait along the bottom, backwards and forwards over the feed area. This works particularly well with baits like bloodworms and red-

Above left: **Higher bulk rig.**

Above: **An evenly strung shot or styl rig**

Pole rollers allow several pole sections to be slid back smoothly and in one go. They also prevent damage to the pole over rough ground.

Basic pole float shapes (from left): body-up for rivers with carbon stem and cane tip; body-down for lakes with carbon stem and cane tip; delicate, slim stillwater pattern with wire stem and nylon tip; bulbous, up in the water float fitted with fibre stem and nylon tip; wire tip and stemmed bloodworm float; caster model with carbon stem, balsa tip and body.

Small pole floats for tackling shallow ledges on the far bank.

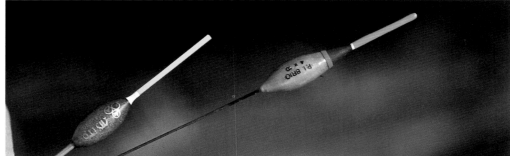

worms. Perch can't resist this movement and it also brings surprising results with species like roach, tench and bream.

On running water, the long pole can be used to slow hookbaits right down, even to a standstill and at distances well beyond the capabilities of rod and line. This is a particularly good winter tactic and has great possibilities when extra water is trotting the tackle through too fast.

LONG POLE RIGS

Most anglers design their own highly individual rigs, but there needs to be a starting point. The following tried and tested tackles will catch you a lot of fish and cover most situations you are likely to come across:

LAKES AND GRAVEL PITS
RIG 1: ON-THE-DROP

Most stillwater pole floats with a pronounced body shape have a gradual taper towards their fine wire, nylon, carbon, or cane tips. These body shapes are referred to as body-down.

On-the-drop rigs can be fished at full depth in shallow swims, or well off bottom in deeper water. But the latter tactic only tends to be productive during the warmer months when the fish are very active.

Strung micro shot, or Styls are best for this type of fishing to give the hookbait a slow fall. Floats are on the small side, usually no heavier than 0.4 of a gram. The best float designs have cane, or carbon stems, so they cock in line with the slowly falling end tackle. Carbon tips are more sensitive for smaller baits, while nylon tips

LAKE AND GRAVEL PIT RIGS

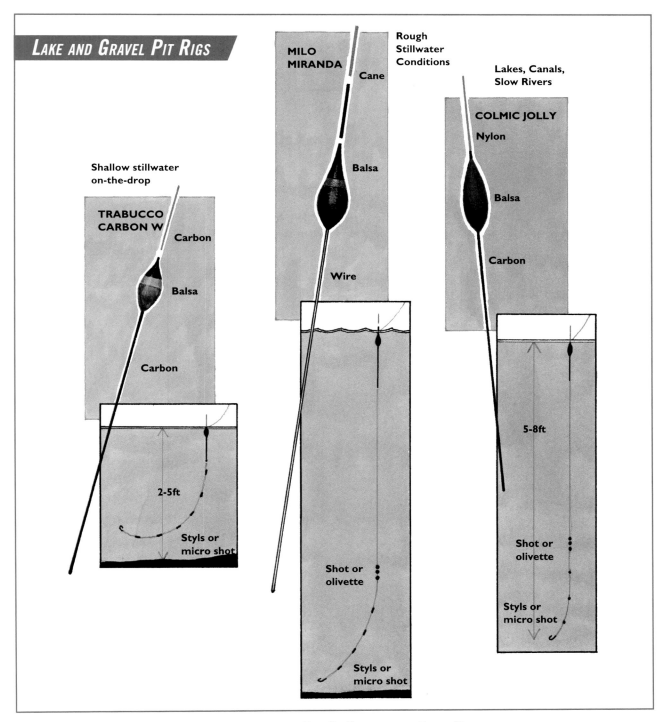

Shallow stillwater on-the-drop

TRABUCCO CARBON W

Carbon

Balsa

Carbon

2-5ft

Styls or micro shot

MILO MIRANDA

Rough Stillwater Conditions

Cane

Balsa

Wire

Shot or olivette

Styls or micro shot

Lakes, Canals, Slow Rivers

COLMIC JOLLY

Nylon

Balsa

Carbon

5-8ft

Shot or olivette

Styls or micro shot

are used for larger baits like maggots and casters.

The floats' weighting can be evenly spread for deeper on-the-drop fishing, (4–8 feet), but it's better to group small weights at half to one-inch intervals halfway down the rig for very shallow work, spreading a couple of tiny dropper shot at wider intervals down to the hook. This still gives the tackle a slow fall if controlled on a tight line, but most importantly, it stops too many tangles.

RIG 2: STANDARD FULL DEPTH

A bulk weight is needed here, but if the swim isn't too deep, strung shot, or Styls are used slightly spread below half depth, to slow the bait down over its last few feet of fall.

There's a wide choice of float sizes here, depending on depth. Floats in the 0.3 to 0.75-gram carrying capacity are used in depths down to eight feet, depending on conditions. Deeper

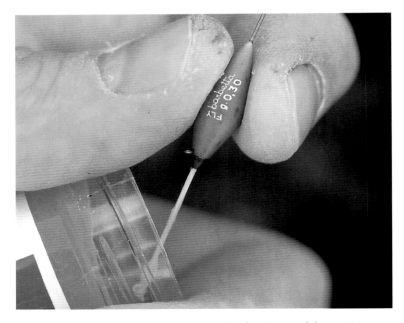

Greasing the sight tip helps make it stick in the surface tension if the shotting is too precise and the float is tending to submerge.

Styl pinchers are essential to pick up these tiny weights and fix them accurately.

RIG 3: BIG FISH

The long pole can account for big fish like tench, bream and carp. A heavy elastic shock absorber is used with 0.10 to 0.15mm hooklengths. Hooks should also be strong and in some situations may have to be forged.

In order to balance this stepped-up tackle, a good degree of presentation is achieved by keeping floats on the small side. These are weighted down with small shot, either strung out, or partly grouped and strung. It's very important to use soft micro shot, because these move if a good fish bolts into weed cover. It's better they slide up your line rather than breaking it.

Normally large offerings are used for this method like double casters or maggots, even sweetcorn, so the float tip needs to be quite buoyant. Thicker nylon, or fibre bristles are best. It's also possible to purchase specialist balsa tipped floats for this type of fishing.

Use body-down float shapes in calm conditions, a body-up design may be better if the rig needs to be held very still in bad drift. Cane or carbon stems are best, although wire can be used in drift.

CANAL

RIG 1: DEEP WATER/MAIN CHANNEL

Small olivettes, or closely grouped small shot can be used to get the bait down quickly. One or two dropper shot will cope with small fish, but the bulk may have to be moved up and some more micro shot evenly spread below to fool larger roach and skimmers.

Float shapes should be slim, or body-down. The float should be stable, so wire, or carbon stems are required. Tip material depends on the baits being used. Use wire for bloodworm and squatts, carbon replaces this if rough conditions are swamping the float and is also applicable to baits like punch, hemp and pinkies. Nylon sight tips are better for bunches of bloodworm, chopped worm, maggots and casters.

Floats carrying from 0.03 to 1 gram are most used on this line.

RIG 2: SHALLOW/ON-THE-DROP

This is small float territory. Tiny floats carrying from just three No. 8 Styls up to 0.3 of a gram are mainly used with spread out micro shot, or Styls from size 7s to 9s.

The float can have carbon, cane, or wire stem material, depending on the rate of fall you want

water may require heavier models carrying anything up to two grams.

Body-down floats are correct for these rigs, stems should be carbon, or wire. Tip material may be wire or carbon for small baits like bloodworm. Nylon is better for supporting maggots, casters, bread punch and redworms.

Below a spread shot, or olivette bulk, try and use several small strung Styls, or micro shot, so the hookbait falls more naturally over the last few feet of its descent.

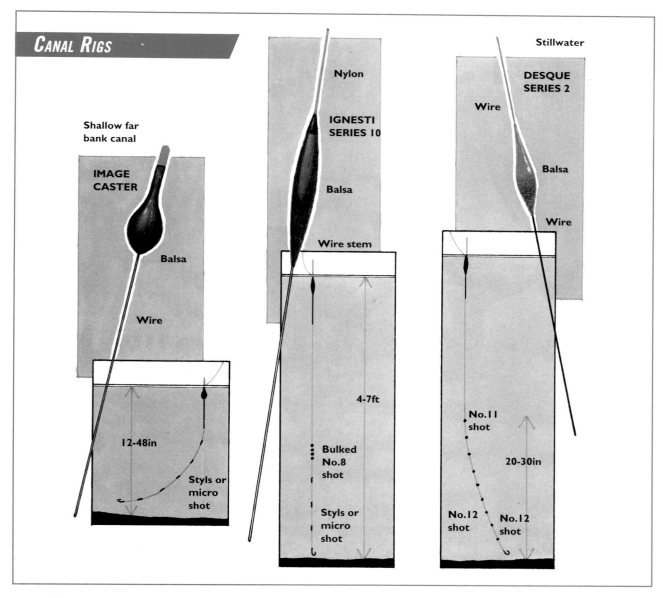

to instill in the hookbait. Tips can be wire, or carbon, but you may have to change to nylon, or balsa if conditions are windy, or the tow is bad.

Body shapes should be slim in calm conditions. A small body-up float may prove more effective if the canal is running a lot, or if there are bad side winds, otherwise use body-down shapes. Round bodies are also worth considering in bad winds.

RIG 3: FAR BANK/BIG FISH

This is again shallow water fishing so the float size should be on the short side and take minimal shot, or strung Styls.

Although the float may only be carrying three or four No. 8 Styls, or the equivalent in micro shot, its tip should be slightly thicker than nor-

mal. This helps visibility when fishing the pole at maximum length and the majority of times baits like casters and maggots are fished over-depth, so the tip should also be quite buoyant. Nylon, or balsa tipped floats are favourite. Stem material can be a short piece of wire, carbon or cane.

RIVERS

RIG 1: BULKED/TROTTING

An olivette is used, unless lack of flow allows a light float, then small shot can form a wider spread bulk, set below half depth. This latter tactic pulls the rig through better – utilising to full advantage what little current there is.

Classic body-up running water pole floats can be used, but round, or rugby ball shaped bodies

Pole River Rigs

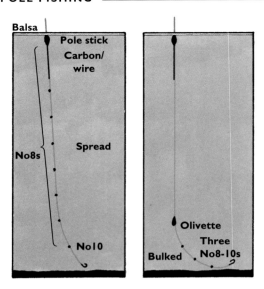

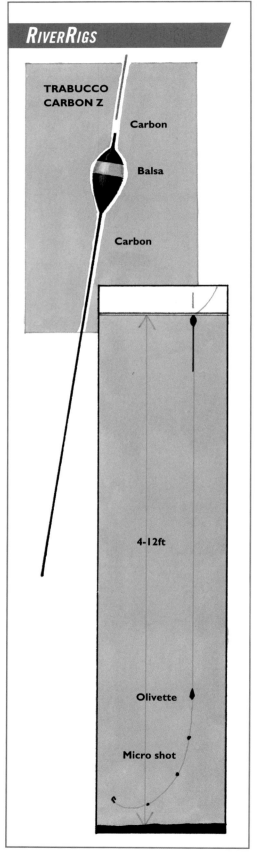

RiverRigs

TRABUCCO CARBON Z

are just as effective. Float capacities of 0.5 to 1.5 are the norm, but in deeper, or faster water there may be a need to step up to 2-4 grams.

Wire, or carbon stems are best for this type of trotting work. The float tip would normally be nylon for most baits and flow rates, but more sensitive carbon, or wire can be introduced in lesser flows especially with smaller baits like bloodworm.

Dropper shot can be kept down to a minimum – 2 or 3 most of the time. No. 8s, or 10s are commonly used.

RIG 2: STRUNG/TROTTING

Similar floats to those above may be used, or more specialised Pole Sticks, which are basically more streamlined versions of the running line stick floats.

No. 8 or 10 shot, or larger Styl weights are evenly spread down the rig, usually tapering down in size slightly towards the hook.

RIG 3: HOLDING BACK

Round, or body-up floats tend to hold back well in flow without riding up out of the water. The tackle is controlled on a tight line and either held stationary, or edged through the swim at different speeds until bites materialise.

Wire stems are the most stable for this technique. Nylon is the best tip material.

Float sizes begin at 0.75 and move up to several grams in faster water. It is also a good idea to try over shotting lighter floats, if bites are difficult to connect with. The float won't sink if you hold it against the flow on a tight line.

The tackle should be fished over-depth and three or four dropper shot, (10s, or 8s) are probably about right.

INDEX